PRIVATE GRAZING AND
PUBLIC LANDS

PRIVATE GRAZING AND

PUBLIC LANDS

Studies of the Local Management
of the Taylor Grazing Act

By WESLEY CALEF

 THE UNIVERSITY OF CHICAGO PRESS

Library of Congress Catalog Number: 60-15396

THE UNIVERSITY OF CHICAGO PRESS, CHICAGO 37
The University of Toronto Press, Toronto 5, Canada

© *1960 by The University of Chicago*
Published 1960. Composed and printed by
THE UNIVERSITY OF CHICAGO PRESS,
Chicago, Illinois, U.S.A.

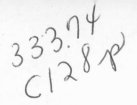

To

MAX BRIDGE   CYRIL JENSEN
LESTER BROOKS   IVAN VICKERS
                JACK WILSON

Sometime district graziers in the Middle Rocky
Mountain basins, who, during the lean and difficult years of the Grazing Service, badgered by
politicians, ignored by those they were supposed
to regulate, unsupported by their department, and
neglected by the electorate, nevertheless carried
on their work with intelligence, energy, and, astonishingly, with enthusiasm.

FOREWORD AND ACKNOWLEDGMENTS

This monograph concerns the use and management of one class of western federal public lands—the "vacant, unappropriated and unreserved lands . . . of the public domain," commonly called Taylor grazing lands. These lands are administered under peculiar circumstances: they are used almost exclusively by a small group of westerners, but ultimate control and responsibility for the lands rests with all the people, the great majority of whom are easterners, largely unaware of and almost completely uninformed about the problem. Thus, the principal aim of my investigations was to provide reliable observations and information primarily for those easterners with whom responsibility rests, bearing on a general question concerning how we—the people of the United States—should act with respect to the Taylor grazing lands. Little can be accomplished toward solution of the problem until its fundamental outlines are better understood and more widely known.

My first contact with the Taylor land problem came in 1947 in connection with a regional study of the Uinta Basin of northeastern Utah.[1] While making that study, I came to realize that the range livestock industry and the Taylor Grazing Act and its appurtenances—grazing district, allotments, permits, district grazier, grazing advisory board, and the like—were largely responsible for the characteristics of land use on 90 per cent of the area of that basin. Consequently, fairly detailed attention was given to the operation of the Taylor grazing district in that area, and the principal contribution of the regional monograph that subsequently appeared was a description of what might be called the operational mechanics of the district. During that summer, numerous signs indicated that the Grazing Service was going through a period of crisis; if by nothing else, it was indicated by the closing of the district office for a few weeks after July 1. These were local manifestations of a struggle between the Department of Interior (the federal agency responsible for administering the Taylor lands) and the western range livestock interests for control of the administration of the Taylor Grazing Act. The struggle focused on matters of grazing fees and annual appropriations; the closing of the local office was simply one expression of a parliamentary

---

[1] Wesley Calef, *Land Associations and Occupance Problems in the Uinta Country* (Chicago: University of Chicago, Department of Geography, 1948).

maneuver by congressional representatives of the livestock interests to force the Interior Department to capitulate by drastically cutting appropriations for administration of the grazing districts. The maneuver was successful. The leaders of the major western livestock associations, encouraged by success in their controversy with the Interior Department, had launched a full-scale campaign for congressional authorization to sell the western public lands on a preferential basis to those ranchers who were using the lands at the time of sale. News or rumors of the appropriations cut and of the campaign for sale of the public lands had penetrated to all parts of the West and had generated vague doubts, unrest, and tension among the Uinta Basin ranchers, particularly the smaller ranchers.

The western livestock associations' campaign generated a rather considerable flow of argument and comment in various publications concerning, particularly, the sale of the public lands.[2] As the controversy continued, neither side advanced very rational or cogent arguments to support its position. The principal argument of the western livestock interests seemed to be that they wanted the land, and therefore it was grossly unfair, illegal, unconstitutional, and immoral for the federal government to continue holding it; moreover, it was "communistic." They advocated that the land be sold at a "reasonable" price, with an absolute preference for the current lessee. Their principal argument not based on legal, ethical, or metaphysical grounds concerned the desirability of getting the disputed lands on the local taxrolls. They did not explain why, in the light of their concern about local revenues, they had successfully thrown all their influence toward diverting half of their grazing fees, which could have been used for any state or county purpose, into developments and improvements on the very range lands they were using; nor did they explain why they had backed a bill which sharply cut the proportion of these fees that were available to the local taxing units. The idea that they would gladly pay as taxes what they had strenuously and successfully opposed as fee allocation did not seem very convincing.

2 Lester Velie, "They Kicked Us off Our Land," *Collier's Magazine*, July 26, and August 9, 1947; A. H. Carhart, "In Defence of Our Public Domain," *The Land*, Summer, 1947; Bernard De Voto, "The West against Itself," *Harper's Magazine*, January, 1947; De Voto, "The Easy Chair," *ibid.*, June, 1947; De Voto, "Sacred Cows and Public Lands," *ibid.*, July, 1948; De Voto, "Statesman on the Lam," *ibid.*, July, 1948; De Voto, "Two Gun Desmond Is Back," *ibid.*, March, 1951. De Voto produced other articles on the same subjects later in *Harper's* for February, May, July, 1953, and August, 1954. Numerous short articles and editorials on the same issues but with much different points of view appeared in most of the issues of the Denver *Record-Stockman* and *The American Cattle Producer*.

The opposition seemed in little better circumstance. They attacked the plan *in toto* as a wholesale landgrab and made no distinctions among the different kinds of land involved. One argument advanced against the scheme was that it would constitute a gift by the federal government to an organized pressure group. It is a little difficult to see why this particular proposed gift aroused such indignation, but a survey of the opposition literature seems to indicate that their objections to the sale of federal lands did not arise so much from the gratuitous nature of the transaction as from a deep emotional antipathy toward the idea of the government's parting with these lands.

Sportsmen's organizations asserted that freedom of hunting would be sharply curtailed under private ownership. This supposition would, if eastern and Texas experience is any guide, be borne out; it was a relatively minor argument. Much more important was a predicted increase in erosion rates under private ownership. This argument was adduced by more writers than any other. No reasons to support the prediction were presented; it is one of the fundamental articles of conservationist dogma that land under government ownership does not erode, under private ownership it does.

Where did the truth lie? What *should* the government do with, to, and for the Taylor grazing land? Immediately a series of related questions arise: Where is the public domain land? What are its characteristics? How is it used? How administered? How did the present situation develop? In the intervening period, answers to these latter questions on a national scale have been presented in a series of first-rate volumes.[3] Consequently, the time seems appropriate for a more detailed scrutiny of these same matters in a much more restricted area. The research reported here is, therefore, more narrowly focused; it consists of fairly detailed, comparative studies of the combinations of land conditions, land tenure, land use, and federal land administration in several specific areas—the various basins of the Middle Rocky Mountains. These basins form a highly distinctive region of the West, embodying a unique association of physical features, cultural arrangements, and historical circumstances. The region, however, has significant characteristics in common with all

[3] Marion Clawson, *The Western Range Livestock Industry* (New York: McGraw-Hill Book Co., 1950); Marion Clawson and Burnell Held, *The Federal Lands: Their Use and Management* (Baltimore: Johns Hopkins Press, 1957); E. Louise Peffer, *The Closing of the Public Domain* (Stanford, Calif.: Stanford University Press, 1951); Mont H. Saunderson, *Western Land and Water Use* (Norman: University of Oklahoma Press, 1950); Samuel T. Dana, *Forest and Range Policy: Its Development in the United States* (New York: McGraw-Hill Book Co., 1956).

of the Intermountain West. Undoubtedly many of the conclusions, judgments, and statements of fact drawn from the studies of the Middle Rocky Mountain basins and reported in this volume are applicable to much wider areas.

Much of this book is concerned with the operation of the Taylor Grazing Act in the Middle Rocky Mountain basins. Ever since the western land problem arose in the second half of the nineteenth century, the land laws and land policy of the United States have undergone a series of changes to cope with the new situation. The federal Congress as well as various state legislative bodies have enacted measures. Stockmen's associations, conservationists, and other interested groups have essayed new solutions to the novel problems of land utilization that developed in the West.

The Taylor Grazing Act of 1934 was the last major federal legislative measure designed to reorganize the use and control of the 140 million acres of "vacant, unappropriated, and unreserved lands . . . of the public domain." But the implications of the act were somewhat broader. One of its fundamental objectives was to stablize the range livestock industry that is so intimately involved in range use. Needless to say, the Taylor Act did not quiet all the controversies attending the western public domain land question; but it did offer a new approach to the problems of western land use and control. Since the passage of the act, a quarter-century has elapsed. In these years a body of experience has accumulated. Before further experiments are instituted, the experience gained from the administration of the Taylor Act should be studied and evaluated.

How has the Taylor Grazing Act worked? What changes in land use or control have resulted? What has been its effect on the land? What aspects of the administration of the act have had especially favorable results? Where has the experience been particularly disappointing or impracticable? The Taylor Act has not been administered in the same way in all parts of the West. It has not produced the same results in all areas. Local reaction has differed widely in different places. Land use practices, techniques, and organizations have been adjusted in various ways to mesh with the administrative practices and conditions resulting from the act. By studying the impact and consequences of the administration of the act in particular localities, we can marshal the volume of experience in western land management that the Taylor Act has furnished. The studies reported here were intended as a step in that direction.

The special studies of the Middle Rocky Mountain basins are presented in Part II. Part I furnishes background material, for readers who are unacquainted with the situation, concerning the western range livestock industry, the western land tenure pattern, and the administration of western public lands.

Part or all of five summers from 1949 to 1958, were spent in the field work for this volume. Altogether a few hundred persons furnished aid or information as the studies progressed; the help of all of them is gratefully acknowledged, but I am particularly indebted to: Allard Caudron, Lander, Wyoming; Marion Clawson, Resources for the Future, Incorporated, Washington, D.C.; Charles Colby, Department of Geography, University of Chicago.

E. N. Munns, formerly of the U.S. Forest Service, gave assistance in obtaining information from that agency. Edward Pierson, Burton Silcock, Riley E. Foreman, James Speelman, and R. Keith Miller, of the Bureau of Land Management in the Department of Interior read and commented on various sections of the manuscript. They are responsible for none of its shortcomings. J. P. Beirne of the Bureau of Land Management made a most helpful special compilation of income and costs by grazing districts for Wyoming. The discussions of terrain features were made more revealing by the map of the physiography of the Middle Rockies, the use of which was permitted by Guy-Harold Smith. R. S. Spratt, John Hay, and Adolph Magagna furnished invaluable information on range use in Wyoming.

The prose style and the logic of the presentation have been improved by the thoughtful suggestions of Jesse Wheeler of the University of Missouri and Melvin Lackey of the University of Chicago, both of whom took time from busy schedules to lend their superior editorial talents to the improvement of this volume. I am profoundly indebted to them.

All financial support for the study came from various research funds supplied by the University of Chicago. The studies could not have been made without that support.

TABLE OF CONTENTS

PART II. TAYLOR ACT ADMINISTRATION IN THE MIDDLE ROCKY MOUNTAIN BASINS

LIST OF ILLUSTRATIONS

FIGURES

PLATES (*following page 76*)

Part One

THE TAYLOR ACT AND
ITS BACKGROUND

Chapter One

THE WESTERN LAND QUESTION

Between the Rockies and the Sierra-Cascade Mountains of the United States stretches a vast, dry, sparsely settled area that has been designated the Intermountain West. It is a wide land with few people (see Fig. 1). Most of the region supports less than a family per square mile, and only the irrigated areas support as many as eighteen persons per square mile. It is a land of few and widely spaced cities; the entire intermountain region contains only five metropolitan areas, and none of them approaches a population of a half-million persons.

It is a land where most economic activity consists of simple exploitation of the region's resources; a land of irrigation farmers, livestock ranchers, dry farmers, lumbermen, loggers, miners, and resort managers. It contains some of the most intensively cultivated land in the United States and the most extensive of agricultural operations.

It is, above all, the land of the range livestock rancher. No other use has been found for most of the land of the Intermountain West. The maps of sheep and cattle distribution (Figs. 2 and 3) indicate clearly that the range livestock industry penetrates to all parts of the region. In fact, it does not indicate the full dispersion of range livestock ranching, because the dots are localized at the ranch headquarters which are more concentrated than are the lands used by the ranches. Everywhere in the Intermountain West land use is devoted mostly to range livestock grazing.

The Intermountain West is also the locus of a land question of vital and historic importance. The crux of the question is how to allocate the use, control, and ownership of the land in the intermountain region to protect the present interests of the inhabitants, while at the same time insuring permanency and stability of settlement. This general problem is, of course, a universal one, but in the Intermountain West it presents itself with a peculiar urgency that lies chiefly in the region's precarious situation with respect to water. The available supplies are insufficient to meet all present demands, and even they will dwindle unless the watersheds are adequately protected. Thus the land question involves not only the irrigation farmers, urban dwellers, and range livestock ranchers who actually use the region's land and water, but also the federal government, which

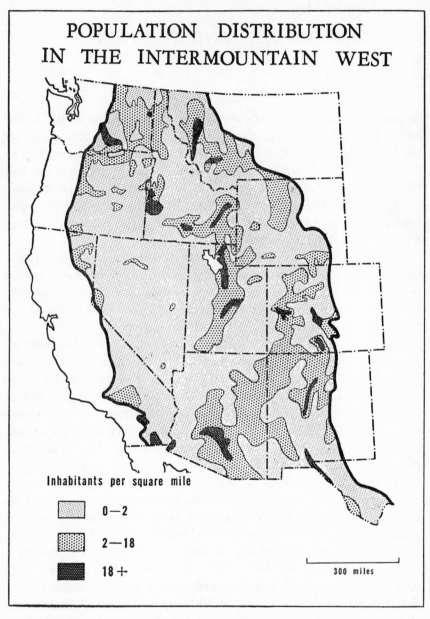

FIG. 1.–Population Distribution in the Intermountain West. (From *Goode's World Atlas* [Rand McNally & Co.], by permission.)

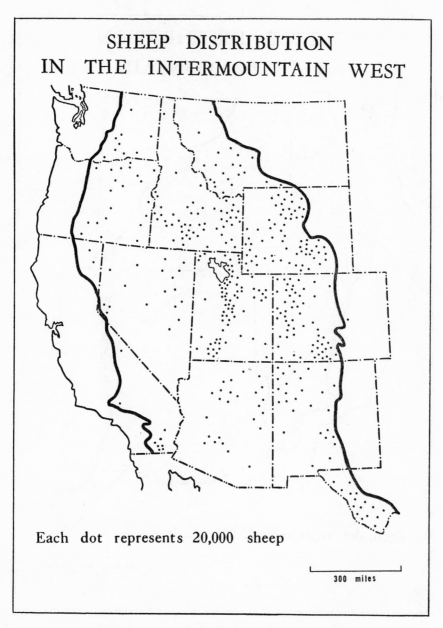

SHEEP DISTRIBUTION IN THE INTERMOUNTAIN WEST

Each dot represents 20,000 sheep

300 miles

Fig. 2.—Sheep Distribution in the Intermountain West

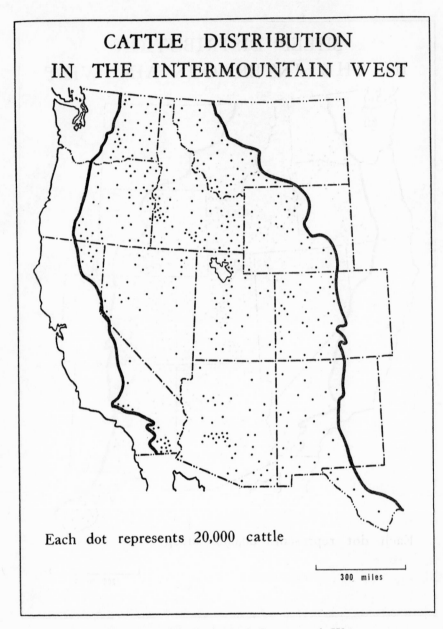

FIG. 3.—Cattle Distribution in the Intermountain West

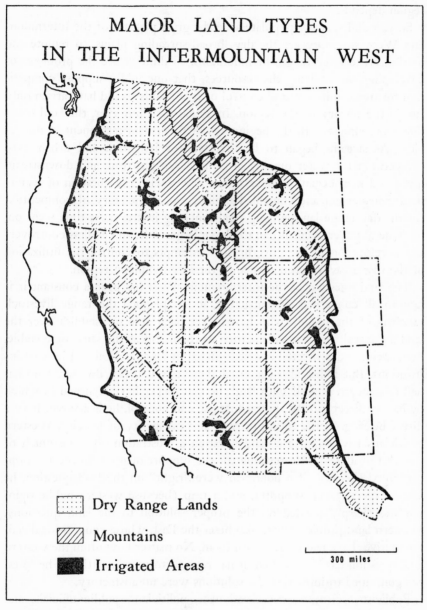

MAJOR LAND TYPES
IN THE INTERMOUNTAIN WEST

Dry Range Lands

Mountains

Irrigated Areas

300 miles

FIG. 4.–Major Land Types in the Intermountain West. (From *Goode's World Atlas* [Rand McNally & Co.], by permission.)

owns and controls the mountain watersheds upon which the life of the region depends.

So vast and sparsely populated are the great plateaus of the Intermountain West, so empty are the dry, broad-spreading plains, so remote and harsh are the lofty ranges of mountains, so difficult are the problems of developing and utilizing the resources, that one might suppose competition for ownership, use, and control of these lands would have arisen only late in the history of the region. In actual fact, however, the land question arose almost with the beginnings of permanent settlement in the region. As streams began to be diverted for irrigation and urban uses, competition for water quickly arose between upstream and downstream users, and men began to concern themselves with the question of watershed management and control. Familiar, too, is the story of competition for the dry range lands among rival ranching interests. As time went on, the federal government began to play a larger role, and endless controversies developed over the government's attempts to control the utilization of the vast areas which it owned in the intermountain region.

The land question of the Intermountain West has been a constant irritant to all concerned. In particular, it has plagued the range livestock ranchers of the region, who have never been able to establish over the land a control that was satisfactory to them and at the same time stable, permanent, and protected and recognized by our political and judicial institutions. But it has also exercised the western urban dweller, who has had to concern himself with lands he may never have seen and in which he has no direct interest, but whose use and control, he is assured, have a direct bearing on the future growth and prosperity of his city. Western politicians have found the land question a frustration (because much of the land produced little revenue for the support of government[1]), an opportunity (because, if a politician were "right" on the land question, he could expect strong support), and a trap (because western public opinion was sharply divided on the proper solution to the land question). Western land problems have also beset the East, whose congressional representatives have had to deal with them. No matter how often the western land question has been settled, it has refused to remain settled. The West has continued to insist that the solutions were unsatisfactory.

Publicists, scientists, conservationists, politicians, public officials, and free-lance writers have addressed themselves to the western land question in books, articles, press releases, and official reports, and the matter has

[1] But not always. When minerals on public lands are exploited under lease or royalty arrangement, the revenue to the government may be substantial.

been debated and investigated endlessly in Congress. Yet today the fundamental issues are still unresolved. Why has this question proved so refractory? Why, after nearly three-quarters of a century of experience, study, controversy, debate, and investigation, do the lands of the Intermountain West still constitute an active and sometimes bitter issue? Partly the answer lies in the complexity of the factors and forces involved. Variations and combinations of physical conditions and cultural circumstances occur from place to place in the West. Thus the nature of the land question is not the same from one locality or region to another. Each citizen sees the problem as it exists in the areas with which he is acquainted, and the solution that he proposes may be radically different from the one advocated in another locality. Variations in the local situation go far toward explaining the sharp divisions in western public opinion about the proper solution for the land problem.

The problem may prove insoluble. The interests of some groups may have to be sacrificed to protect or satisfy the interests of other groups. The decisions will necessarily be political ones, and a discouraging confusion of issues and proposed solutions already exists. We can expect a wise resolution of the question only if we know clearly the extent of the various interests in and claims on the lands of the intermountain region, and the minimum physical and social safeguards that are necessary to protect those interests adequately.

Water: A Major Key to the Land Problem

The most important key to the western land problem is water. It is the critical element in the Intermountain West, the limiting factor in the economic development and occupance of this region. Water is scarce in relation to land and resources.

The precipitation in the lowlands of the intermountain country is not adequate to support cultivated agriculture. Only the heights of the mountain ranges and the highest plateaus receive enough moisture to produce a luxuriant growth of vegetation and a surplus of water. Consequently, all water that is used for cultivated agriculture, for cities, and for industry is transported water. It may be transported naturally by streams, or it may be collected and transported by artificial devices such as reservoirs, conduits, canals, flumes, or irrigation ditches; it may flow in underground aquifers and be pumped to the surface; but whatever the means, the collection and concentration of water is an inescapable prerequisite for cultivated agriculture, urbanism, and industry. The great water problem is, however, simply scarcity of water. Were all the water of the Intermountain West made available to agriculture, it would be sufficient to permit cultivated agriculture on only a small portion of the lands of the region.[2]

Nearly all the population of the Intermountain West lives in irrigated areas; most of the cities are so located. But the total acreage of such lands is comparatively small. Of the total land area of eleven western states, only 2.7 per cent (20.5 million acres) is irrigated, and nearly a third of this (6.6 million acres) is in California. Wyoming has about 1.5 million acres of irrigated land, representing somewhat less than 3 per cent of the state's total area. Most of Wyoming's irrigated land is in the Middle Rocky Mountain basins. But despite the small acreage of irrigated land in the Intermountain West, this land is important in three ways. It is the most productive agricultural land. It may be integrated with use of the dry lands. It uses water that actually or potentially could be used for other purposes.

It is important to remember that irrigated agriculture is not the only use for water in the Intermountain West. Urban needs for water must be met from the limited transported supply. Mining and manufacturing make demands upon it. Water for urban and industrial purposes reduces the supply available for cultivated agriculture and this limits its actual or potential expansion.

The supply of available water from a land area can be diminished or modified in four principal ways: (1) The proportion of the precipitation that is retained on the land can be increased and either used or dissipated on the land surface where it falls; this reduces the quantity of water available for transportation and use elsewhere. (2) The proportion of water that runs off can be increased. (3) The quality of the water can be impaired by certain land management practices. Increases in the salt content or silt content of water are familiar examples. (4) The time distribution, or rate, of water production can be modified greatly by land management practices. These four modifications of the supply of available water from a land area are intimately interrelated; if changes in one of them are induced, change in some others will generally follow.

Since the quantity and quality of water and the rate of water production from an area can be greatly modified by land use practices, all water users must be concerned with the management of their watershed lands. The westerner wants a guarantee that future changes in practices on the watersheds will not adversely affect his supply of water and thus place his economic life in jeopardy. He is deeply interested in the ownership and

2 See, for example, Morris E. Garnsey, *America's New Frontier: The Mountain West* (New York: Alfred A. Knopf, 1950).

control of watershed lands, because ownership and control carry with them the power to modify the water production from these lands.

The relationships of water and land are the paramount facts of western resources management, but all lands do not have the same relationship to water; the relationship varies historically, but particularly it varies with different land types, with their location, and with their arrangement.

A Gross Land Classification for the Intermountain West

To facilitate the line of analysis undertaken here, a classification based on water relations of the land is used.

A Water Relations Classification
of Western Land

 I. Lands of large water surplus (mountain lands)
  A. Forest lands
  B. Grass and shrub lands (grazing lands)
  C. Waste lands (no economic use except as watersheds)
 II. Irrigated lands (lands of high water consumption)
  A. Irrigated grasslands
  B. Irrigated lands bearing crops other than grass
 III. Lands of small water surplus or deficiency
  A. Grazing lands
  B. Waste lands
  C. Lands most valuable for non-agricultural purposes

The major groupings of land in the classification are based on water relationships; their distribution is shown in Figure 4. The mountain lands produce a large surplus of water, much of which is collected and applied for intensive cultivated agriculture on the irrigated lands. In the third group are those lands which either produce a small surplus of water or have a deficiency, but are not irrigable. A knowledge of the salient characteristics of each of the three major kinds of land is a prerequisite for any real understanding of the intermountain land problem.

THE MOUNTAIN LANDS

Without its mighty mountain ranges, the entire Intermountain West might well be a vast low-lying desert or dry steppe, a monumental barrier to transportation, inhabited by a sparse, scattered population of graziers. Certain it is that the mountain lands are the great source of water for intermountain cities, industry, and agriculture. The massive bulk of the western mountains and their rough and jagged topography cause sufficient lifting and mixing of air masses to produce two, three, or, in their higher

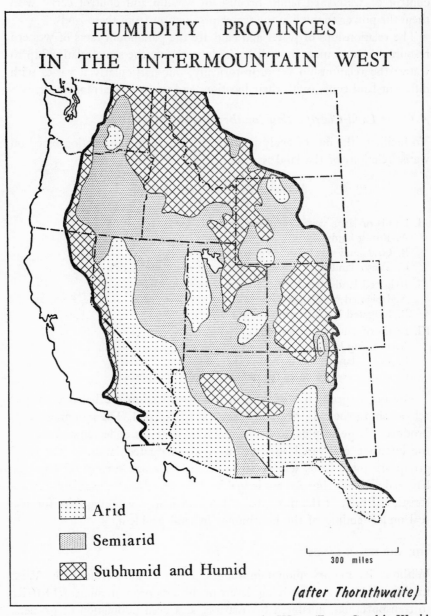

HUMIDITY PROVINCES
IN THE INTERMOUNTAIN WEST

Arid

Semiarid

Subhumid and Humid

300 miles

(after Thornthwaite)

FIG. 5.–Humidity Provinces in the Intermountain West. (From *Goode's World Atlas* [Rand McNally & Co.], by permission.)

12 |

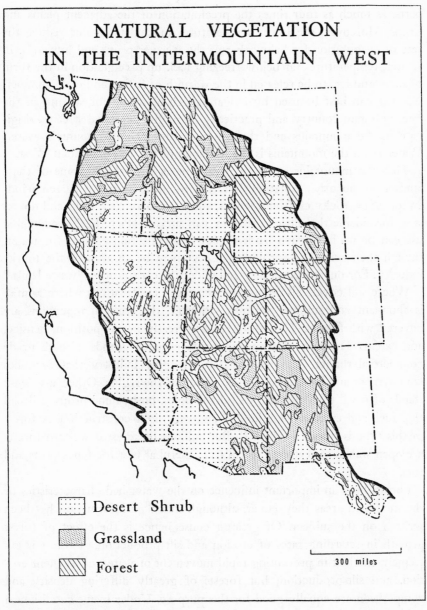

NATURAL VEGETATION
IN THE INTERMOUNTAIN WEST

:::::: Desert Shrub

▨ Grassland

▨ Forest

300 miles

FIG. 6.—Natural Vegetation in the Intermountain West. (From *Goode's World Atlas* [Rand McNally & Co.], by permission.)

parts, as much as four times the precipitation of the adjacent plains and basins. Moreover, the lower temperatures of the mountains reduce the rate of evaporation far below that of the warmer plains and lowlands. In winter, temperatures far below freezing lock up precipitation in the form of snow and ice, to be released in the warmth of spring and early summer, when it can best be used by irrigators. All of the major streams in the intermountain country and practically all of the perennial streams, originate in the mountains and their flow is sustained by mountain water. Water from the mountains is the lifeblood of the Intermountain West.

Thus the mountains are most important as watersheds. Some of these lands have no other function. The environment of many barren windswept crags, rocky cliffs and ledges, and great bare rock walls and domes is so formidable that little vegetation can survive (Plate I). No economic use can be made of such lands except as a collection ground for water, though their wild and forbidding aspect may be an asset to the tourist industry. For our purposes they fall under the classification "waste lands."

Where soil covers all or parts of the rocks at elevations where rainfall is abundant and summer warmth sufficient, the western mountains are covered with forests. These forests vary greatly in composition, density, and extent. The best of them constitute excellent stands of high grade commercial timber, supporting a large logging industry that furnishes employment and income to the population of the region. Others are dense stands of small trees that are useful for poles, posts, mine props, railroad ties, fuel, and even for box lumber and very light construction. A forest of this type is shown in Plate II. But millions of acres of western forests are open stands of scattered, small trees useful at best for fence posts and fuel.

Forests have an important influence on the watershed characteristics of the mountain areas they cover, although much misinformation has been written on the subject. Of greatest consequence is the effect of forest growth in retarding rates of erosion and silt-production. A forest is extremely efficient in preventing rapid movement of water, consequent erosion, and silt-production; but forests of greatly differing density and composition are equally good for this purpose. Under many conditions a fairly open forest of shrublike trees will hold erosion to normal proportions, although this depends in part on the type and distribution of precipitation. Under most circumstances forests tend to distribute the flow of water more evenly; they reduce the peak flows and increase the low-water flow. Recent research indicates, however, that this is not an invariable concomitant of forest cover.[3]

The most widespread misconception about the effect of forests concerns their effect on total water yield. They differ widely. Some forests cause a greater annual flow of water than would be the case if the land were under some other type of cover, other forests produce large decreases in the total annual stream flow, and still others apparently have little effect one way or the other. In an assessment of the role of the forest lands in the intermountain land management scene, these three distinct forest effects—high efficiency in erosion prevention, moderate efficiency in control of flow, and widely varying efficiency in enlarging or decreasing total annual flow—should be kept in mind.

Interspersed among the forests, occupying notable areas in the higher elevations of the mountain lands but attaining their greatest extent in the lower, drier reaches of the mountains and in the foothills are lands covered predominantly with grass. Like the forested areas, these grasslands generally produce large surpluses of water (Plate III). Particularly in the middle and higher elevations of the mountains are verdant areas—the mountain meadows—covered with an uninterrupted sward of grass. At the lowest elevations the grasslands are mixed with shrubs and brush. The density of the brush component differs from place to place; in some places only a few bushes per acre interrupt the grass cover, while in other places shrubs and bushes will be so numerous as completely to hide the grass in an oblique view.

The efficacy of a grass cover in preventing erosion depends largely upon the density of the grasses. A dense tight sod of long grass is nearly as efficient as a forest in the prevention of erosion and silt-production. It is a highly resistant surface almost completely immune to the effects of running water. With decreases in the density of the grass cover, however, the efficiency of running water in picking up and transporting sediment increases rapidly. With very short grass, even a stand of fairly high density may be unable to resist the erosive effects of concentrated running water.

Although their primary function is to serve as a watershed, the mountain grasslands also have an important secondary function—production of forage for range livestock. Reconciling the requirements of these two

[3] E. A. Colman, *Vegetation and Watershed Management* (New York: Ronald Press Co., 1953).

functions constitutes a major problem in land management and one of the thorniest branches of the land question in the Intermountain West.

IRRIGATED AND IRRIGABLE LANDS

Most intermountain irrigated lands are located on the floodplains and terraces of perennial streams (see Plate IV). It is here that water is most easily and cheaply available. The only exceptions are scattered districts of ground water irrigation[4] and a few very extensive irrigated districts where enough water is available to irrigate sections of the interstream divides.

The value of irrigated land is an expression of approximately the same factors that determine the value of land in humid areas—climate, soil, drainage, topography, relative prices of the various crops, and location of the land with respect to markets, transportation, and marketing organizations. One factor that ordinarily does not enter into humid land values is of critical importance in the valuation of irrigated land—the quantity of irrigation water available and its cost. The finest irrigable land in the West without a water supply will have only a tiny fraction of the value it would have with water available. The primary economic consideration respecting irrigable land is whether or not it is associated with rights to irrigation water. If water is available the land will be worth from ten times to, in extreme cases, as much as a thousand times what the value would be without a water supply. Again we encounter the primary fact about western land: the land-water relationship is paramount.

The importance of water rights in the Intermountain West cannot be overstressed. Western water law makes it possible for a citizen to establish a claim, a "water right," to a specified part of the flow of water in a stream, and this claim will be defended and protected by the courts. "Rights" are assigned on a basis of chronological priority; the earliest valid claim takes precedence over all others, the second takes a share of the remainder, the third takes a share of what is left from the first two claims, and so on until all the water that flows in the stream has been appropriated. The simplest example would be a valid claim by an irrigation farmer to all the flow of a small creek. No one else, even though he might own riparian land along the creek, would be legally permitted to remove water from the creek. Even if the farmer did not use all the water, he would still maintain his rights to it. Only when it passed farther down the river system could it be used by others, and by them only as long as the water "owner" did not choose to divert it onto his land.

[4] Irrigation with water pumped to the surface from underground aquifers.

Water rights and land ownership are not legally tied together. The water provided by a water right can be applied first to one piece of land and then to another, or it may be used for some other purpose. However, the value of the land is a joint valuation of the land and the water.

Irrigated land is not a major factor in the western land problem, but it could make significant contributions to its solution. The products from irrigated lands can be used to supplement and complement range forage utilization. When seasonal range forage supplies are poorly balanced, irrigated crops can be used to even out the feed supply. When climatic variations cause failure of the range forage supply, irrigated crops can be used to substitute.

RANGE LANDS—LANDS OF SMALL WATER SURPLUS OR DEFICIENCY

Range lands embrace all the lands of lower elevation except the irrigated lands. Nearly all range lands are characterized by precipitation totals that are inadequate to permit cultivated agriculture. Most of these lands produce a small surplus of water, owing to the fact that part of the precipitation comes in the form of rare, sudden, heavy downpours. For a short period there is more water than the land surface can absorb; for a few hours or a few days every arroyo, creek, and river bed is a torrent of mud and water. But soon after the rain ceases, the water courses dry up, and then for weeks, months, or even years all the available water will be captured by the air, the vegetation, and the ground.

Although the precipitation of the range lands is inadequate for cultivated plants, it is sufficient to produce vegetation. There are marked differences in temperature, precipitation, and soil conditions from place to place, and the result is a wide diversity in plant associations. Broad areas of the range lands are covered largely with grass, here closely spaced, there only in widely scattered clumps, as in Plate V. Other areas support a vegetation composed largely of bushes and shrubs. But the preponderance of range land supports a mixture of brush and grasses. Generally the bushes are low. Various species of sagebrush are the most widely known of range shrubs. Growing beneath and adjacent to the bushes and shrubs are the inconspicuous grasses.

The only economic use that has yet been discovered for most range land is the pasturing of range livestock. The market value of range land is determined mostly by the value of the forage it produces. Range forage is not sown and not cultivated; it is natural vegetation. Commonly it consists partly of browse and partly of grasses, and production per unit of area is sparse. The only economical method of harvesting the forage is to turn grazing animals onto the land. Since range forage is neither sown nor cultivated, the only cost of production is the harvesting cost; but the value of forage produced on a unit area of range land and, consequently, the market value of the land itself, is not always strictly proportional to the total quantity of feed produced. Additional factors include the relative amounts of different plant species and seasonal kinds of range within a district, the relative accessibility of various pieces of range land, the availability of water for the livestock, and many others. All of these factors grow out of the relationships between the range lands and the organizations and practices that have been developed to utilize the forage. To understand these relationships requires a knowledge of the nature and function of the western range livestock type of agricultural production, described in the following chapter.

Chapter Two

THE WESTERN RANGE
LIVESTOCK INDUSTRY

The cowboy is the universal symbol of the western range livestock industry. Riding the range, herding his bunch of cattle, enduring storm, blizzard, heat, and drought, he epitomizes the style of agriculture that was developed to exploit the natural forage resources of the range lands. But durable though he may be as a symbol, the cowboy is disappearing from the range as a new style of ranching develops, based on fences to control cattle. It is a shift from a more extensive, primitive type of range land use to a more intensive and tightly controlled method of range ranching.

We have seen previously that the only feasible method of harvesting the naturally produced grasses and shrubs of the western ranges is to turn livestock onto the ranges to graze. In the Intermountain West, cattle, sheep, and horses are the types of livestock used to harvest range forage. The operating agricultural unit is called a ranch, and range livestock ranches are either cattle ranches, sheep ranches, or (some of them) combination cattle and sheep ranches. Not all livestock ranches, however, are range livestock ranches. In the irrigated sections are livestock ranchers (usually cattlemen) who graze their stock exclusively on irrigated land. The distinctive feature of a range livestock ranch is the use of dry, unirrigated range land as pasture for at least part of the year. Such a ranch is a commercial operation. The products of the ranch are sold in the national livestock market. The animals produced are sold exclusively as meat animals or as breeding stock for the production of meat animals. Beyond this, range livestock ranches exhibit considerable variety. Some are exclusively livestock operations. Others have livestock production as merely one function, with grain, fruit, vegetable, or dairy production from irrigated land as major or minor additional functions and sources of income.

Most western range livestock ranches, however, derive all of their agricultural income from the sale of animals or wool. A typical ranchstead consists of a ranch house and outbuildings located in an irrigated river valley. Adjacent to the house are irrigated fields of hay and grain, and pasture. For part of the year the livestock graze or are fed on the irrigated lands adjoining the ranchstead, and for part of the year they are herded or allowed to roam searching for feed on the dry range lands.

Cattle Ranching

The objective of meat animal production is to deliver a salable animal at the packing house. To accomplish this, a highly intricate system of production has been developed on the range lands and irrigated lands of the West and the grain-producing farms of the eastern Great Plains and the Corn Belt. The different groups of farmers and ranchers specialize to a high degree. The cattle rancher of the intermountain range lands produces calves and carries them through their period of most rapid growth. Then the animals are bought by eastern grain farmers or western irrigation farmers, who feed them on their more succulent and productive pastures but, especially, on grains or other concentrated feeds until the animals are "finished" for delivery to the packing house.

The American consumer will pay a premium for fat beef but the fat must be white, not yellow. Cattle can be fattened on grass, but the fat of grass-fed cattle is yellow. Consequently, cattle can be most profitably fattened on concentrated feeds, particularly grain.[1] But young cattle will grow well and enlarge their bone structure on rougher and less concentrated feeds. Cows of beef breeds will maintain themselves and produce healthy calves on rough pastures, though more concentrated feed is highly desirable for the period preceding calving. The Intermountain West contains millions of acres of rough, sparse pasture, whereas the irrigated lands of California and the humid fertile plains of the Mississippi Valley produce high value concentrated feeds or lush pasture. These characteristics of the American cattle market, the growth pattern of livestock, and the gross regional pattern of land types account for the regional specialization in American meat-production.

The western range cattle rancher is primarily a producer of young cattle. The range lands are breeding grounds for the commercial beef cattle industry. The basis of the rancher's operations is a supply of cheap feed—the grass and browse of the dry range lands. The typical range cattle ranch of the Intermountain West comprises a large herd of cows, a small herd of bulls, and a bunch of young animals; the young animals may all be nearly the same age, or they may be of various ages. The cow

---

[1] Sometimes grass-fat cattle will be fed grain for a very short period—just long enough to change the fat from yellow to white.

herd might be called the physical working capital of the ranch; certainly it is the center of operations. Commonly when a western rancher is asked the size of his herd of cattle he will give the number of mature cows on the ranch. Frequently, newspaper advertisements of ranches for sale will list the ranch size as being a "200-cow" or "400-cow" ranch.

THE YEARLY CYCLE ON THE RANCH

Because seasonal conditions of range vegetation, climate, and water supply vary widely over the Intermountain West, the timing of the yearly round of activity differs considerably from place to place. Since this study is concerned primarily with the Middle Rocky Mountain basins, the production sequence that will be described is the one prevailing in that area, but the same general pattern, with local variations, characterizes the entire Intermountain West.

The calves are born in the late winter or spring. During the spring, summer, and early fall the cows and their calves are on the open range. Feed supplies are scarcest during the winter and the more rigorous weather conditions of that season bring the highest death losses from exposure, disease, and accidents. Consequently, fall or early winter marks the beginning of the sale of stock from the ranches of the Middle Rocky Mountain basins. On some ranches all the calves except those needed for replacement of the cow herd are sold. Normally, a range cow will produce from four to seven calves during her lifetime. A few cows can be expected to die and some cows will need to be culled at an early age; thus to maintain a constant number in the cow herd, most of the heifer calves must be carried over for replacement. If all the rest of the calves are sold, the ranch is known as a "cow and calf ranch." Ranches of this type are not very numerous in the Middle Rocky Mountain basins.

Other ranchers will elect to carry over the winter a larger proportion of the previous spring's calf crop. The decision hinges on a wide variety of circumstances. The most important single factor is the ratio of the summer feed supply to the winter feed supply. A rancher whose winter feed supply is very small in comparison with his summer supply will cut his herd as drastically as possible in the fall. If he carries part of his calf crop over the winter, he may sell some of the animals in the spring. As a normal procedure, however, if a rancher carries calves over the winter, he will keep them on his own ranges during the summer. A rancher with a great preponderance of summer feed may elect to buy some cattle with which to stock his ranges in the spring.

In the spring another calf crop will be dropped, and thus the ranges will be stocked with cows and calves and yearlings. In the fall of the second year it is normal for all the yearlings to be sold, together with the normal proportion of the calf crop sold. Twenty or thirty years ago a high proportion of the yearling steers were held over a second winter and marketed the following autumn. This practice has largely disappeared, as a steadily increasing demand for smaller cuts of beef has set in motion a trend toward marketing younger cattle. Few steers are now kept on the range for more than two summers.

Whether sold as calves or as yearling steers, very few animals go directly from the range to the packing house. Almost without exception, the animals are 'finished," either in the major irrigated areas of the West or in the grain-producing areas of the eastern Great Plains or the Corn Belt. Sales of cattle to feeders are almost always accomplished in one of three ways: (1) by direct negotiation between the range rancher and an individual buyer, (2) by auction sales at local sales markets, or (3) by sales through central markets such as the great stockyards at Chicago, Omaha, Denver, and Ogden or in such smaller central markets as Billings, Montana; Sioux City, Iowa; or Stockton, California.

In direct negotiation the buyer commonly calls at the ranch, picks out the cattle he wants to buy, and negotiates the purchase. Some Corn Belt feeders buy cattle from the same range rancher year after year. In such cases the sale negotiations may be carried on entirely by correspondence. Cattle may also be bought on the ranch by a professional cattle-buyer who purchases feeders for individual farmers or for an association of Corn Belt or irrigation farmers. A third type of buyer is the individual livestock dealer. He travels from ranch to ranch, many times with a truck on which he hauls away his purchases. He is willing to buy odd lots, but ordinarily his prices are lower than the prevailing prices.

The rise of local auctions to a position of major importance in range livestock sales is a comparatively recent development; but they now account for about a third of all western cattle sales, though the percentage varies considerably from state to state.

A large percentage of cattle leaving the ranges go by truck or rail to the major central livestock markets. Not many of them, however, go directly to the slaughterhouse. Instead, they are bought by commercial feeders or, more commonly, by cattle-buyers purchasing for feeding interests. The cattle then are transported to the feed lots of the cattle-feeder or to the farm of a grain farmer or irrigation farmer.

In general, the production schedules of range livestock cattle ranches conform to the pattern described; but there are almost endless variations in marketing procedure—variations from ranch to ranch, and variations on the same ranch from year to year. If the price of cattle is high and the rancher believes there will be a downward trend, he may sell all his yearlings, all his calves, and perhaps some of his cows. Conversely, if prices are low but the rancher believes they will rise, he may elect to keep all his calves, though normally he will still market all his long yearling steers.[2] A rancher who is building up his cattle herd will follow a different marketing pattern from a rancher whose ranges are fully stocked. Ranges in poor condition may cause increased stock marketings; excellent range conditions may slow down the marketing rate.

Although numerous factors are of importance in influencing the individual rancher's decisions about producing and marketing his cattle (and by no means all of them have been mentioned), the one factor that pervades all his operations, that sets the limits within which he must operate, and, moreover, is of greatest concern to us in analyzing the western land problem, is the seasonal supply of feed. Cattle should eat and drink every day. That is the paramount fact on a western range livestock ranch. Winter or summer, the cattle need food and water. Of course, cattle can survive short periods without water, and much longer periods with inadequate food or even no food. But when food and water are inadequate for short periods growth ceases, and as the period of inadequate nourishment lengthens, loss of weight (shrinkage) begins. Periods of any length during which stock are poorly nourished result in smaller calf crops and increased losses from disease and exposure. Moreover, lower marketing weights, poorer conditioned cattle for sale, increased death losses, and smaller calf crops will cause profits to vanish—not just the profits of one year but of several years. The losses from a single year of high death rate, a small calf crop, and low prices for poorly conditioned cattle may wipe out the profits of two or three good years.

The feed supply on a ranch, then, is not a simple matter of total annual supply, but of having a sufficient supply at all times during the year. We have seen already that cattle numbers can be varied seasonally to bring them into closer conformance with the feed supply. Moreover, it is standard practice to vary the rate of feeding. During periods of minimum feed supply the rancher may feed his cattle only enough to maintain health and body weight while in periods of abundant feed the young cattle grow rapidly and the older cattle become sleek and well fleshed.

---

[2] A "long yearling" is an animal several months more than one year old.

Range ranchers have three possible sources of feed. First, they can turn their cattle onto the naturally produced forage of the range lands. Second, they can grow feed for their livestock on their own irrigated land. Third, they can purchase feed for their stock. This all seems simple enough; but the nice balancing of cattle numbers and the feed supply in relation to the price of cattle and the price of feed is one of the most critical elements in the success or failure of a ranching operation. The three sources of feed can be combined in seemingly endless variations. Even if our purview is limited to the Middle Rocky Mountain basins, a wide range of successful combinations can be discerned. At one extreme are the ranchers who depend almost wholly on range land forage to support their herds throughout the entire year. Some highly successful ranchers keep their stock on range feed throughout the year in some years, and during others, when weather conditions make it impossible for the cattle to graze the range, they buy feed, both hay and grain. At the other extreme is the rancher who turns his cattle onto the range for a period of only a month or two, and for the rest of the year grazes them on irrigated pastures or feeds them hay and grain from irrigated fields. There are, for that matter, livestock ranchers in all the irrigated sections of the West who confine their operations entirely to irrigated land, but they are not range ranchers and so for the moment do not concern us except to indicate the gamut of possibilities in meeting the feed requirements of a ranch. By far the most common type of range rancher is the man who depends partly on range land, partly on irrigated hay and pasture, and partly on purchases of concentrated feed such as grain, cottonseed cake, or soybean cake.

The forage-production of a piece of range land is subject to large variations from year to year. Best-known are the variations resulting from fluctuations in precipitation. Abnormally large amounts of precipitation will produce an abundance of forage, and an extended drought may cause the range feed supply to vanish; but other influences affect the annual production or usefulness of the range feed supply.

In general, a rancher who has both a supply of range forage and feed produced on irrigated land will plan to use the range forage whenever it is available and to utilize his tame hay and irrigated pasture, together with some purchased feed, to carry the cattle through periods when range feed is not available.

We have been speaking of the rancher's available supply of range forage as though it were homogeneous; but this is by no means the case. Ranges vary in the quantity of forage they produce, in the quality of forage, in accessibility, and in the season or seasons when they can be used. The amounts of different kinds of range that a rancher has at his disposal are nearly as important as the total quantity of range forage. Three main kinds of range are recognized according to season of use: summer range, spring-fall range, and winter range.

SUMMER RANGE

Summer ranges are high mountain ranges. During the short mountain summer the abundant precipitation and cool temperatures produce lush, succulent, nutritious pasture of high carrying capacity (see Plate III). The best of these ranges are almost equal to humid lowland pastures in carrying capacity. The rancher who has high summer range for his cattle depends on it to produce rapid growth in his young stock and to fatten the older cows to endure the period of poorer feed during the ensuing winter. It is obvious that summer range in the humid mountains is a great asset to a range rancher. It is also obvious, however, that summer range is highly seasonal range. Until the winter snows have melted and the summer sun has started the grasses growing vigorously, it is unavailable, and after the first hard frosts and snows of autumn the cattle must be brought down to lower and warmer lands.

In the Middle Rockies the high summer ranges are rarely available before the middle of June, and they must be vacated by the end of September. In late spring and early summer there is no climatic reason why the summer ranges cannot be utilized, but the grasses must be given a period in which to grow and develop root systems. If they are grazed too early, the total forage-production will be greatly diminished, and if too early pasturing persists, the carrying capacity of the range will be lessened. The important point is that this source of feed is available for only three months a year. Although it is highly valuable—ranchers who have it depend upon their summer range to produce maximum gains in their livestock—summer range forage is available only when it can be grazed, for it cannot be stored except in the flesh of the cattle.

SPRING-FALL RANGE

At lower elevations in the mountains and in the very highest parts of some of the floors of Middle Rockies basins are lands with higher temperatures but less precipitation than the high mountains. These are the spring-fall ranges. Because the warmth of spring reaches them earlier, these ranges can be pastured a month or two before the high summer ranges are available. In autumn the heavy frosts and snows are a little tardier than they are in the higher mountain meadows. The land, however, is high enough to have moderate precipitation, and the grasses are green and succulent during the summer. Thus the spring-fall ranges, as their name implies, are used by ranchers to pasture their cattle in the spring before the high mountain pastures are ready to be grazed and again in the fall for a month or two before the onset of winter covers them with snow. However, these ranges can also be used in summer if necessary. If a rancher owns a piece of spring-fall range and has no access to high summer pastures, he may keep his stock on these ranges for approximately six months, from about April 15 to October 15.

WINTER RANGE

The lowlands (in the Middle Rocky Mountain region, the floors of the basins) are the winter ranges. These are the lands of lowest precipitation and of highest temperatures, though, for periods, they may be bitterly cold in winter. The term "winter range" is somewhat misleading. Provided water is available these ranges can be grazed at any time. A rancher who has access only to so-called winter range may use it during any part of the year, or, for that matter, at all times in the year. It is called winter range because it is a source of range forage during the winter, when the summer and spring-fall ranges are inaccessible. A rancher who has two types of range obviously will use forage from the higher ranges when it is available and reserve the lower, warmer winter range for use during the winter season.

A ranch with an ideal combination of forage supply sources will operate in the Middle Rocky Mountain region on about the following schedule. In the summer the cattle are grazed on the green, highly palatable grasses of the high summer range. Around the middle of September, they are brought down to the spring-fall range. About November 1 they are herded into the lowlands and grazed on the winter range, where they remain until mid-April. If the winter range is in good condition and if the weather is not too inclement, the cattle will maintain themselves in moderately good condition on the winter range grasses. Perhaps they may be fed a little supplemental hay or even smaller rations of concentrated feed. In March the cows are brought onto the irrigated pastures of the ranch or onto fenced winter range near the ranch headquarters. Here the calves are born. Toward the middle or end of April the cows and calves are moved to the spring-fall range. For a period of two months they slowly work their way up the mountain slopes, and about mid-June they reach the high summer range.

The foregoing, as we have said, is an ideal situation. The procedure on a ranch without access to summer range would be like that described, except that the cattle would remain on the spring-fall range from April to October or November. Some areas are so high that they cannot be said to have a true winter range, because the snows of winter completely bury the range vegetation. In such areas cattle must be grazed on irrigated pasture when it is not too deeply covered with snow, and fed hay and more concentrated feeds the rest of the winter. A rancher who has neither summer range nor spring-fall range may alternate his cattle between irrigated pastures and range land, or he may keep his cattle on the winter range throughout the year.

It is this possibility of endless variation in feed sources that makes the range land problem so confusing to an outsider. He sees that successful ranchers operate with almost every possible combination of range land and irrigated land; still, he knows that there is pressure by ranchers, as a group, for more range land. Few ranchers have all the range land of all types that they would like. Many ranchers are continually trying to expand their holdings or rights to range forage.[3] The pressure for additional range forage arises from numerous factors. Expansion of feed sources is necessary if the size of the ranching operations is to be increased. Additional range forage is in many cases desirable in order to balance the annual feed supply. In some cases range forage is the most economical source of feed; but not always. The factors involved in range forage costs are considered next.

COSTS OF RANGE FORAGE

The intermountain range livestock industry depends for its existence on a supply of cheap feed. The cheapest feed in general is the naturally produced, relatively low-grade forage of the range lands. The reservation, "in general," is very important. It has often been said that nature produces the range forage and all the rancher need do is turn his cattle onto the range to reap the harvest. Considerable light will be cast on the range problem if we examine this proposition in some detail.

[3] Some ranchers are not interested in increasing their supply of range forage. Those who are financially overextended may find they have insufficient livestock to stock their ranges. If their financial position improves and their ranges become fully stocked, they may then enter the market for additional forage sources. Elderly ranchers who gradually are reducing the scale of their operations find it easy to dispose of cattle and will not be searching for additional forage sources. A third group that exerts little pressure for additional range forage are those ranchers who, probably for reasons of individual temperament, find it more satisfactory to operate largely on irrigated land. They regard range forage as merely a seasonal supplement to their irrigated hay and pasture.

Suppose that immediately adjacent to his ranch headquarters a rancher has control of sixteen sections (square miles) of winter range land. He decides to carry all his stock on this land throughout the year and use his irrigated hay for supplemental feeding whenever it is needed. Forage production on this particular piece of winter range is such that eight acres are required to feed one cow for one month. The rancher makes the following simple calculation:

$$\begin{array}{r} 640 \text{ acres per section} \\ \times\ 16 \text{ sections} \\ \hline 10,240 \text{ acres} \end{array}$$

Eight acres are required to feed a cow for a month. Hence,

$$\frac{10,240 \text{ acres}}{8} = 1280 \text{ animal unit months.}$$

(An animal unit month, hereafter abbreviated "a.u.m.," is the amount of forage necessary to support one cow or five sheep for one month.)

Because our rancher wishes to carry his stock on the range throughout the year, each cow will use twelve a.u.m.'s of forage per year from the range. Hence, the rancher divides the total available number of a.u.m.'s by twelve:

$$\frac{1280}{12} = 106.$$

Thus, if he has calculated the carrying capacity properly, he can keep 106 head of cattle throughout the year on his sixteen sections of range.

What happens when the rancher turns these cows onto the range? They will immediately turn back to his irrigated pasture if not prevented from doing so. Clearly he must fence his irrigated land. Sixteen square miles is admittedly a substantial piece of land, but what is to prevent his cattle from wandering off his property? They certainly will if there is good grazing and water on the adjacent properties. In the course of two weeks some of the cattle may wander ten or fifteen miles beyond the boundaries of the ranch. The owner of the cattle may have no objection to this, but his neighbors most certainly will. Thus he must take some action to control his cattle. He can either fence his land or he can herd the cattle. If his lands lie in a sixteen-section square, he will find it necessary to construct sixteen miles of fence merely to inclose his range. In the late 1950's it would have been possible to do the fencing for approximately $950 per mile. This figure is less than the cost of contract fence construction, but by doing much of the work himself he might reach it, or even a slightly lower figure.

Sixteen miles of fence at $950 per mile yields a total fencing cost of $15,200. This represents $1.50 per acre merely for external fencing. In terms of animals, however, it means he must make a capital investment of nearly $150 per cow. At 5 per cent on his investment, the rancher has now incurred expenses of roughly $7.50 per year per cow plus maintenance costs merely to fence the range lands which his cattle will use. Clearly there are very real costs involved in harvesting this gift of nature. If the rancher wished to maintain greater control over cattle movement and fenced his sixteen sections into four pastures of four sections each, this would require a minimum of eight miles of internal fencing, which would increase all the figures given above by 50 per cent, i.e., $11.25 annually or 94 cents per month. If he decided to control the movements of the cattle by having them herded by a single rider, this would cost him at present prices a minimum of $2400 annually for wages and maintenance, and he would have the additional expense of horses and feed for them. The annual cost for herding expenses would amount to $25 or more per cow.

Part of his range may be so far from water that the cattle cannot or will not reach and utilize the forage in that section. In that case, a water source must be provided in the area where none exists. This will necessitate drilling a well and installing a pump or windmill, or building a reservoir, at a cost of a few hundred to a few thousand dollars. If it is the latter figure, the rancher may decide that it is economically not feasible to utilize the forage produced in that part of his range, in which case the total number of a.u.m.'s of forage must be decreased, and unit costs for fencing will rise.

We have here touched on one of the most critical aspects of the utilization of range land for raising cattle. So far as cattle-production is concerned, range forage without water is worthless. Cattle must have water to drink every day. If water is available, they will tend to stay near it and wander out in search of food. If there is only a single source of water and feed is very scarce, cattle will journey four or five miles away from the water source. Most western livestock men claim, however, that it would be most unusual for a cow or steer to travel more than four miles from water in search of forage. Where water sources are widely scattered, cattle will graze the range very unevenly, especially if forage is relatively abundant. They will graze heavily near the water, but will leave forage relatively untouched on the areas farthest from the water. To some extent this grazing pattern can be modified by careful herding, but unless the control is close, the pattern just described will prevail.

A cattle rancher who is appraising the carrying capacity of a piece of range land must consider carefully the water supply conditions on the range. Are water sources numerous and well distributed? If not, how much will it cost to develop the necessary new sources? Can the distribution pattern be modified by careful herding or by judicious placing of fences? We will see later that the water problem becomes much more involved if combined with a complex land tenure pattern.

To return, however, to the costs of harvesting range forage; we have been assuming that the range lands are immediately adjacent to the ranch headquarters, but if some sections are located a considerable distance from the ranch, transportation or trailing costs to move the stock to and from the forage, and transportation costs for hauling feed to the livestock or for hauling sick or weak cattle home must be added to the total harvesting costs. Thus, even if the forage were available for harvest absolutely free, there would still be substantial costs associated with its exploitation.

Of course, there is no forage available for free use. Nowhere in the Intermountain West is any land available for such use. If a rancher is to obtain a supply of range forage he must pay for it, either by purchasing the land outright or by paying an annual fee for a grazing lease. Thus the interest on his investment in range land or the annual grazing rental fees he pays must be added to the cost of the range forage. The direct cost of range forage is a matter of the utmost importance to the entire intermountain range livestock industry. We shall defer our consideration of it for a more extended treatment later. Here it is only necessary to point out that the cost of acquiring range forage in conjunction with harvesting costs will determine whether or not range forage is cheap forage.

Sheep Ranching

The foregoing discussion applies only to cattle ranching. Sheep ranching, the other major component of the intermountain range livestock industry, exhibits problems and methods materially different from those of cattle ranching.

Western sheep ranchers have an adage that they quote repeatedly to the effect that: "The sheepman has only two paydays a year." It is a homely way of saying that the sheep rancher markets only two products—wool and lambs. In the yearly cycle of operations each product is harvested, so to speak, at a definite time, and during the remainder of the year nothing is ready for sale. The sheep are sheared in the spring and the lambs are marketed in the fall. Over the enormous expanse of the Intermountain West shearing times vary and marketing dates for lambs vary, but on the great majority of ranches, spring brings the wool crop and lambs leave the range in autumn.

A sheep rancher with ample financial resources is in a more favorable marketing position than a cattle rancher with respect to his wool crop and in a less favorable position with respect to his lamb crop. Wool can be stored for several years with no deterioration. A sheep rancher who can afford to do so may store his wool and wait until he feels the market is satisfactory for selling. Lambs, however, are a more perishable commodity than cattle. This results from the nature of the American consumer market for mutton. American consumers will pay a high price only for lamb.[4] Considerable amounts of mutton are consumed, but there is such a great differential between lamb and mutton prices that mutton might be thought of as a cheap by-product of lamb and wool. Hence, a sheep rancher has fewer options than a cattle rancher in the disposition of his meat animals. If the cattle grower holds his calves in the fall because the market is abnormally low, he knows that his animals will continue to appreciate in value. A sheep rancher, however, ordinarily cannot hold his lambs more than a few weeks or months, because his market is for lambs and nothing else. (Of course he must retain a large portion of his ewe lambs to replenish the herd of breeding ewes.)

The sheep rancher markets his lambs and ewes in the same manner and through the same channels as the cattle producer, but he does not use the same markets in the same proportion. Livestock auctions, so important in the cattle trade, are of little importance in marketing sheep. Less than a tenth of all sheep sales in the intermountain country are made at local livestock auctions.[5] As compared with cattle a larger proportion of lambs go directly from the range to the packing house. The leading single method of marketing is consigning lambs to a commission firm at a terminal market.

The range sheep rancher has one possible escape from complete de-

[4] Almost all of the United States lamb crop is sold in urban centers, and an astonishingly high percentage of it is consumed in just a few of the very largest metropolitan centers. See Marion Clawson, *The Western Range Livestock Industry* (New York: McGraw-Hill Book Co., 1950).

[5] Harold Abel and D. A. Broadbent, *Trade in Western Livestock at Auctions. I. Development, Relative Importance, Operations* (Logan: Utah Agricultural Experiment Station *Bulletin* 352, 1952), p. 42.

pendence on fall prices for lambs. Dealers and buyers in the intermountain region will contract in the spring to purchase a rancher's entire lamb crop at a specified price in the fall. This gives the rancher one alternative to selling at the market price in the autumn. If he can make a profit at the contract price, he may if he wishes sign the contract and eliminate all speculation concerning the fall price of lambs. But if he feels that the lamb market in the fall will be higher, he will refuse to contract for his lambs and will take the market price when the lambs are delivered.

The standardization of products and marketing times, and, particularly, the drastic drop in prices for older animals, gives a greater degree of regularity to the annual cycle of operations on a sheep ranch than on a cattle ranch.

The typical sheep ranch does not differ greatly in appearance from the typical cattle ranch. If range lambing is practiced, it may well be impossible to tell from the sparse array of sheds and corrals whether a ranch produces sheep, cattle, or both. In some parts of the intermountain region shed lambing is practiced, and, where this is the case, the lambing sheds give evidence that sheep are being raised.

The range sheep rancher depends upon the same sources of feed as does the cattleman. He recognizes the same three classes of range land and uses them in the same way. If he has access to high mountain summer range he uses it and depends on it to put maximum weight gains on his lambs. If spring-fall range is available, he uses it at those seasons, and if he has no summer range the sheep are kept on the spring-fall range during the summer. In rare instances sheep will be kept on winter range the year round. The hay, grain, and pasture produced on the rancher's irrigated lands are used for supplemental and emergency feeding, and he can and does purchase feed for the same purposes.

In late fall the ewes and the rams are put on winter range for the breeding season. In the Middle Rocky Mountain basins the winter ranges are the basin floors. Throughout the winter weak or sick sheep will be trucked or trailed into the ranch headquarters to be fed and cared for, while hay, grain, and cottonseed meal or soybean meal will be brought out to the herd to supplement the range forage. If the ranch practices shed lambing, the ewes are brought, in late winter or early spring, to the lambing sheds, where the lambs are born. When the spring-fall range is ready for use, the flocks are trailed to the new range. If the rancher practices range lambing, the spring range generally is the lambing ground. The arrival of full summer sees the bands of sheep trailed to the high mountain pastures and in early fall they trail down again to the lower elevations of the spring-fall range. In the fall, when the sheep leave the spring-fall range, the lambs are taken out of the flocks and shipped to market. Some may go directly to the packers, but most of them will go to an irrigated farm or a midwestern grain farm for further feeding before they are finally sent to market. As the bands come down to the winter ranges the older ewes are examined and the ones not deemed worth carrying another year are culled out and sent to market also. Generally, it is the condition of the teeth that determines whether a ewe will be culled, but injuries, poor condition, or sickness are other common causes for removing ewes from the breeding flock.

A variation of the foregoing procedure is sufficiently important in the intermountain country to merit mention. A ewe lamb is not bred during its first winter. Hence, all such lambs intended as replacements for the ewe flock will have to be carried on the range for an additional year. Some sheep ranchers have enough high-grade summer range that they are able to market grass-fat lambs directly to the packers in the fall, or they may have an inadequate amount of winter range and consequently will want to use as large a proportion as possible of their summer range for the mother ewes and their lambs. These specialists in fat lamb production market all their lambs in the fall and buy replacements for their breeding stock.

The sheep ranches of the intermountain region show the same variation in feed sources from ranch to ranch as do the cattle ranches, but, in general, sheep ranchers use range forage to meet a much larger proportion of their total annual feed requirements than do cattle ranchers. Sheep ranchers follow the same seasonal patterns of range use as cattlemen, but the sheepman's range problems and especially his harvesting costs are quite different from the cattleman's. Sheep in the intermountain region are almost invariably herded. Only if they are practically within sight and sound of the rancher are they left untended even in fenced pastures. Sheep are too defenseless to be left alone. A vicious stray dog might kill several thousand dollars worth of sheep in a short time. Exceptions to the herding pattern can be found, but they are rare. Herding costs are part of the sheep rancher's harvesting costs. In the late 1950's a sheepherder's salary was $150 to $200 per month plus his food. Herders' salaries are a major part of the expense of sheep-raising on the range. Consequently, sheep numbers are fairly sensitive to labor costs. Since 1942 labor costs for sheepherding have risen fairly steadily and sheep numbers have dwindled, though in recent years there has been relatively little change either in herding costs or in numbers. Many other factors have influenced the steep drop in sheep numbers, but the ranchers themselves list labor costs as possibly the most important factor.

By incurring the cost of herding, a sheep rancher eliminates or mitigates some problems and obtains certain distinct advantages. First, he needs no fences to control the movements of his livestock, since they are controlled by herding; he may, however, find it necessary to fence against trespass on his range. Furthermore, herding, if properly done, gives maximum control over utilization of the range. All the forage on all parts of the range can be used. If the vegetation cover in an area is in poor condition, the herder can have the range grazed lightly in those spots and then quickly move the band to another part of the range.

The sheepman has a major advantage in range utilization arising from the fact that sheep can graze ranges on which there is no water supply. On a range where morning dew is abundant, sheep can graze the range for a month or more with no access to water, and in winter they can obtain all the water they need by eating snow. Consequently, sheep can graze enormous sections of the Intermountain West that cannot be used for cattle, or cannot be used until large capital investments have been made to procure additional sources of water.

The Sheep-Cattle Ranch

Some range livestock ranches produce both sheep and cattle; many of them are small. Larger ranches commonly specialize in one kind of animal or the other. The most common example of a large sheep-cattle ranch is one which is changing over from one type of animal to the other. In recent years the change almost invariably has been from sheep to cattle.

Ranchers carrying both sheep and cattle may graze both types of livestock on the same range at the same time, may graze them on the same range at different times, or may keep them on entirely separate ranges. Huge areas of the Intermountain West are grazed by cattle at certain times and by sheep at other times in the year, but in most cases the sheep will be the property of one ranch, the cattle of another. If grazing management is good, range types containing grass, weeds, and shrubs will produce their maximum returns if they are grazed by both cattle and sheep. Cattle graze entirely on grass if it is available. Sheep prefer browsing on the shrubs, but will also eat the weeds. Thus maximum utilization of the forage will result from grazing both types of stock over such ranges.

Summary

It may be useful at this point to summarize the major points in the fore-going chapters. We have seen that two major groups are vitally concerned with the unirrigated lands which compose all but a tiny fraction of the intermountain region. The interests of the water-user groups—irrigation farmers, urban dwellers, miners, and industrialists—focus on the watershed properties of these lands. Any characteristic of the land or any action taken on the land which affects its water-yielding properties is critically important to them. For the range livestock ranchers, the focus of interest is the forage resources of the range lands. The complex inter-relationships among the commercial range livestock industry, the national markets for meat products, and the physical characteristics of the range lands have been outlined. Finally, it has been noted that ownership and control of most intermountain range lands is not directly in the hands of either of the two most interested groups but is vested in a wide variety of other persons, voluntary associations, and branches of various levels of government. Lands held by these diverse owners and administering agencies are interspersed in a complex fashion so that the pattern of land tenure in many areas forms a veritable geographic jigsaw puzzle. The land tenure pattern greatly affects the range livestock industry and is a major factor in the intermountain land problem. It is discussed in chapter iii.

Chapter Three

THE LAND TENURE PATTERN AND THE RANGE LIVESTOCK INDUSTRY

The lands of the Intermountain West are under the jurisdiction of a remarkable diversity of private and public owners and agencies. Included among these are private individuals and enterprises, voluntary associations, and agencies of various levels of government. Many areas exhibit a complex intermixture of different jurisdictions and ownerships. This situation seriously complicates the operations of range livestock ranchers. In order to understand why this is so, it will be necessary to examine the over-all pattern of land ownership, jurisdiction, and administration in its relation to the range livestock industry of the Intermountain West.[1]

Land Tenure in the Intermountain West

Contrasts in the land tenure pattern are one of the major cultural differences between eastern and western United States. The outstanding feature of western land tenure is the high proportion of government ownership, particularly federal ownership. In the East, on the other hand, most land is privately owned. The differences, however, do not lie simply in the contrasting proportions of federal land. In the East most of the large federal properties were in private hands for a time and have been reacquired by the national government through purchase. But in the West, particularly in the intermountain region, most federal lands have been the property of the national government ever since they were added to the national territory. There has been no history of alienation and reacquisition.

The federal establishment is the premier landholder of the Intermountain West. In eleven states lying wholly or in large part within the intermountain region the federal government owns a third or more of the entire land area of each state and 53 per cent of all land in the eleven

---

[1] It would contribute nothing to the main line of thought in this book to consider all of the various types of land tenure and jurisdiction in the intermountain country. Attention will therefore be centered on those aspects that most affect the range livestock industry. An extended discussion of the status and management of western federal lands may be found in Marion Clawson and Burnell Held, *The Federal Lands: Their Use and Management* (Baltimore: Johns Hopkins Press, 1957).

states.[2] In six states, lands of the national government embrace more than half of the area of each state, and in three states the federal government still owns more than two-thirds of all land.

Three principal circumstances may be adduced to account for the high proportion of federally owned land in the Intermountain West. In the first place, the land laws that provided a method for settlers to patent land from the government were suited only to cultivable lands. Only a small fraction of western land is cultivable, and as a result most of the land could not legally be alienated from the federal government under the existing laws. In the second place, much of the land was not thought to be worth acquiring or deemed necessary to acquire by those who were using it. The final circumstance was the withdrawal of enormous acreages from entry by the government in order to reserve them for the common benefit and use of the entire nation.

Considerable areas of land in the intermountain region are owned by the individual states. Originally this land was granted to the states by the federal government for the purpose of supporting education. Such grants generally constituted about 5 per cent of the area of the state and were the sixteenth and thirty-sixth sections of each township. It is difficult to generalize on the characteristics and administration of state-owned land. Some states sold large acreages of land for revenue. Others retained their original acreage but traded land on an acre-for-acre basis with private owners, thus greatly modifying the original areal pattern of grants. Some states have leased their state land on very long leases which are transferable, and state administration consists of little else than collecting rental fees and transferring lease assignments. Other states have undertaken more active forms of administration. It is impracticable to consider here the many variations from state to state in the areal pattern and administration of state-owned land. In later chapters we shall examine some details of state land distribution and management in the Middle Rocky Mountain basins.

It is so common to stress the fact that more than half the land of the Intermountain West is still in public ownership, that one tends to overlook the huge area which has passed into private hands. Despite the obstacles interposed by inappropriate land laws, private owners have acquired nearly half of all land. However, privately owned land tends to be concentrated in particular areas, and in four states much less than a third of the land is in private holdings.

[2] U.S. Congress, House Report No. 3116, *Area, in Acres, of Lands in Federal Ownership: Administering Agencies by States* (81 Cong., 2d sess., Sept. 19, 1950), pp. 6–10.

In the remainder of this chapter we shall focus our attention on the relationships between the range livestock industry and several major types of land according to jurisdiction: national forest land, privately owned irrigated land, privately owned dry land, and state-owned land. Discussion of the federally owned land administered under the Taylor Grazing Act of 1934 will be reserved for chapter v.

The National Forests and the Range Livestock Industry

If we look at the gross pattern of land tenure and jurisdiction in the Intermountain West, we discover a definite tendency for covariation between dominant forms of land tenure and the major land types described in chapter i. The lowest elevations, the irrigated lands along the streams, are private land. The lands at intermediate elevations are areas of mixed land tenure—state, federal, and private land. Most of the higher mountain areas are occupied by national forests. The high correlation between mountains and national forest is shown in Figure 7.

We should not be misled by the term "forests." Large areas of the national forests are tree-covered, but great acreages are grassy meadows or shrub land. The national forests incorporate most of the true summer range, which we have previously noted as one of the most important assets of the range livestock industry.

The national forests of the Intermountain West were largely created during the later nineteenth and early twentieth centuries.[3] A series of actions by the legislative and executive branches of the federal government reserved and appropriated the mountainous parts of the public domain and designated them national forests. The principal interest in these lands at that time lay in their timber resources. But the West was imperfectly known, at least to the officials drawing the forest boundaries, and very extensive untimbered sections were included.[4]

To manage and administer the new Forests an agency, the Division of Forestry, was created in the Department of Interior. It later became the United States Forest Service. Bitter political battles have been fought within the executive branch of the federal government over the transfer

[3] Space permits only the sketchiest description of the origin of the various land tenure types, their development, the agencies that administer them, and the codes and rules under which they are administered. The details included here are those deemed necessary to an understanding of the problems of intermountain land management.

[4] Because of the interspersed pattern of timbered and untimbered areas, it would have been impossible to exclude many of the non-forested areas even had it been considered desirable.

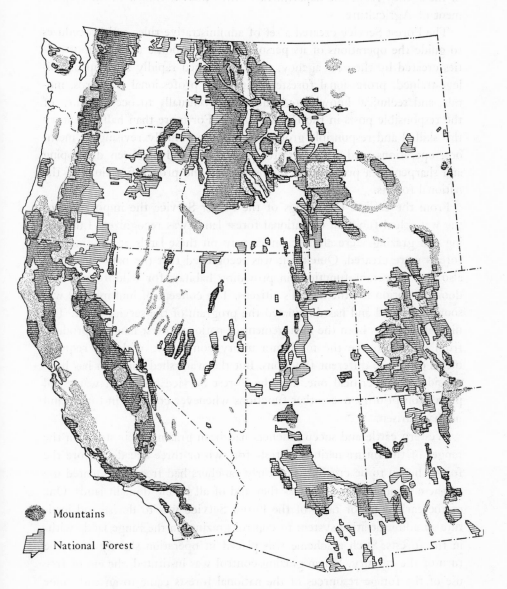

Mountains

National Forest

Fig. 7.—Areal Relations of Mountains and National Forest

of the agency from one department to the other. It is now in the Department of Agriculture.

The Forest Service created a set of administrative rules and procedures to guide the operations of its personnel. As a response to the opportunities created by the new agency, there developed rapidly a group of college-trained, professional foresters with high professional standards, morale, and technical knowledge, who came eventually to occupy most of the responsible posts in the Forest Service. For more than half a century this skilled and responsible group has been continually revising its methods, operations, and administrative procedures and has been developing and sharpening a professional philosophy of the proper functions of the national forests.

From the earliest beginnings of the Forest Service the importance of the watershed function of national forest lands was recognized. Lumbering and grazing were already under way on these lands at the time the forests were created. Quickly it was recognized that the national forests also had important functions in providing habitats for wildlife and outdoor recreation for the nation's citizens. The concept of multiple use was soon developed and has dominated the program of the service since. The ultimate aim has been the management of national forest lands to produce from each resource the maximum utility compatible with the requirements of all the different functions. But the watershed function has been considered the critical one, and the Forest Service has given watershed protection priority over other functions whenever conflicts in forest land use have arisen.

Western cattle and sheep ranchers had been grazing their stock on the ranges of the future national forests for two or three decades before the forests began to be created. The early ranchers had free, unregulated use of these summer ranges, just as they did of all public domain lands. One of the earliest major tasks of the Forest Service was to devise and institute an administrative system to control grazing on the range lands within the forests. Such a scheme was placed in operation shortly after the turn of the century. When grazing control was instituted, the era of free use of the forage resources of the national forests came to an end, since the new system required payment of a fee for each animal grazed.

The grazing control scheme devised by the Forest Service was a remarkably fine administrative and land management system when we consider the time at which it was developed. Its fundamental features have remained unchanged down to the present, though there have been changes in detail. The following discussion outlines the present-day features of the system.

Grazing Administration on the National Forests

A national forest is a definitely delimited area within which all federally owned lands are national forest lands. All laws, rules, and regulations pertaining to national forests apply to these lands. Broad areas of nearly all national forests are exclusively federal land, but lands with other types of tenure are commonly included within national forest boundaries. In certain sections of some national forests in the intermountain region there is a complex interspersion of federal, state, and private holdings.

A national forest is subdivided into several "units," the number of units varying somewhat with the size of the forest. The units are laid out on a multiple-purpose basis. The types of land, the means of access, and the use made of the land are all taken into consideration in drawing unit boundaries. For purposes of grazing administration the units are further subdivided into "allotments" that are the basic unit areas of forest grazing administration. Allotment boundaries are commonly drawn in conformance with physical features of the area. A large grassy meadow surrounded by dense forest might be delimited as an allotment, or a creek valley, a ridge top, or a glacial cirque.

Each allotment is surveyed to determine approximately the quantity of forage produced annually and the period during which the allotment should be grazed. The allotments were very rapidly and sketchily surveyed decades ago, but are resurveyed almost annually to observe such factors as vegetation growth and condition, intrusions of noxious weeds and poisonous plants, and evidences of accelerated erosion.

The estimated annual production of forage on an allotment is expressed in animal unit months. It must be understood that the animal unit month does not represent an actual weight of forage. Clearly, poor cattle on lush pastures will use much more forage than cattle on very poor range. Neither is it a measure of grazing effect on forage production. A hundred a.u.m.'s of grazing on a piece of range in poor condition might seriously impair future productivity, whereas a hundred a.u.m.'s of grazing on another range would have no effect on productivity. The animal unit month is simply a convenient device for expressing the concept of a given number of cattle grazing for a given number of days.

If some of the forage is used by game animals, a portion of the total production is assigned for game use. In many forests approximately 10 per cent of the animal unit months of forage is assigned for such use, though in many forests the proportion is much smaller.

The remaining forage is available for grazing lease by range livestock ranchers. The "grazing lease" or "forest permit" contains the following provisions: (1) the number of cattle or sheep and the number of days they are permitted to graze, (2) the dates on which grazing shall begin and end, (3) the route by which the grazing area will be reached and the approximate rate at which the stock must move along the route, (4) the route which the stock will follow when leaving the grazing lands and the approximate speed at which they will move, (5) the allotment or allotments on which the stock will graze, and (6) the amount of the annual fee to be charged for the number of animal unit months permitted (the number of cattle multiplied by the number of days, divided by thirty equals the number of animal unit months for which the Forest Service will charge). In addition, if the cattle or sheep are to be herded, the grazing lease will specify the grazing route to be followed while the herd is on the allotment and the number of days the animals are to be grazed on each part of the allotment.

Grazing fees on the national forests are somewhat variable, but the variations are not great. The two variables that are taken into consideration in setting fees are the market price of cattle and the ranchers' operating costs on a particular forest. As market prices for cattle and sheep rise, grazing fees rise; a drop in livestock prices brings a reduction in grazing fees. Slightly lower fees are charged in forests that are difficult or expensive of access, are located a long way from transportation lines, or have some other local condition that increases ranchers' production costs.

The supply of summer range forage is completely inadequate to meet the demand, so the Forest Service must decide who is to receive permits. It was one of the remarkable achievements of the Forest Service that it insisted from the beginning of grazing control that the national forest ranges should be managed so as to contribute to permanency of settlement and to the stabilization of the livestock industry as an integrated part of western agriculture, and that the service was able to devise a permit system that had the desired effect. The key provision in the system was the "base property" requirement for the issuance of national forest grazing permits. This requirement has had the effect of giving complete priority in forest permits to permanently established local landholders. It has made it virtually impossible for a rancher to use national forest ranges as part of a year-round livestock operation carried on entirely on public lands. The base property requirement demands that the holder of a national forest grazing permit have a year-round livestock operation and that for part of the year he support his livestock on his own private property, either irrigated land or privately owned range land.

When the original forest permits were issued, priority was given the local rancher who owned and worked irrigated land, who may also have owned dry range land, and whose livestock had previously grazed the national forest ranges. Since there were enough such ranchers to take up all the available forage, they became the original permittees and obtained grazing privileges to the exclusion of all others. The grazing privilege was tied to a base property. Ownership of the base property, therefore, was a prerequisite for the issuance of a permit.

The Forest Service has always held that the use of national forest land for grazing was a privilege and not a right, and that the service was free to revoke grazing permits at any time. But the ranchers, quite naturally, have insisted that grazing permits once issued were grazing rights (in fact, property rights) which could not be withdrawn or cancelled by the Forest Service. The matter has not been tested extensively in the courts, but the few decisions handed down indicate that the courts probably would not permit the service to cancel or drastically cut permits to individuals, but that the service unquestionably can reduce permits when the interests of the forest demand it.[5]

Although the service has never abandoned the position that grazing "privileges" can be revoked at its discretion, in actual practice permits are renewed year after year to the same individuals. Moreover, except in unusual circumstances they are renewed annually for the same number of a.u.m.'s.

Consistent with its position that grazing permits are revocable or modifiable privileges, the Forest Service has also steadfastly maintained that its permits were not transferable or assignable except at the discretion of the service. In practice, however, the Forest Service has almost invariably transferred grazing permits when the base properties to which such permits were tied have changed hands; though not always for the same number of a.u.m.'s. The Forest Service has permitted transfers of grazing rights from one person to another but more rarely has permitted transfers from one base property to another. The permit is attached to the base property. A rancher with a permit to graze livestock on the national for-

[5] For a more complete discussion of the legal status of Forest Service grazing permits, see Jack Holmes, "The Public Land Question in New Mexico" (Albuquerque: Department of Government, Division of Research *Publication* XI, University of New Mexico, 1947).

ests cannot just offer his permit for sale to anyone interested in buying it, while still retaining his base property. The Forest Service commonly would not issue a permit to the purchaser. Thus, in effect, the way to purchase grazing privileges on a national forest is to purchase the base property of the existing permit. If the grazing permit has value, it will appear in the price paid for the base property.

The Forest Service has never made any secret of its view that livestock numbers and grazing pressure on the national forests should be reduced. Reductions on some forests have already been very large. The earliest surveys greatly overestimated the carrying capacity of many forest ranges, and this has been an important contributing factor to the Forest Service's perennial problem of effecting grazing reductions.

Relation of Irrigated Private Land to the Range Livestock Industry

Only a tiny fraction of the Intermountain West is irrigated. So much emotional appeal has been generated by the idea of making the desert bloom, and so much publicity has been given the high returns per acre of some western irrigated lands, that there is a tendency to forget what a minuscule proportion of all land is actually "under the ditch." Even in the case of privately owned land the percentage under irrigation is only around 6 per cent. Nevertheless, the irrigated lands are tremendously important to the range livestock industry, because irrigated areas make possible the efficient utilization of extensive areas of dry range land for livestock production that otherwise would be uneconomical to use. This is particularly true of irrigated lands located at such high altitudes that temperature conditions will permit only hay or grain to be produced (in some places only hay can be produced). On many of these lands the costs of production are relatively high. Hay is a low-value crop that ordinarily will not stand high transportation costs to reach a market. Grain produced on these small patches of high-altitude irrigated land is much too expensive to be sold in competition with that produced by extensive, machine methods on the Great Plains or in the Midwest. The only other choice is to use the hay and grain to feed livestock, either dairy cattle or beef cattle. Irrigated meadows are used for pasture and hay production, and the grain is fed as supplemental feed. Ordinarily this is not a very profitable procedure. In a strict economic sense, these lands are marginal or submarginal; they are barely worth exploiting, or they fail to bring the operator a return on his investment.

These same irrigated lands may be highly valuable, however, if they are operated as part of a livestock enterprise which also utilizes the sur-

rounding and adjacent dry lands. We have explained previously the crucial necessity in the operation of a cattle or sheep ranch to provide feed
for the livestock regularly throughout the year, else the operation of a
ranch becomes unprofitable if not impossible. Throughout extensive sections of the Intermountain West there is a period in the year when no
dry land feed is available. In the northern part of the region it occurs in
the winter season, when it may be so cold or the snow may be so deep
as to make grazing difficult or impossible. In the southern intermountain
area the heat of summer is generally the period when range forage is unavailable. Moreover, on many ranches there is a serious seasonal imbal-
ance in the forage supply. That is, a ranch may have access to far more
winter range than summer range; or the ranch may be totally lacking in
spring range. If the ranch has a deficiency in summer range, the cattle
may be fed on irrigated pastures during the summer season. Quite elaborate arrangements are worked out. For example, the rancher may have
the right to take certain amounts of water from a stream only during periods of high water but will have the right to remove certain additional
quantities of water at any time. When his cattle come off the winter
range, he will turn them onto pastures which can be irrigated only during the period of peak flows in early summer. From fields which can be
irrigated throughout the summer he will take a cutting of hay and then
will turn his livestock into these fields when his pastures which depend
on peak flows begin to dry up. Or a rancher who lacks spring range might
pasture cattle or sheep in all his irrigated hay fields for a period in the
spring and then cut hay from the fields after the livestock has been turned
onto the summer range.

Under some circumstances relatively unproductive irrigated lands located at high altitudes may acquire an astonishingly high value because
they make it possible to use range lands that otherwise could be used only
with difficulty. Under more usual circumstances such irrigated lands
make it possible to use the available range forage much more efficiently
than would otherwise be the case.

Even irrigated land that is capable of growing fruits, vegetables, sugar
beets, cotton, or other high-value products may be used for hay-produc-
tion under exceptional circumstances. If a small acreage of such land is
surrounded by extensive areas of range land, it may be more profitable to
raise hay and grain for use in a livestock enterprise based primarily upon
range land, than to produce high-value crops for sale. It is not necessary
for every range livestock rancher to raise his own feed. Enough hay and
grain may be produced and offered for sale by irrigation farmers so that

it is unnecessary for all the local ranchers to produce their own supplies.[6]

The role of privately owned irrigated land in the totality of agricultural land use in the intermountain region varies from place to place. So far as the utilization of the dry lands is concerned, the irrigated lands serve as a source of supplemental feed at those periods in the year when the range forage supply disappears or is least profitable to use. In unusual circumstances such lands make possible the utilization of range forage that might otherwise have such high harvesting costs as to be submarginal. More often, they introduce a large element of flexibility into the annual feed supply and thereby make utilization of dry land forage more efficient and profitable. Under these circumstances irrigated lands not integrated into a range livestock enterprise are much less economically used than they would be if they were so integrated.

The Role of Privately Owned Dry Lands

Fifteen times more private land in the West is unirrigated than is irrigated. Since use of the public lands outside of national forests and national parks was neither regulated nor leased until the early 1930's, why were private dry lands acquired? Under what circumstances did they pass into private ownership? How are they used?

Millions of acres of private land in the Intermountain West were acquired for purposes which lie outside our present concern. Some were acquired because they contained valuable timber or minerals or because they were thought to be irrigable. Others were acquired as sites for cities. Tens of millions of acres came into private ownership through land grants to railroads. Such lands were not brought into private ownership because of any particular physical property of the land itself but simply as part of an arbitrary pattern of railroad land grants. Most of the remaining private land of the intermountain country was brought into private ownership for one of two purposes: either it was acquired to give access to or control over a source of water on the range, or it was acquired because it was a particularly good piece of range. Unirrigated private range land is consequently found in three general types of location: in strips along rail lines; near a stream, pond, or spring; or high enough in the foothills of the mountains to produce good forage.

Most private land was alienated from federal ownership under the pro-

---

[6] For a detailed description of this process and a bibliography, see Jacquelyn Beyer, "Integration of Grazing and Crop Agriculture: Resources Management Problems in the Uncompahgre Valley Irrigation Project" (Chicago: Department of Geography Research Paper No. 52, University of Chicago, 1957).

visions of the Homestead Act. A surprisingly high proportion came into private ownership during the twentieth century.[7] Probably most private range land in the western states was originally obtained by various degrees of fraud in connection with the Homestead Act. Millions of acres were also obtained under the provisions of the Timber and Stone Act and the Desert Land Act, but the total obtained under both acts was only a fraction of that obtained under homestead entry. Some specific parcels of private land came into private ownership by a process of trading other private land for state owned land; this procedure did not increase the total amount of private land but merely changed its location.

We have seen previously that the value of much dry range land is determined by the value of the forage it produces, but some private range lands have values considerably in excess of the value of their forage production. Range lands which permit or control access to water supplies and thereby make possible use of the range, or give control of range grazing, will reflect this access or control in their valuation. In theory, practically all western range land grazing is now controlled either under private property rights or under federal regulation of the grazing use of government land; nevertheless, extralegal competition is still important. Consequently, a piece of land containing a water source that controls cattle grazing on an extensive area still has value far greater than the value of the forage it produces. Grazing on Taylor lands and on national forests is not completely flexible because it involves regulation by an agency. The freedom of action possible on privately owned lands in a system characterized by such rigidities is valuable and consequently adds value to privately owned range land.

During periods of scanty forage induced by adverse weather conditions or during periods of high livestock numbers, the relative value of privately owned range land, either for lease or for purchase, advances sharply because such land is the only possible source of increased forage. Federal ranges cannot suddenly be heavily stocked, and there is normally no possibility of suddenly increasing the supply of forage from irrigated lands.

State Land

The quantity, quality, location, and administration of western state-owned land varies greatly from state to state. This is attributable partly to the varying quantities of land which the states originally acquired

[7] See E. Louise Peffer, *The Closing of the Public Domain* (Stanford, Calif.: Stanford University Press, 1951), p. 353.

from the federal government, but more particularly to the administrative policies pursued by individual states after obtaining title.

In some ways the states handle their lands as does a private landlord, that is, for a cash rental. State land leased for grazing purposes (nearly all) carries no stipulations concerning number of livestock to be grazed, season of use, or length of grazing period. These matters are entirely within the discretion of the lessee. In four major ways, however, the states' practices are decidedly different from those of a private landlord. First, the states grant ten-year leases on their lands, a period several times longer than the average of private land leases. Second, and more important, these leases are almost automatically renewable. Only unusual circumstances will cause a state land administrative agency to refuse a lease renewal requested by the lessee (and the lessee almost invariably does want it renewed). Third, state lands are leased for much less than the going rate for leases on private range land of comparable productivity, though in general the rentals are somewhat higher than for public domain land of equal forage production and location.[8] Lastly, leases on state land are assignable, and upon expiration of a lease the state will automatically renew it to the assignee.

These four characteristics of state rental practice make a lease of state grazing land a valuable property. Such land can be regarded and used as private property without any investment in purchasing land[9] and without the necessity of paying any direct taxes on the state-owned property.[10] Consequently, state land leases are bought and sold;[11] under certain circumstances they may be pledged as security for bank loans. In the operation of a livestock ranching enterprise they are regarded almost as the equivalent of private land.

[8] Despite the extensive acreage of state lands in the intermountain region, and despite the fact that for decades one of the most widely advocated solutions to the problem of the western dry lands has been to grant these lands to the states for their administration or disposal, there has not been, to my knowledge, a single careful detailed study of the administration and utilization of state-owned western lands. Such an investigation would be a major contribution to our understanding of the use of western range lands.

[9] Although a man who acquired his lease through purchase may have a considerable investment in the lease itself.

[10] State land leases are taxed in indirect ways—by increasing the valuation of the ranch.

[11] The market for state land leases is not an entirely free one. Much state land can normally be used only by a comparatively small number of ranchers whose properties are suitably oriented to it.

Chapter Four

THE TAYLOR GRAZING LANDS

In the Intermountain West, two types of federally owned land are especially significant to the range livestock industry: the national forests and the Taylor grazing lands. Use of the national forests for grazing has been described in the preceding chapter. The Taylor grazing lands are the lands which were organized into grazing districts under the Taylor Grazing Act of 1934.

Background of the Taylor Act

The Taylor grazing districts were formed from the "vacant, unappropriated, and unreserved" lands of the public domain. Nearly all of the 754 million acres of land in the eleven western states originally fell in this category. But through homesteading and other means of alienation, the federal government has transferred nearly half of this land to private owners or to individual western states. Tremendous acreages have been reserved for use as national forests, Indian reservations, or national parks. We have previously noted that the national forests administered by the Forest Service of the Department of Agriculture include about a third of all federal land in the eleven western states, or between a fifth and a sixth (18 per cent) of all western land. Considerably greater areas are administered by the Department of Interior, which is responsible for more western land than any other federal agency. Of the 247 million acres under its jurisdiction in the western states, 11.6 million acres are controlled by the National Park Service, while the Bureau of Indian Affairs supervises about 46 million acres of western Indian lands. But the branch of the Interior Department which administers far more western land than any other is the Bureau of Land Management. It has approximately 179 million acres under its jurisdiction. This acreage represents about a fourth of all western land and nearly half of the western land remaining under federal ownership. Of the 179 million acres, approximately 147 million are located in organized grazing districts administered under the provisions of the Taylor Grazing Act. Since this land accounts for one acre in five of all land in the eleven western states, it is apparent that the Taylor grazing districts and the act under which they are administered are of great importance in western land use.

The "vacant, unappropriated, and unreserved" lands of the public domain that were organized into grazing districts under the Taylor Act have been described as the lands nobody wanted. They might better be described as the lands that were wanted least. These were the lands that could not be patented under the provisions of the Homestead Act, or that were not patented because their forage was so poor, or because particular ranchers thought they could control them through their possession of adjacent water sources and land.

The fact that scores of millions of acres of western land remained unappropriated and unreserved until the 1930's was partially the result of conflicting opinions regarding their disposition. For several decades after settlement of the West began, it was the settled policy of the federal government to place the public lands in private ownership as soon as possible. In time this policy began to be questioned, but the majority of the interested parties still thought the government should dispose of its unreserved and unappropriated lands. However, they were unable to agree on a method of disposition. The controversy began at about the opening of the century and has continued since. The solutions most widely and forcefully advocated were: (1) sell the land to grazing users at some extremely low price, (2) give the land away in small blocks to homesteaders, (3) deed the land to the states, and (4) have the federal government lease the land to private persons. No agreement on a single course of action could be reached, and consequently no changes were made.

It is unnecessary to record here the political history of these lands prior to the passage of the Taylor Grazing Act; the story has been adequately treated elsewhere.[1] As we have seen, however, approximately 147 million acres did remain in federal ownership under the jurisdiction of the General Land Office; but there was practically no administration of it. A substantial proportion was not even surveyed. About the only management or administration that was accorded this land was to keep ranchers from fencing it. Grazing was almost the sole means of utilizing the land, and the land was open to such use for anyone who wished to use it. It was a great commons.

During the early decades of grazing on the western range, the use of public land as a commons was not unsatisfactory to the majority of active western ranchers. By control of water sources, by legal fencing of their own properties and illegal fencing of federal property, by grazing-terri-

[1] Peffer, *op. cit.*

tory agreements among themselves, and by extralegal threats and pressures to fend off intruders, most ranchers were able to evolve a fairly satisfactory system for using the forage resources of the public lands to support their ranching operations. But as grazing intensity increased, both legal and extralegal methods were less effective in preventing federal range land use by others, and the situation became increasingly unsatisfactory for the established ranchers. Eventually, a slow but steady attrition of the very best lands by homesteading placed additional strains on many range graziers.

Despite the deteriorating situation of the graziers, nothing was done because no agreement could be reached about what should be done. However, from the early years of the twentieth century there was a gradual drift toward the idea of leasing the use of federal land resources. The grazing leases on the national forests were the earliest large-scale application of this idea. Although bitterly opposed by the sheep graziers, the leasing program was supported (albeit at times somewhat ambiguously) by many cattle ranchers. Another application of the idea was the leasing of mineral lands for exploitation. These might be lands owned outright by the federal government or lands on which the mineral rights had been reserved by the government when the surface was alienated.

For several decades, however, the leasing principle was not applied to the grazing lands of the public domain with which we are here concerned, and conditions on these lands continued to deteriorate steadily. As it became increasingly difficult to control the use of the public ranges, overgrazing became more and more widespread. This led to decreased forage-production and, in some places, to accelerated erosion. Inability to forbid use of the public ranges to others made it increasingly difficult for established ranchers to maintain balanced year-round livestock operations based partly on public land.

The temporal conjunction of several circumstances accounts in large measure for the introduction of a leasing system on the public grazing lands and for the particular time at which it was instituted. Shortly after the beginning of his administration, President Hoover and members of his cabinet proposed (1929) that the remainder of the unreserved public lands be turned over to the states in which the lands were located, with the mineral rights reserved to the federal government. Immediately the eastern conservation interests began to oppose this proposal with all the strength they could muster. Unexpectedly, however, the western states showed no enthusiasm for taking title to the remaining public domain lands within their boundaries. Particularly, they did not want the lands without the mineral rights. Although the Hoover administration pushed its proposal vigorously, within a year it was clear that there was no real chance that the transfer to the states would be made. Most of the proponents of transfer to the states then threw their influence behind groups that were proposing other measures, including a leasing system.

A second circumstance was the onset of the Great Depression of the 1930's. Agriculture had shared relatively little in the prosperity of the 1920's, and with the coming of the depression, the situation of farmers and ranchers rapidly became critical. Economic stringency intensified the ranchers' desire to obtain somehow control of their grazing resources. Meanwhile, their troubles were being multiplied by the unusually severe drought which beset them during most of the decade of the thirties. The extraordinary difficulties engendered by drought and depression put the nation in a favorable mood for social experimentation. And coincident with these events, several key political figures changed their minds about either the temporary or the ultimate disposition of federally owned western land. Among them was Congressman Edward T. Taylor of Colorado.

The law[2] which bears Congressman Taylor's name was passed by the Congress in 1934. It put an end to the free common use of the remaining "vacant, unappropriated, and unreserved" federal lands in the western states and substituted a system of leasing these lands for grazing.

Most of the lands affected by the Taylor Act were then useful for nothing but extensive grazing. For half a century they had been grazed by the livestock of local ranchers, though in later decades grazing by itinerant (so-called "tramp") sheep bands had become increasingly common. Such bands were not based on any private property, but were grazed exclusively on public land. In some places federal land existed in large, solid blocks, but elsewhere it was intermixed, often in a complex and intricate manner, with private and state-owned land. The federal lands were in no way physically separated from private and state land, and the economics of range grazing, particularly in the depression period, made it unfeasible to fence the land. Property boundary lines were often completely obscure. The purpose of the Taylor Act was to regularize and control grazing on the public range so as to bring some order into the existing situation.

Main Provisions of the Act

The three objectives of the Taylor Grazing Act are set forth in the preamble: (1) "to stop injury to the public grazing lands by preventing

[2] The Taylor Grazing Act of June 28, 1934 (48 Stat. 1269).

overgrazing," (2) "to provide for their orderly use, improvement, and development," and (3) "to stabilize the livestock industry dependent upon the public range."[3] Prior to the passage of the act the federal government had exerted only the slightest control over use of the surface resources of the unreserved and unappropriated public domain. The major change envisaged by the act was the orderly regulation of grazing on the public range in the hope and belief that such action would stop the deterioration of the range and stabilize the range livestock industry.

The act laid down a general policy and specified the major methods to be used in regulating grazing use of the western unreserved "public lands pending . . . final disposal."[4] It authorized the Secretary of the Interior to establish grazing districts. Lands previously reserved by the federal government for national forests, national parks, reservoir sites, reclamation projects, and the like were specifically excluded. After a grazing district had been established, the forage resources of the federal lands within the district were to be leased for a fee to the holders of "grazing permits." The basic devices for leasing the use of grazing resources were similar (though not identical) to those developed by the Forest Service about three decades earlier (see pp. 41–43). The payment of a fee for a stipulated number of a.u.m.'s of grazing, leasing solely to holders of permits, freedom from trespass by other graziers, and the confinement of each rancher's grazing activities to a stipulated area called an allotment were all devices used previously by the Forest Service. They had also been used in two grazing districts organized just prior to the passage of

[3] All quoted material in this section is from the Taylor Grazing Act as amended unless otherwise noted.

[4] The circumstances surrounding the inclusion of the "pending" phrase in the act make a fascinating historical study. Many of the stoutest backers of the bill—western representatives and senators, including Congressman Taylor—were convinced that the public domain lands should be transferred to the states or should eventually pass into private ownership. Many of them were supporting the Taylor Bill simply because they believed there was no hope at that time of getting the type of disposal of these lands that they desired. Partly at their insistence and partly to anticipate opposition the "pending" phrase was included. The inclusion of the phrase, however, was nearly as serious a threat to the successful passage of the act as its omission would have been. The Secretary of Agriculture—who had never been an enthusiastic supporter of the bill, because it placed administration of the Taylor Act in the Department of the Interior—advised President Franklin D. Roosevelt to veto the bill, partly because of the "pending" phrase, which he chose to interpret as making the bill merely a stopgap measure. Probably too much emphasis has been placed on the phrase. One Congress cannot irrevocably commit the people of the United States and their congressional representatives to a particular course of action. Future Congresses will act with respect to these lands in the way they think best, which is what they would have done with or without the inclusion of the "pending" phrase in the Taylor Act.

the Taylor Act. These districts utilized land from the unreserved public domain and were similar to those subsequently organized under the Taylor Act.

The law provided that before a district could be established a hearing must be held. Public notice of the hearing was to be given well in advance. One of the most important stipulations of the act then followed: that publication of the notice of the hearing was to have the effect of withdrawing all lands in the district from all forms of entry. Section 7 of the act empowered the Secretary of Interior to classify lands within a district as being more useful for some purpose other than grazing and then to dispose of them under the "applicable public land laws." A particular piece of land would be so classified and alienated upon request by someone wishing to make entry on it. It was stated that lands should not be "subject to disposition, settlement, or occupation until after the same have been classified. . . ." With these provisions of the act the tens of millions of acres of unreserved public land became subject to classification for the first time, and the principle was established that they should not be used in ways to which their physical characteristics were unsuited. Although it provided for reopening of lands eventually classified as being suitable for agriculture, the act had the effect of closing most lands against alienation from federal ownership.

The Secretary of Interior was authorized, after the districts had been formed, to make such rules and regulations for their administration and regulation as were "necessary to accomplish the purposes of this Act. . . ." The latter passage is the specific authorization for the *Federal Range Code for Grazing Districts*, which has now grown to a twenty-six-page document setting forth the rules and regulations by which the Department of Interior administers and regulates grazing districts. Wilful violations of the Taylor Act or the *Federal Range Code* were made punishable by fines. The act also authorized the Secretary to study erosion and flood control on these lands.

Those western members of Congress who were particularly interested in the Taylor Act had very concrete ideas concerning the regulation and administration of the grazing districts. Consequently, the act gave the Secretary a number of specific directives. He was to issue permits to graze livestock on the grazing districts. Reasonable annual fees should be charged for permits. Permits were to be issued to citizens and corporations, with preference to persons within or near a district who were private landowners and had been in the livestock business prior to January 1, 1934. Ten years was the maximum time a given permit could run, but

permits were to be subject to renewal, and renewals were to have preference. The Secretary was to "specify from time to time numbers of
stock and seasons of use." The Secretary could "remit, reduce, refund"
grazing fees.

Improvements designed to increase the utility of the range were clearly
desirable. Section 4 of the act authorized construction of "fences, wells,
reservoirs, and other improvements." Such structures might be built either by the government or by a permittee.

Section 8 of the Taylor Grazing Act was designed to make possible
some consolidation and simplification of the difficult and complex land
tenure pattern found in many western areas. To this end the Secretary
was empowered to accept gifts of land lying within a grazing district and
to trade lands. Lands to be traded could be either within or outside of a
grazing district. The lands to be traded, however, had to be of equal
value; or more specifically, the private lands to be traded had to be at
least equal in value to the public lands. Lands could be traded either with
private parties or with the states. When federal lands were known or
thought to contain minerals, the Secretary was directed to reserve the
mineral rights when making exchanges. In all exchanges, such mineral
rights could be reserved by either party.

From the standpoint of the western stockmen probably the most satisfactory part of the entire Taylor Grazing Act was Section 9, which instructed the Secretary to make regulations "for cooperation with local
associations of stockmen" in the administration of the districts. The section also authorized the Secretary to accept "contributions toward the
administration, protection, and improvement" of a district.

Sections 10 and 11 prescribed the disposition of grazing receipts. Discussion of this will be deferred to a later section, where the history of
grazing fees and receipts and their disposition will be reviewed (pp. 72–
76).

Section 12 directed the Secretary to co-operate with the Forest Service
in co-ordinating grazing by livestock that used both grazing district land
and national forest land. Section 13 specified that the President might
transfer federal lands within a grazing district to a national forest if it
were deemed desirable. Similarly, national forest lands might be transferred to grazing districts.

By amending a previous law, the Taylor Act authorized the Secretary
of Interior to sell at public auction by bids any isolated tract of land not
exceeding 760 acres. However, owners of adjacent lands had the privilege of buying the land if they met the highest bid price. Such isolated

tracts had to be sold for at least their appraised value, but they could not be sold for more than three times their appraised value to owners of contiguous land. Any rough or mountainous areas up to 160 acres in size, whether isolated or not, could be sold to owners of adjacent lands.

The Secretary of the Interior was authorized to lease, upon "such terms and conditions" as he might prescribe, any vacant, unappropriated and unreserved public lands whose situation did not warrant their inclusion in a grazing district. Preference in issuing such leases was to be given owners of contiguous land. Areas up to 320 acres in size that were classified as suitable for agriculture could be taken up by individuals under the various applicable public land laws. The federal lands of the grazing districts were specifically asserted to be open to hunting, fishing, and prospecting for minerals.

Ever since the Taylor Act was passed, the western livestock interests have sought constantly to tighten and extend their influence on its administration. The first amendment to the act, passed in 1936, contained a stipulation requiring every higher level administrative officer, including district graziers, to have been a resident of a western public land state for at least a year prior to appointment. The same section also directed the Civil Service Commission to "give consideration to . . . practical range experience" in determining eligibility for appointment. By giving preference to westerners and persons with practical range experience in the public land states, the livestock interests felt they would insure an administration sympathetic to their viewpoint. In particular, this would forestall the possible appointment of an eastern conservationist with an unsympathetic attitude and scant knowledge of the western range livestock industry.

The original version of the Taylor Act called only for "cooperation with local associations of stockmen." An amendment passed in 1939 (Section 18 of the act as amended) gave specific legal status to the "advisory board of local stockmen." Under the amendment each board was required to have not less than five nor more than twelve members. One member of the advisory board might be a wildlife representative appointed by the Secretary of Interior. The other board members were to be "recommended" to the Secretary by an "election conducted under rules and regulations prescribed by the Secretary," but no member could take office "until appointed by the Secretary. . . ." This gave the Secretary an absolute veto on any appointment to a grazing advisory board. The Secretary was empowered to remove any board member "for the good of the service." The board was required to meet at least once a year.

The function of these boards is entirely advisory, and the Secretary can overrule them whenever he desires. However, except in cases of emergency, the law requires the Secretary to "request the advice of the advisory board in advance of the promulgation of any rules and regulations affecting the district."

The stipulations we have just reviewed constitute the principal features of the Taylor Grazing Act. The passage of the act was a major piece of legislation. It was intended to reverse policy completely with respect to the unreserved public domain from free, unregulated, common use to leased, regulated, exclusive use.

Such a radical change in policy, involving so many people and so many millions of acres of land, was not something that could be accomplished overnight. The process of creating an organization to administer the districts and to make contact with all interested parties took several months. To organize districts and implement the act throughout the eleven western states took several years, and in some respects the process of instituting and implementing the act has continued down to the present.

Implementing the Taylor Grazing Act

Almost immediately after passage of the Taylor Grazing Act the Interior Department took steps to implement it. The first move was to hold a series of conferences in the various western states during the months of July, August, and September, 1934 to inform people of what was intended, explain the purpose of the act, and sound out the stockmen's opinions concerning its operation.

Reactions to the passage of the act, as evidenced at the hearings, differed sharply from place to place in the West. In some areas ranchers entertained doubts and serious anxiety abut the way in which the new law would affect their operations. Some of the hearings were tense, explosive, rough; rumors circulated that the Department of Interior representatives were to be run out of town by local ranchers. Ranchers appearing at the hearings issued belligerent statements that they would shoot anyone trespassing on "their" range and declaring that they were not going to have their ranching operations run by any government man.[5] In contrast, the hearings in other areas were very quiet. They consisted mostly of an endless series of questions by local ranchers about how the act was to be administered—questions which in many cases the Interior representatives

[5] Personal conversations with some of the men who held the early hearings, particularly Mr. Lester Brooks, then District Grazier, Wyoming Grazing District, Lander, Wyoming.

were unable to answer. Meanwhile a small flood of inquiries was reaching the Interior Department offices in Washington, D.C. To deal with them Secretary Ickes appointed a temporary Director in Charge of Grazing, but, within three months after the act became law, F. R. Carpenter was appointed Director of Grazing. Mr. Carpenter was from the same section of the country, western Colorado, as the sponsor of the act, Congressman Taylor. He was an attorney acquainted with the range livestock industry. His appointment was reassuring to the stockmen because his general point of view was wholly sympathetic to the western range livestock industry.

The new Director proceeded promptly with measures necessary to implement the act. He began to recruit a staff from the other divisions of the Interior Department. He issued notices of the state-wide public hearings that were required by the Taylor Act before grazing districts could be organized. During December, 1934, and January, 1935, these hearings were held. At the meetings those in attendance elected state committees of stockmen to draw up boundaries for the grazing districts. These committees were organized in all the western states "and recommended the establishment of 50 districts involving an aggregate area of approximately 142,000,000 acres of vacant, unreserved, unappropriated public land."[6] Only thirty-two grazing districts were actually organized, since the law provided that only 80 million acres of public land could be included in such districts. Those districts having the most pressing problems or presumed to be the easiest to administer were organized first. The committees' recommendations were, of course, almost a mandate to Congress to increase the amount of public land eligible for inclusion in grazing districts. A bill to increase the eligible area to 142 million acres was introduced into Congress in 1935, but it carried certain other provisions which caused the President to veto it.[7] A bill raising the limit to 142 million acres was passed in 1936.

As soon as the state-wide hearings were completed, Department of Interior representatives known as district graziers were sent into various areas to organize districts. In some cases a single district grazier was sent to organize one of the new districts. In other cases two or more Interior Department men undertook the task.

During the first year after passage of the Taylor Act, rapid progress was made toward the actual organization of the districts. By June 30, 1935, thirty-two grazing districts had been organized, and by the end of

[6] U.S. Department of Interior, *Annual Report, 1935*, p. 15.

[7] See Peffer, *op. cit.*, p. 222.

the 1935–36 fiscal year the entire 80 million acres authorized for inclusion had been organized into thirty-seven operating districts. The districts contained a total of 198 million acres in all ownerships. At this time the Division of Grazing had sixty employees, of whom forty-seven worked outside the Washington office. This represented one field employee for each 4.2 million acres to be supervised and administered.

Various provisions of the Taylor Act, already reviewed, provided means for alienating lands within grazing districts, but they stipulated that no land could be alienated until it had been classified as suitable for the purposes for which it was being entered. In November, 1934, just a few months after the passage of the Taylor Grazing Act, the President withdrew all public lands in the western states from entry until they had been classified. Of course, this did not stop the alienation of the land under entries already filed. Nor did it stop filings of new applications. Public domain lands continued to be patented at a rate greater than a million acres per year until 1940. Original entries dropped precipitously after 1935, but they continued to run in excess of one hundred thousand acres per year throughout the rest of the 1930's. Nevertheless, classification during the early years of the act was rigorous. Lands were not classified as being suitable for agriculture (or some other purpose) unless they really were adjudged to be suitable. During that period public land was disposed of, not on the basis of fulfilling the letter of unrealistic land laws, but in accordance with its potentialities.

It is highly significant that the first instructions issued by the new Director of Grazing were "rules providing for special elections for district advisors to assist in the management of grazing districts."[8] The early election of these stockmen-advisors was necessary for two reasons. One was the provision in the Taylor Act which called on the Division of Grazing to co-operate with local stockmen and to permit them to take an active part in the administration of the districts. Thus, it was highly desirable that the stockmen-advisors be elected before administration and regulation had advanced very far. Second, before any progress could be made in organizing the grazing districts, it was absolutely essential to have the advice and counsel of some local stockmen, because the system of permit allocation and priorities to be set up necessitated information concerning the previous range activities of the applicants. Such information could be obtained only from local range livestock ranchers. The members of the advisory boards received no regular salary but were paid $5 per day for each day of active service, largely to cover their travel ex-

[8] U.S. Department of Interior, Division of Grazing, "Circular No. 1."

penses and subsistence. The advisory board members were the effective governing and administrative body of each grazing district.[9]

A second circular was issued about a month later. It was entitled "Rules for the Guidance of District Advisors in Recommending the Issuance of Grazing Licenses." The circular stated that the Department of Interior would issue one-year "temporary revocable licenses"[10] pending the completion of land classification within the districts and final decisions on the various relationships between the ranchers' private property and their former use of federal range land. These relationships, when determined, would provide the basis for issuing permanent grazing permits.

The crucial task in implementing the Taylor Act was the internal organization of the grazing districts, that is, the assignment of grazing licenses or grazing permits, and the exclusion and removal of unlicensed and unauthorized users from the federal lands within the district. This proved to be an extraordinarily complex and difficult undertaking. The source of the difficulty lay in the desire of the ranchers to graze more livestock on the range than it would support. Much of the range had been seriously overgrazed previously, and most livestock operators knew this to be the case; but almost no livestock operator wanted to cut down his individual use any more than was absolutely necessary.

The framers of the Taylor Act were, of course, perfectly aware there was far more use of the range than was desirable; therefore, if some use and users were to be eliminated, a system of priorities had to be set up. A general system of preferences was enunciated in the act, preference "to those within or near a district who are landowners engaged in the livestock business, bona fide occupants or settlers, or owners of water or water rights. . . ." "Circular No. 2" set forth the preferences in detail. Applicants were placed in one of three classes in order of priority:

Priority 1. Qualified applicants with dependent commensurate property and with prior use of public grazing land.

Priority 2. Qualified applicants with prior use but not adequate commensurate property.

Priority 3. Qualified applicants with adequate commensurate property but without prior use.

In many districts if an applicant was placed in priorities 2 or 3, he was effectively eliminated from the district because all of the available graz-

[9] For an analysis and description of the role of western ranchers in the administration of the Taylor grazing districts, see John D. McGowen, "Cowboy Joe, Administrator," University of Wyoming *Publications*, Vol. XI, No. 5 (Sept., 1944), pp. 65–90.

[10] U.S. Department of Interior, *Annual Report, 1935*, p. 16.

ing would be necessary to satisfy the claims of those in priority 1. However, this was not always the case.

Early in the year following the appearance of "Circular No. 2," the Division of Grazing held in Salt Lake City a western regional meeting of the representatives of all the organized districts. At this meeting the range livestock ranchers took the Division of Grazing to task for its order of priorities. They demanded that priorities 2 and 3 be reversed because the priority system gave the detested "tramp" sheepman a priority over a local land-owning applicant who did not have a history of previous range use. Shortly thereafter a new circular was issued changing the order of priority. The new order was designed to eliminate the "tramp" operator and largely did so; it also helped to stablize the livestock industry because it assured that use of the dry federal range lands for grazing purposes would be integrated at least partially with the water supplies and irrigated lands of the adjoining areas. It will be recalled that the preference system of permits for grazing on the national forests accomplished the same result.

The prior use requirement was defined as actual grazing of the federal ranges of the district for three of the five years during the period June 28, 1929 to June 28, 1934. This was a period of drought and depression, and some local ranchers who had long used the federal ranges had either stopped doing so during the priority period or had reduced their herds to unusually small size. Later on, when increased precipitation had boosted forage production on the range and the market for cattle had improved, these ranchers came to the grazing district advisory boards with applications for range grazing permits. As late as the summer of 1953 I sat in the office of a Wyoming grazing district and listened to an applicant request a permit based on regular use of the range during the 1920's, although he had never contacted the grazing district office previously nor had his cattle ever used the federal lands since 1929.

The foregoing two preference requirements (dependent commensurate property and prior use of the range) were the only specific instructions available to district graziers and district advisory boards when they began issuing "temporary permits" to graze the lands of their districts. These permits ran for one year. It will be recalled that one of the principal objects of the Taylor Act was "to stop injury to the public grazing lands by preventing overgrazing," and that the Secretary of Interior was empowered to specify numbers of stock and seasons of use. Nevertheless, in virtually all cases, the number of livestock licensed under temporary permits was greater than the range could properly support. Clearly, numbers needed to be reduced, but to effect such reductions proved an exceedingly thorny problem, as will subsequently appear.

During the period when the temporary permits were being issued and later when permits were being renewed, the district graziers and the advisory boards held what might best be described as public hearings in attempting to arrive at an allocation of priorities and permits. These "hearings" were critically important since they made possible the decisions that were necessary for the Taylor Act to function in specific local situations. Before considering them, however, let us look for a moment at the general setting within which the act had to be implemented.

Issuing the Original Taylor Permits

In attempting to implement the Taylor Grazing Act the participants were not trying to create a new situation out of nothing, but to modify an existing arrangement. During the days and evenings when the Interior men and their local rancher-advisers were conducting the lengthy hearings to determine the allocation of grazing permits, the cattle of the ranchers on the advisory committee and of the ranchers who were appearing at the hearings were wandering over the very ranges that were being allocated. Just how many cattle there were, where they were, and to whom they belonged were matters commonly unknown and often disputed. Bands of sheep under the care of herders and dogs were being slowly moved across the same ranges. Some of the sheep belonged to local ranchers, some belonged to ranchers with headquarters scores of miles away, sometimes on the opposite side of a mountain range; and some of the sheep belonged to herds operated by men who had no headquarters. These cattle and sheep grazed an intricately divided and interspersed pattern of private, state-owned, and federally owned lands. How much or when each band of sheep or bunch of cattle used each piece of property was doubtful or unknown. Whether the amount of use and the spatial or temporal pattern of use that year was generally comparable to that of previous years was imperfectly known. Since the differences from year to year could not be stated with any precision, it was exceedingly difficult to specify the grazing pattern that constituted "normal use."

Further difficulties lay in the fact that little or nothing was known scientifically about the condition of the ranges, the amount of forage production, or the trends of range condition. Over vast areas of the West this was a period of drought; hence, even if it were agreed (as it usually was not) that range conditions and forage production were deteriorating, it would have been impossible in many circumstances to say with any degree of certainty whether the deterioration was due to overgrazing and abuse of the range or was simply an ephemeral condition attributable to drought. In short, no one could say anything with any certainty about either the current condition or the long-range trends of the range. One major objective of the Taylor Act was to bring the level of grazing use into approximate conformance with forage production in order that the range livestock industry be "stabilized." However, since there were absolutely no reliable scientific data concerning range condition nor concerning that elusive quantity "carrying capacity," there could be no reliable opinion on the reduction in numbers necessary to bring range use into conformance with carrying capacity.

Permits were to be issued on a priority system based on property ownership and on previous range use. Property ownership was easy to establish. Previous range utilization is best described as chaotic, or nearly so, but it was on the basis of the available precedents that range permits were to be issued. A less structured situation is difficult to imagine. Few precedents were available; such data as existed were conflicting, debatable, and almost never susceptible of proof.

Reactions to the situation were diverse and extraordinarily interesting. As might have been anticipated, the large-scale, aggressive, alert, politically conscious ranchers tended to seize the initiative and secure election to the advisory boards. Many of them were officials of, or at least active in, the various western livestock associations. Many of the larger ranchers were urban dwellers—bankers, real estate dealers, lawyers, lumbermen, or merchants. They were active in political life and alert to legislative actions affecting their interest. Not all large-scale operators, however, were active and influential in the hearings. In some cases failure to participate actively and effectually appears to have been due to a misguided contempt for the whole procedure, a notion that it was simply a *pro forma* process that would have no overt effect on range land use. Other ranchers neglected the hearings probably from failure to realize their significance, and perhaps in some cases simply from a personal inability to function effectively in such a situation. Everyone concerned with the situation, however, realized that, whatever the reality, it must not be made to appear that the hearings were dominated by the big ranchers and their livestock associations.[11] Consequently, some aggressive, active, in-

---

[11] It should perhaps be made explicit that western range livestock ranchers have trade associations as do other industrial or professional groups—they are called live-

terested, and politically adept small ranchers became highly influential in the advisory boards.

When a rancher appeared at the hearings in connection with his permit application, he was commonly asked to state the terms of the permit for which he was applying; that is, how many head of livestock he wished to graze, where, how long, and at what seasons.[12] Next he was questioned about the location and extent of the private property ("base property," "commensurable land," or "dependent property") which he had used to support his range livestock herd previously and which he proposed to use in the future. It will be recalled that ownership of local property was one of the requirements for receiving a permit that had been written into the Taylor Act. As to whether the property had been used to support a range livestock herd during the years immediately preceding the hearings there could be argument, and on many occasions there were fiercely held contradictory views.

In fact, by far the most common source of disagreement and argument was the applicant's previous history of range use. An applicant would almost always request the largest permit that he felt he could possibly substantiate. He would then assert that in the past he had used the public ranges to graze the number and kinds of livestock, for the period, and time of year, for which he was applying. Very commonly a member of the advisory board acquainted with the area in question or another rancher interested in a permit in the same area would contradict some or perhaps all of the applicant's statements. They might assert that the applicant had not grazed more than half the numbers that he claimed, that his stock had always grazed on the west side of Sheep Mountain only, and that they had never grazed south of Big Sandy Draw, except during very dry periods, when they had been allowed to trail down to Joe Smith's spring. The applicant would argue otherwise. Witnesses would be called to testify, who would then corroborate or contradict points in the opposing statements. In some cases they might elaborate; for instance, a witness might explain that in 1932 the applicant had actu-

---

stock associations. Both cattle producers and sheep ranchers have a national association. The national associations are closely affiliated with state groups and local associations. Their objectives are to promote the interests of the western range livestock industry. In general they represent the views and interests of the large ranchers, but some small ranchers are active and influential in the organizations.

[12] Sometimes several applicants for permits in the same general area would appear at the hearing more or less simultaneously, while at other times and in other places applicants would appear individually.

ally grazed the number of livestock he claimed on the particular range, but that normally he had never used that range, and had been permitted to do so that year only because the winter snow had completely covered his normal forage supply.

The entire hearing procedure was in part a test of the applicant's political, forensic, and rhetorical skill. The general tendency was to make such claims as could not definitely be made to appear extremely unlikely. Suppose, by way of illustration, that an applicant had in fact generally grazed 100 head of cattle on a particular piece of public range from the middle of September, when they came down off the national forest lands, until approximately the middle of December, when they were brought onto the irrigated lands of the ranch headquarters. If the applicant were to claim that he had grazed 200 head of cattle on this range for three months in the fall and for three months in the spring, every informed person would flatly contradict his assertions, and no one could be found to substantiate his statements. If, however, he claimed that he had grazed 130 to 145 head of cattle on the range for three months in the autumn and for one month in the spring, and coupled this with the assertion that he and Jones had used the range in common, each with approximately 135 head (an assertion which Jones had previously made) and added that their western boundary had been the crest of Rocky Ridge (a claim which Smith had been trying to substantiate), he could reasonably expect that Jones and Smith would corroborate his statements to the letter. Although some others would flatly contradict his statements, some would admit that, although they thought the applicant grazed only 100 head here in the fall, it was possible that he had grazed a few more in the fall and had them there for a month in the spring also. The net effect was to make it clear that the only information available was conflicting testimony, and that it was impossible to prove conclusively that the applicant's claims were invalid. The ability to talk persuasively, confidently, and (perhaps) cleverly was undoubtedly an asset in such a situation. Time and again in talking to ranchers or to Interior Department officials about some apparently anomalous result of the hearing process, I was told: "Well, so-and-so was just a better talker, that's all."

Rhetorical effectiveness was not, however, the sole determinant of the influence of a man's views. Some ranchers carried to the hearings other assets which gave increased weight to their views or strengthened their bargaining position. A rancher, whether a member of the advisory board or appearing as an applicant before the board, who had strong influence within either of the major political parties or within one or more of the western livestock associations, might find himself in a more favorable position than he would have been if not involved in politics. The views of a rancher-banker might be given great weight simply because of his ability to wield considerable power over the economy. On the whole, however, such considerations were of comparatively small importance. Ranchers buy in a fairly open market and sell their products in a national and impersonal market. On the whole they are probably less impressed by, or fearful of, retaliatory political or economic power than almost any group of substantial size in American society.

In some cases the local range property holdings of a rancher were potent sources of bargaining power. A man who controlled all sources of water on part of the range lands of a district (to take an extreme case) and who threatened, if his permit application were substantially reduced, to retire onto his private lands and simultaneously close off access for anyone else to his water supplies, obviously held a whip-hand over all the cattle ranchers who had formerly used that area and the applicant's water. Ordinarily no individual rancher was in so strong a position as this, but usually certain ranchers, because of the size, nature, and location of their holdings, were in a more powerful bargaining position than others. By threatening to close off water sources, or to string long fences on their private property (thus making long detours necessary for livestock to reach certain parts of the range) or to prohibit trailing across their lands, or to engage in other types of unco-operative activity, some ranchers could assure themselves more favorable and preferential consideration in the granting of permits and allotments than could their less favorably situated neighbors.

It is easy, however, to exaggerate the efficacy of range pressure by control of water or by fencing. Consider again a rancher who completely controls water supplies on an area of range. By refusing everyone access to his water supplies he could place an absolute interdiction on use of that range by cattle, but his control of water supplies would have no effect whatever on use of the range by bands of sheep (see p. 34). Thus the possibility of sheep use on the area was at least a partial counter to any threatened closure of water supplies. Moreover, there was the additional possibility of developing new water sources on the dry ranges either by constructing reservoirs or by drilling wells.

The effectiveness of sheep use of range lands otherwise controlled by ownership of water sources is well illustrated by the experience in Nevada. Nevada has a larger proportion of public domain land and fewer water sources than any other western state. Large Nevada ranchers long achieved effective control of great sections of the public domain by establishing complete control of water sources, and consequently opposed any regulation of the public ranges. Many of them finally came to support federal leasing of these ranges as a result of large-scale winter invasions of "their" public lands by bands of sheep whose use of the range they could prevent neither by legal methods through ownership of water supplies nor successfully by extralegal methods.

All ranchers, including sheep ranchers, may be susceptible to range-

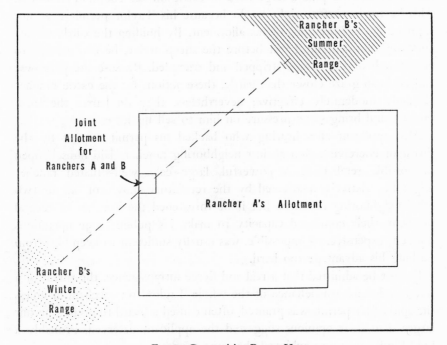

FIG. 8.—Competitive Range Use

use pressure if they use federal range lands. Figure 8 illustrates a current case of pressure being applied by one rancher against another under Taylor administration in the Middle Rocky Mountain basins. The location of the area is not specified for reasons that will soon be apparent. As indicated by Figure 8, the large cattle allotment (containing many tens of thousands of acres) is assigned to a large-scale cattle rancher, whose Taylor permit allows him to graze cattle on that range for most of the year. One small part of the large allotment is used in common. A sheep rancher uses it for two weeks in both spring and fall to interrupt the long migrations of his sheep bands from the winter range to the summer range and back. In spring, the sheep are trailed to the small allotment from the winter range, allowed to rest and feed for two weeks, and then trailed on to the summer range. The procedure is reversed in autumn. The rancher who owns the large allotment has tried repeatedly to buy the sheep rancher's rights on the common allotment, but without success. He is now attempting to force the sale. His ranch is so large that his cattle are herded, and their movements can thus be controlled. In the spring and fall somewhat before the sheep bands are to arrive the cattle rancher puts a large herd of cattle on the common allotment. This he has a perfect right to do because his Taylor permit does not stipulate any subdivisions of his allotment. By holding the cattle on the common allotment until just before the sheep arrive, he can manage to have much of the forage stripped and trampled. Because sheep browse and also can graze closer than cattle, these actions by the cattle rancher are only moderately effective; nevertheless, they do harass the small rancher and bring some pressure on him to sell his lease.

Any applicant at a hearing who backed his permit request by the threat of coercive action against neighboring ranchers laid himself open to possible retaliation. A powerful, large-scale, well-situated rancher might be relatively unaffected by the retaliatory moves of one or two small neighboring ranchers, but if he threatened the interests of several of them, their combined capacity to make his public range operations difficult, expensive, or impossible, was usually sufficient to keep him from pushing his advantage too hard.

It must be admitted that a real and fierce intransigence, the threat of a bitter and stubborn defiance of the whole Taylor Act mechanism unless the applicant's permit was granted, often caused a board to grant a permit larger than their opinions suggested the applicant deserved. Probably a bold bluff sometimes achieved the same results.

Thus at the permit application hearings the problem of the district grazier and his advisory board of stockmen was to achieve some approximation of justice in a situation where a large share of the essential facts were unknown, misrepresented, or in dispute. Concerning one range user, however, the tramp sheepman, there was no argument. Everyone present at the hearings wanted him completely removed from the range, and the basis for his elimination was clearly and unequivocally stated in the *Federal Range Code*. In most areas he swiftly disappeared from the scene.

The tests and criteria for the allocation of permits among the local property holders were based almost entirely on previous land use, but in most areas the picture of previous use bordered on chaos. In such a situation the only feasible move was some sort of temporizing measure that would: (1) furnish a much longer time in which to organize range land use, (2) permit the western range livestock industry to keep functioning without serious dislocation, (3) at the same time permit the federal government to begin leasing the use of its land, and (4) establish at least a semblance of government control over grazing on the public range. In line with these objectives, the policy followed at the permit hearings was to give everyone approximately the permit he applied for unless the majority of neighboring range land users objected. In the latter case the permit was reduced only to a figure in which the other ranchers concerned would acquiesce. The temporary permits as finally issued stipulated the number of stock permitted on the range, where they were to be grazed, and at what season they were to be grazed on each area.

The average Taylor grazing district contains approximately three million acres of land, an area far too big to be administered or used in one piece. The districts are divided into subareas called units; which also are too large, each district being divided into just a few units. So units, in turn, are divided into numerous allotments that vary greatly in size; the smallest may contain only a few hundred acres, the largest, several tens of thousands of acres. The allotments are basically similar to those of the national forests. In some cases a small Taylor allotment may be used exclusively by a single rancher, whose permits allow him to use the allotment almost like private property. Often the only limitations will be those stipulating the types of livestock he is permitted to graze, the total number of a.u.m.'s of grazing, and a short period in the year when grazing is not permitted. At the other extreme would be an allotment as large as one hundred thousand acres, used in common by fifty or sixty ranchers grazing both sheep and cattle on it for various periods at various seasons of the year. A wide variety of intermediate types occur between these two extremes. Various combinations of livestock and grazing areas are found in the permits issued for particular units. Herded sheep, for example, may be confined to particular allotments within a unit, while cattle are permitted to graze over the entire unit. Such complexities make the administration of a unit difficult.

As soon as the permits had been issued, it was generally apparent to all concerned—the Department of Interior representatives, the members of the advisory boards, and the ranchers—that the situation was entirely unsatisfactory. In most districts permits had been issued for many more livestock than the range could properly support. Many, perhaps a majority of the permittees, were dissatisfied with the areas which they were permitted to graze, or the grazing season, or some other aspect of their own or their neighbors' permits. Most permittees were anxious to work out some mutually agreeable modification of all the permits in each part of the district as soon as possible, and adjudication procedures to accomplish this began to be developed almost immediately. But such procedures have not accomplished any rapid change in the situation; on the whole the process of modifying the grazing pattern and grazing intensity has proceeded very slowly, with numerous halts and interruptions.

Range Adjudication and Grazing Administration

Range adjudication may be defined as the process of making changes in the allocations and priorities governing the use of range resources that were stipulated under the original temporary permits. The Taylor Act provided that as soon as the carrying capacity of the range in a grazing district had been established, permits could be issued for terms as long as ten years. Most ranchers were anxious to obtain these ten-year permits and thus had an incentive to complete the adjudication.

One provision of the act made it virtually impossible to revoke a permit if the permittee did not violate the rules established in the act and in the *Federal Range Code*. The relevant clause (in Section 3 of the Taylor Act) states that "no permittee complying with the rules and regulations laid down by the Secretary of the Interior shall be denied the renewal of such permit, if such denial will impair the value of the grazing unit of the permittee, when such unit is pledged as security for any *bona fide* loan." Since cancellation of a permit would inevitably impair the value of a grazing unit, any rancher who was granted an original one-year permit could make himself invulnerable to cancellation by merely pledging the unit as security for a small loan.

Several other circumstances were of greater importance in making range adjudication and readjustment extremely difficult: (1) much of the range has never been surveyed and its carrying capacity is not accurately known, (2) ranchers, including members of the district advisory boards, have been reluctant to give up any part of their class-1 demands,[13] (3) administrative personnel have usually been scanty; at times, with district offices closed down or operating with only a district grazier and clerk, progress in range readjustment has been nil or conditions have actually deteriorated, (4) changes from one type of livestock to another have created difficulties (in recent years this has been mostly a change

[13] Class-1 demands are those obtained under priority 1 as specified in grazing "Circular 2" (see p. 60).

from sheep to cattle), (5) there have been changes in ranch ownership and associated changes in the ownership of grazing permits; in many cases such sales have involved either combining or splitting ranch units, (6) year-to-year changes in range conditions have occurred, usually traceable to variations in precipitation.

The range grazing patterns that prevailed after the first permits were issued were generally chaotic, because they were based on the previous anarchic range use practices. One obvious line of action in nearly every district was to try to organize a more rational grazing pattern. In the area best known to me, the Middle Rocky Mountain basins, a majority of ranchers in all the Taylor grazing districts were willing to co-operate in a program of range reorganization, but there were generally some ranchers who preferred no changes at all, either because they were satisfied with current conditions or because they preferred to have range management as disorganized as possible in order to increase their own freedom of action.

As long as changes in range organization were kept separate from questions of cuts in the permittees class-1 demands, progress could be made. Among the methods used to simplify and rationalize the grazing pattern were: exchanges of land use, changes in the season of use, changing joint allotments to individual allotments or vice versa, new fencing, and allotment boundary changes.

The licensees were unwilling to decrease the number of a.u.m.'s of use as stipulated in their annual or term permits if it could possibly be avoided. Numerous ways of avoiding formal cuts were available. It could be argued that the carrying capacity of the range would increase, hence cuts were not necessary. Many ranchers argued that their permits should not be cut, but that their neighbors' permits should be; this was an effective way of preventing any reduction. The *Federal Range Code* provides that a rancher may apply for and be granted "non-use"; that is, a rancher asks to graze the range for fewer a.u.m.'s than his permit entitles him, and he pays only for the number that he actually uses. He can take such non-use for as long as the District Manager will approve, though commonly the bureau tends to draw the line at five consecutive years. By doing this regularly, a rancher reduces the amount of his range use without reducing the size of his permit. In some cases a rancher will not use all the a.u.m.'s of grazing that his permit entitles him, but will pay the full fee called for by the permit, thus reducing use without even taking non-use. It should be noted that very large prorated cuts were made in permitted stock numbers in some districts where the situation demanded it and where the district grazier was particularly forceful, aggressive, or persuasive, or where the district advisory board took strong leadership.

To develop and maintain a rational range grazing land plan has proved difficult in most areas exhibiting a complex land tenure pattern or where numerous small operators use the range. Reorganization plans are generally worked out through long-continued conversations among the ranchers, the grazing district advisory board, and the district grazier. By exchanges of range use and by other processes of give and take, a whole series of interlocking informal agreements is created, and these agreements add up to a range grazing plan without any changes in the ranchers' formal claims and permits. The agreements may be entirely oral with nothing to enforce them except their mutual acceptability. They are recognized by the Bureau of Land Management (or the BLM) only if they are reduced to writing and approved by the range manager.[14] Sometimes there is not even a face-to-face agreement; three or four ranchers will gradually adjust their practices to each other, and these practices will become stabilized and routinized.

A complex, informal organization of this sort is extremely precarious; almost anything can upset it. The most prevalent cause of disruption is a change in ownership of one of the ranches involved in the agreement. The new owner may read his permit, consult with the district grazier concerning the boundaries of his allotments, and then proceed to operate according to the letter of his permit. He may under such circumstances shatter in several particulars a delicately negotiated, fragile set of range agreements perhaps involving the practices of a dozen ranchers. It may be several years before the situation can be stabilized again.

Grazing Fees

One other administrative problem, the grazing fee, is of sufficient importance to be treated in detail. To begin with, it must be clearly understood that grazing fees from the Taylor grazing lands are negligible from the viewpoint of the total federal revenue. Grazing fees from such lands in 1956 totaled less than $2.4 million; this figure was only a small fraction of a *hundredth of 1 per cent* of total federal income. Such an infinitesimal percentage can scarcely command even a moment's consideration by a Congress almost overwhelmed with a multitude of fiscal and legislative problems. When we recall that this income is derived from lands scattered over all the western states, it becomes clear that even if it were all turned over to the states the grazing revenue from the Taylor

[14] Sec. 161, 6 (g) of the *Federal Range Code*.

lands would be only a minor item in the revenue picture of state governments. We must look elsewhere for the actual or potential importance of grazing fees.

Grazing fees are important to range livestock ranchers because they affect their costs of production. Such fees therefore have an effect on the stability of the range livestock industry. The level of fees may affect ranchers' grazing practices and thereby indirectly have an effect on range land conditions. Indirect effects on range conditions will also be exerted by grazing fees that are reinvested in structures and other "improvements" on the range. If these fees were turned over to local taxing units (counties, school districts, etc.), in lieu of taxes, they would be an important item in local tax revenues.

On any comparative basis, grazing fees on the Taylor lands are very low. Part of the explanation is historical. The original fees were established in the depression of the 1930's, when nearly all range livestock ranchers were having difficulty in remaining financially solvent. Ranchers were then extremely reluctant to add grazing fees to their operating costs. The very low first fee (5 cents per a.u.m.) was designed partly to enlist rancher co-operation and acquiescence in Taylor Act administration. The original Taylor grazing fees were approximately a third the size of those being charged on the national forests at that time[15] and represented an even smaller fraction of private land leasing fees. For the first year after the formation of each district no grazing fees at all were charged.

Throughout the history of Taylor Act administration, only a small part of the total grazing receipts has gone ultimately into the federal treasury. The Taylor Act called for a payment of 5 cents per a.u.m. for grazing on all lands coming under its provisions, whether incorporated in grazing districts or not. A three-way split of the receipts was authorized. Half of all receipts were to be turned over to the states in which they were collected, with the state legislatures being required to expend the monies in the counties where collected. I found it a startling exemplification of the political power of the range stockmen to discover that these funds were invariably turned over to the grazing district advisory boards to be expended for range improvements, in spite of the stringent need of many western counties (particularly in the 1930's) for school, road, and other funds.

An additional fourth of the original grazing fees was indirectly turned over to the Secretary of Interior for use in range improvement work.

[15] Clawson and Held, *op. cit.*, p. 221.

Thus, it is not unrealistic to view the Taylor Grazing Act as, in effect, forcing the range livestock ranchers to invest 3¾ cents per a.u.m. in the development of the federal ranges to which they were being granted exclusive grazing use.

Only a fourth of the fees as originally provided in the Taylor Act were actually brought into the federal treasury as miscellaneous receipts. All during the early years of grazing district administration, the receipts from grazing leases were totally inadequate to meet the costs of managing the grazing districts.

As the years went by in the administration of the Taylor Act, a series of interrelated developments eventually produced an increase in grazing fees. The market price of livestock rose. Toward the end of the 1930's range forage conditions began to improve markedly under the influence of increased precipitation. The costs of operating the Grazing Service rose fairly steeply, mostly because of a steadily increasing number of employees on the payroll. As administration costs mounted, the disparity between these costs and the almost stable grazing lease receipts began to widen. By the mid-1940's the House of Representatives was pressing strongly for a change, either lower appropriations for the Grazing Service or increased fees. The Department of Interior had been anticipating this demand for several years. The matter of an increase in fees was called to the attention of the National Advisory Board Council only in 1944, but internal discussion and studies within the Interior Department had taken place somewhat earlier, and as early as 1940 the department had made some tentative suggestions that higher fees would be in order. However, the western range likestock interests, abetted by several western senators, successfully opposed any fee increases until 1947. In 1946 the Congress drastically cut appropriations for the Grazing Service to bring them somewhat closer to the figures for grazing district receipts.

No one seriously argued at this time that the grazing district license holders were paying for the forage what it was worth. On the contrary, it was well known that permittees were paying a relatively small fraction of the value of the forage. The western ranching interests did not want to pay fees representing the true value of the forage, and they were particularly desirous not to have any principle established under which grazing fees would ever be related to the value of forage. Largely because of the lack of any interested and intelligent opposition in Congress, they were able to establish temporarily the principle that range grazing fees should be based on the cost of administering the grazing districts. With this principle in effect, a modest rise in fees from 5 cents to 8 cents per a.u.m. took place in 1947. The new fee was divided into two parts and disposed of differently from the original 5-cent fee.

If grazing fees were to be based on costs of administration, presumably they should be set sufficiently high to meet most of these costs. To achieve this and simultaneously keep fees as low as possible, they proposed to reduce drastically the state and county share of grazing receipts. They felt that, if the half of the grazing fee which went to the states and counties could be used to defray administrative costs, there would be less pressure in Congress to increase grazing fees. These proposals found expression in a section of the Interior Department Appropriations Act of 1947. A fourth of the fee, 2 cents per a.u.m., was designated as a range improvement fee. This was all to be returned to the district where collected for range improvement work. The balance of the fee, 6 cents per a.u.m., was called the grazing fee; of this part the counties were to receive only 12½ per cent. Fees collected on Section-15 lands—federal lands outside organized grazing districts—would continue to be distributed in the previous manner.

Despite the 1947 fee increase, Congress and the Department of Interior were convinced that the fees were still far too low. In 1950–51 the total fee was raised to 12 cents per a.u.m. and in the fiscal year ending June 30, 1955, it was raised to 15 cents.

The Interior Department at present maintains that the cost-of-administration basis for determining fees has been abandoned, as indicated by the following statement in the *Annual Report of the Secretary of Interior for 1955:* "The highlight of grazing administration in the past year was the adoption of a new formula for determining grazing fees. Instead of basing fees on administrative costs, the new formula provides for charging grazing fees equal to the average price per pound of cattle and sheep at Western markets."[16]

The application of the foregoing formula called for an increase in grazing fees to 17 cents per a.u.m. on January 1, 1957; however, because of serious drought conditions in the western states the increase was postponed until January 1, 1958. This formula is of the same type as that adopted decades earlier by the Forest Service. It results, however, in much lower prices than those charged by the Forest Service. Both fees are based on the price of livestock, but in different ways. In 1955, when the Taylor grazing district fees had just been raised 25 per cent to 15 cents per a.u.m., the average national forest grazing charge was 37 cents per a.u.m.,

16 P. 280.

about two and a half times as much.[17] We have pointed out previously that the animal unit month is not a precise standard of measurement; on the average, an animal unit month on a national forest probably represents more and better available forage than does an animal unit month on a grazing district range. Even with this difference taken into consideration, however, grazing district charges are much lower.

The Administrative Staff

When Director Carpenter began to assemble a staff to organize and administer the newly authorized grazing districts, there were almost no professional range managers in the United States except a few in the Forest Service or on the faculties of western agricultural colleges. Thus the newly appointed Director had to recruit a staff where he could find it. The original staff of thirty-five employees was recruited from within the Interior Department, more than half from the Geological Survey and the rest from the General Land Office and the Division of Investigations. This staff was organized into a Division of Grazing, which was an independent division of the Department of Interior; the Director reported directly to the Secretary of Interior.

The new Director believed in "the principle of decentralizing administration."[18] He set up an administrative office in Washington, D.C., but he also established a field headquarters in Salt Lake City, Utah, and eight regional offices, one in each of the eleven western states except California, Wyoming, and Washington.[19] Each regional office was in the charge of a regional grazier. The decentralized organization gave persons affected by the Taylor Act easy access to responsible administrative personnel. By July 1, 1936, an additional twenty-five employees had joined the division's staff. All these men were from the western states, and had been recruited from various activities. The division wanted men with "practical" experience and a knowledge of western range practices. Some of the early staff were college-trained and some were not; but the college education of almost none had been in range management. A year later the staff had been increased to ninety employees. The field men in particular were selected for their knowledge of the western range country, including some experience with range livestock ranching and ability to work and negotiate with the ranchers. The criteria used in selecting the staff during these

17 A few years earlier (1952) the national forest grazing fees had been 64¢ per a.u.m.

18 U.S. Department of Interior, *Annual Report, 1935*, p. 12.

19 There are no organized grazing districts in the state of Washington.

PLATE I.—Areas near the crest of the Wind River Range. The barren, rocky lands in the background are valuable only as watershed and scenery.

PLATE II.—A dense coniferous forest in the Medicine Bow Mountains of southern Wyoming. This land produces a large surplus of water but almost no livestock forage.

PLATE III.—Mountain grasslands. Such areas produce a considerable surplus of water. (Photo by Jack Rottier, BLM.)

PLATE IV.—Irrigated lands along the Wind River in central Wyoming. The irrigated fields on both sides of the river produce grass, used for both hay and pasture.

PLATE V.—Winter range on the floor of the Shoshone–Wind River Basin about fifty miles east of Lander. This forage can be used throughout the year, but is commonly reserved for winter use. The land rarely produces any runoff.

PLATE VI.—Flat floor of the eastern section of the Shoshone–Wind River Basin. The low hills of the so-called Granite Range are in the background.

PLATE VII.—One of the large hogbacks flanking the Wind River Range on the north. Some notion of the scale can be gathered by noting that the dark patch in the center of the photo represents a ranchstead and all the irrigated land of the ranch.

PLATE VIII.—Main house of R. W. Spratt and Sons Ranch. It is much more impressive than most western ranch houses.

PLATE IX.—The west end of a ridge essentially impassable for cattle on the R. W. Spratt and Sons Ranch. The cattle do not climb the ridge to use any of the forage on the other side, to the right of this view.

PLATE X.—Reservoir in the central part of the Shoshone–Wind River Basin. Before this reservoir was built, the land was unavailable for cattle use in spring, summer, and fall. Note the evidence of severe overgrazing in the vicinity of the reservoir. (Photo by R. K. Pierson, BLM)

PLATE XI.—A major silt-producing area. These badlands, with much loose rock debris on the surface and almost devoid of vegetation, are located just east of Boysen Reservoir in the northern part of the Shoshone–Wind River Basin.

PLATE XII.—Water-spreader in central section of Shoshone–Wind River Basin. The sinuous ridge is the dam that diverts the water. The dark area to the left is greener grass and shrubs caused by small amounts of runoff trapped behind the spreader.

PLATE XIII.—Forest Service range improvement plot near the crest of the Owl Creek Mountains. The much superior stand of grass within the fenced area is obvious. Only a few such plots are being operated in the entire Middle Rocky Mountain region.

PLATE XIV.—Excellent grass range in the Laramie Basin. Except for short periods in the winter when it is covered with snow, this highly productive range can be grazed throughout the year.

PLATE XV.—View across the Northeast Range. In the left foreground can be seen an inconspicuous concrete marker at a major property line corner, where pieces of federal, state, and private property join. Most property corners have no such marking; consequently, it can be understood why it is so easy to claim unwitting trespass.

PLATE XVI.—Pinedale, Wyoming, an isolated ranching market town and a minor resort center. Almost the entire village is in view.

PLATE XVII.—Willow meadows along the Upper Green River floodplain.

PLATE XVIII.—Sparse vegetation on the floor of the Big Horn Basin. Badlands in the background support almost no vegetation. Such surfaces clearly have almost no resistance to erosion.

PLATE XIX.—A large gully developing in the northeastern part of the Big Horn Basin

first years and the original operating directives given by Carpenter, the first director, imparted a character to the organization that it has retained in considerable measure to the present.

Only minor changes were made in the original structure of the organization during the first ten years. The most important development was the formation of the National Advisory Council of Stockmen, made up of two district advisory board members from each of the eight regions. The council was organized primarily to provide a channel of direct communication between the western livestock interests and Washington, D.C. That it was representative of the views and opinions of all western stockmen is doubtful, but it did represent the views of the most influential livestock men—the large-scale ranchers. In 1939 the name of the organization was changed from Division of Grazing to Grazing Service, and some internal reorganization was effected, but the essential operations continued to be carried on in about the same manner as previously.

During the 1930's Civilian Conservation Corps camps were used for range improvement and rehabilitation work; at peak strength as many as ninety camps were in operation. Although range management was at a relatively primitive level in those days, the work of the CCC was highly valuable because of the pressing need for a number of major range improvements—especially truck trails, new water sources, and new fences.

From its establishment in 1939 until about 1942 the Grazing Service grew steadily. At one stage the total number of employees exceeded 400, though a shortage of manpower during World War II caused the number to drop. At the close of the war the service began once more to increase its staff rapidly. It also began to reach out for additional functions and to compete with the General Land Office for authorization, funds, and personnel to carry out various functions with respect to the public lands. The steady increase in appropriations for range improvement and administration without any commensurate increase in grazing receipts so disturbed many eastern Congressmen, however, that the 1947 appropriation of the service was cut drastically.[20] Early in July, 1946, a Presidential Reorganization Plan combined the Grazing Service and the old General Land Office (which had handled nearly all non-grazing administrative matters relating to the unreserved and unappropriated public domain even after the Taylor Act became effective) into a new agency, the Bureau of Land Management. The Grazing Division of the new bureau was absolutely starved for operating funds; the decrease in appropriations was so

[20] A great many other factors entered into the Grazing Service appropriations cuts, but they are not germane here. For a full account see Peffer, *op. cit.*, pp. 260–78.

drastic that nearly two-thirds of the personnel had to be released. So great was the decline in the range administrative force that the division became wholly inadequate to discharge its duties. Hundreds of Taylor Act permittees were unwilling that the range allocation arrangements made under the provisions of the Taylor Act should expire merely from lack of supervision and enforcement, and they were especially fearful of the old pre-Taylor anarchic range conditions. Therefore, grazing district advisory boards in many cases appropriated money to support the activities of the Grazing Division in their district. During the year grazing fees rose from 5 cents per a.u.m. to 8 cents, but this did not save the division from a further appropriations cut the following year. Although the low level of grazing fees was highly important to some key eastern congressmen on the House Appropriations Committee, the real struggle was for control of federal policy with respect to the administration of the Taylor Grazing District lands. The question was whether or not the Department of Interior would manage these lands in strict conformance with the views of the Grazing District Advisory Boards, the state and national advisory board councils, and the major livestock associations. The apparent points of conflict—grazing fees, fee distribution, appropriations—were more in the nature of symbols of the underlying struggle than major issues in themselves. The contest ended in a complete victory for the western range livestock interests. Temporarily, at least, the Bureau of Land Management would administer the Taylor lands in conformance with the views of the industry it was supposed to regulate. Where the public interest came into conflict with the local grazing interests, the latter would prevail.

These were difficult times for the Grazing Division employees. Almost from day to day they did not know whether they would retain their positions. Promotions and salary raises were nearly non-existent. Many employees received severance pay and were temporarily unemployed; some were transferred to other sections of the Interior Department. However, as soon as the principle of control by the western livestock interests had been established, a deficiency appropriation was passed by Congress and grazing administration began to take on some semblance of normalcy.

Interestingly enough, some of the older grazing administration technicians look back on the stringent times of the latter 1940's almost as the good old days. It must not be forgotten that most grazing technicians are westerners and many of them have close ties with the western livestock industry. Some of these men feel that their only important function is to "maintain order on the range," as one district grazier expressed it. In the days of meager appropriations a district grazier and a single clerk with the aid and advice of the local advisory board would manage an entire district. They would collect fees, disburse range improvement fees, issue range improvement permits, settle range disputes, and keep the frequency and extent of trespass and overgrazing from becoming unseemly. Some older technicians feel that is all the bureau should do.

Appropriations have risen steadily since 1947. In 1950 they were roughly 50 per cent greater than in 1947, but the whole period from 1946 through 1951 was one of inadequate supervision, management, and improvement of the public ranges. After the Grazing Service had become part of the new Bureau of Land Management, some minor shifts and changes in administrative procedures designed further to decentralize public land administration were put into effect. The merger also had the second, perhaps unintended, effect of de-emphasizing the relative importance of grazing administration. The major revenues and administrative duties of the newly formed bureau were related to minerals leasing and royalties and the sale of timber-cutting rights on public lands in the West Coast states.

The 1952 elections brought a Republican national administration into power for the first time in twenty years. It was anticipated in many quarters that changes in public land management accompanying the political changes would be profound. It was widely predicted that there would be a sharp increase in the rate of disposal of the federal lands and a general relaxation in regulations and controls. No such developments took place. This was partly attributable to the fact that no new, drastically different legislation was enacted. Bureau administration continued to be carried out largely in conformance with the existing laws relating to the public lands.

However, as soon as a survey of the situation could be completed, the administrative organization for management of the public lands received a thorough revision. It conformed to the general pattern of thought and policy adhered to by the new Republican administration. One objective was to "decentralize" land management administration thoroughly.[21] A

---

[21] Decentralization of public land administration is a shibboleth to which high federal officials uniformly adhere, at least in public statements. When the Grazing Service was formed, the Director took great pride in announcing that its administration was to be decentralized. A minor reorganization in the Grazing Division in the late 1930's was reported as bringing about increased decentralization. When some of the activities of the Grazing Service were moved out of Washington during the early years of World War II to release space for agencies more closely associated with defense, it was announced that the move resulted in greater decentralization of administration. Marion Clawson brought about a reorganization of the Bureau of Land Management shortly

second objective was to re-emphasize the importance of the states. To achieve these ends the seven regional offices that long had been a feature of grazing administration were consolidated into three "area offices" in Denver, Colorado, Portland, Oregon, and Salt Lake City, Utah. Within each of the eleven western states was created a new state office. The latter is "the operating office for field personnel and exercises authority over all other BLM offices in the respective States, which include the land offices, grazing district offices and district forestry offices."[22]

Since 1952 the BLM has grown rapidly. The budget of the bureau increased approximately 50 per cent from its low point in 1947 until 1952, at which time it was roughly $7 million. From 1952 until 1957 it approximately tripled, rising to about $22 million by 1957. The proportional share of the total bureau budget assigned to range improvement and management has remained roughly the same throughout the period. Increases in personnel did not keep up with the budget growth; in 1951 the bureau employees numbered 1,220, but by 1956 the number had risen only to 2,260. This situation can be partly explained by the inability of the BLM to recruit trained people at the salaries the bureau is authorized to pay for the beginning grades of employment.

Administration and Organization of Grazing Districts

Administration of a grazing district is the responsibility of the district office staff and the grazing district advisory board. To understand the problems of district range management demands an appreciation of the size of grazing districts, the kinds of management problems that are encountered, and lastly, the unit-area productivity of Western ranges. For illustrative purposes a large district in southwestern Wyoming—Wyoming Grazing District 4—will serve satisfactorily.

Wyoming Grazing District 4 is the largest district in that state, incorporating 4.6 million acres drawn from the vacant, unreserved, and unappropriated public domain. But the district administration also manages grazing on a quarter-million acres of other federal lands within the boundaries of the district. From the eastern to the western boundary of the district is almost 130 miles. Its maximum north-south dimension is about

---

after he became director; this was advertised as increasing the degree of decentralization. The major reorganization instituted by the Republican administration after it took control was announced as decentralization to bring the administration of public land closer to the citizenry.

[22] U.S. Department of Interior, *Annual Report, 1954*, p. 262.

100 miles. A district this large would form a rectangle extending from Chicago nearly as far east as Fort Wayne, Indiana, and as far south as Lafayette, Indiana; from Philadelphia north far into the Pocono Mountains and west as far as Gettysburg; or from Atlanta, Georgia, west as far as Birmingham, Alabama, and south to Montgomery, Alabama, and Columbus, Georgia. However, this huge tract of grazing land, larger in area than Massachusetts or New Hampshire, supports the equivalent of only about 50,000 cattle on a year-round basis, plus substantial amounts of wildlife. Its low productivity becomes clearly apparent when the number of livestock it supports is compared with the number supported on lands of comparable extent in three parts of the humid East: Indiana-Illinois, Pennsylvania, and Alabama-Georgia (see Table 1). It is unnecessary to

TABLE 1

NUMBER OF DOMESTIC ANIMALS IN SOUTHWESTERN WYOMING
AND IN THREE EASTERN AREAS OF COMPARABLE SIZE*

States	Cattle	Sheep	Horses and Mules	Poultry	Hogs
Wyoming, S.W........	64,000	317,000	9,000	45,000	6,000
Indiana-Illinois.......	641,000	149,000	22,000	4,500,000	1,600,000
Pennsylvania.........	490,000	42,000	38,000	8,100,000	50,000
Alabama-Georgia......	215,000	1,000	60,000	1,300,000	125,000

* Data from U.S. Census of Agriculture.

labor the comparison brought out in Table 1; the enormously greater productivity of all the eastern areas is quickly seen. The Illinois-Indiana area, the most striking contrast, produces 10 times more cattle, nearly half as many sheep, 100 times more poultry, more than 200 times as many hogs, and more than twice as many horses as this land of the cowboy!

The extremely low productivity of western range land must be constantly kept in mind when assessing the intensity of land administration and management in the district. Production per acre is so meager that only a very low level of investment in administration and management will produce an economic return.

Wyoming Grazing District 4 has ten full-time permanent employees: a district manager, three range managers, an administrative assistant, two clerks, two range conservationists, and an operator general. However, the district has authorization for additional employees as soon as qualified applicants can be found. Some districts have a few more employees than this, others have a few less. If this situation is looked at from an agronomic or ecologic viewpoint, it would appear that eight men with a little clerical help cannot effectively manage and supervise all surface use on 4.6 million acres of vacant public land, plus grazing use on a large area of associated private land, except at a rather low level of managerial intensity. If the range area were divided equally for management, inspection, and administrative purposes among the district technicians, each would have nearly a thousand square miles to administer. In other words, the managerial staff is too small to have any chance of adjusting the intensity, frequency, and timing of grazing use in such a way that the ranges will be utilized in the most effective and productive manner. Nor can they inspect and study the condition and trend of range vegetation and the water relationships of the land in sufficient detail to have accurate, precise, up-to-date information on the physical well-being of the lands under their jurisdiction. It is impossible for two range conservationists to carry on much more than a token program for physical control of water in the district.[23]

It is enlightening to assess federal management of the public lands in terms of private management of lands of comparable character. We might think of the vacant public lands of the Bridger Basin as being divided into eleven ranches of 400,000 acres each; only a handful of ranches this large still remain in the United States. Quite apart from the management of the cattle, the active manager of such a ranch would find his task a large one, and the eleven ranches would require eleven managers. A ranch of 400,000 acres would probably utilize several fulltime employees for fence construction and repair, reservoir construction and maintenance, range reseeding, noxious weed control, and other details of range management. Eleven times this number of employees would be necessary to bring about a comparable level of physical management on the range lands of District 4.[24] Admittedly the ranchers whose cattle and sheep graze the ranges of the district furnish some supervision and contribute in various degrees to the physical management and maintenance of the range. But even if we assume a level of management and maintenance only half as intensive as that just postulated, we still must conclude that the federal

[23] Range conservationists do not actually execute soil and moisture projects; construction, grading, etc. are contracted. The conservationists make preliminary studies, devise and draw up the plans, supervise, administer, and inspect the work, and after completion of the project inspect it from time to time to see how it is functioning.

[24] Actually the manpower available in a district has been slightly understated. Range survey, an indispensable aid for effective management, is sometimes carried on by fulltime range surveyors sent out from the BLM area office. In addition, temporary employees are sometimes used for major soil and moisture projects. In terms of the total management task, however, the additional personnel are relatively unimportant.

government's falls significantly below the level normally maintained by private management on comparable land. It must be stressed that this is not a very good comparison, largely because it is so difficult to decide how much of a ranch staff's time is devoted to range management as contrasted with cattle management. However, comparisons are useful, and comparisons in this field are hard to find. This one may be helpful if not construed too closely.

Range supervision and inspection by the BLM personnel is done principally during travel over the district for other purposes or in response to specific complaints of illegal practices on the range. There is no help for this situation under present conditions. The duties necessary for adequate supervision are simply too numerous and time-consuming to be discharged intensively by the relatively few technicians in the district offices. The situation has improved in recent years, but management and administration still appear inadequate.[25] However, the intensity of management may be as great as the low productivity of the land will justify. Unit productivity of the land is so low that it can economically support only a relatively light burden of administrative costs.

Perhaps the very size of the district to be administered gives some idea of the magnitude of the management job, but the variety and multiplicity of the tasks necessary for administration of a district cannot be properly appreciated until one has seen an office functioning for some time.

In all except the smallest districts there is specialization of function, and the chief officer, the district manager, devotes his time largely to general administration. His principal duties may be summarized as follows:

1. Management of the office and equipment of the district: An office must be rented, heated, lighted, and furnished. These matters are handled by the clerical and administrative personnel on a regular, routine basis, but they claim some attention from the district manager.

[25] It is extremely difficult to arrive at a firm conclusion regarding the effectiveness of range management in a district. In commenting upon an early draft of this section some of the BLM technicians of District 4 were in complete disagreement with these statements. They maintained that range use was satisfactory, supervision adequate, range survey accurate and comprehensive, and the soil and moisture program just what the district required. Undoubtedly some of the disagreement concerns terminology and the vagueness of the terms used here to describe the efficiency of management. Perhaps the best that can be done is to note, as is done here, that some BLM personnel strongly assert that the circumstances of district range management are much better than described in this section. One point on which there seems to be no disagreement is the steady improvement in recent years in most technical aspects of district management. Progress has been substantial.

2. Management of equipment and supplies: Tools for range improvement work and for fire-fighting must be requisitioned, stored, assigned to workers, repaired, and written off and replaced when worn out. Office equipment and materials must be procured. Corrals must be rented occasionally or regularly for animals of unknown ownership found in trespass. Bulldozers, spraying equipment, fence construction machinery, graders, trucks, and well-drilling equipment must be leased or contracted for from time to time. Cars and trucks for use in the management of the district must be purchased, serviced, and repaired. Some districts own or rent horses. All of these actions require the proper use of order and requisition forms as well as the other fiscal and accounting paraphernalia customarily associated with a large bureaucracy like the BLM. They can be largely handled by the administrative assistant, but the district manager has over-all responsibility.

3. Personnel management: In larger districts that have several employees, numerous problems of personnel management fall on the district manager. He must see that new people are hired when authorized, check employee attendance, see that payroll forms are properly prepared and dispatched, arrange for vacations, prepare employee work evaluation reports, assign duties, attempt to secure raises and promotions for deserving members of his staff, settle disputes, maintain staff morale, and attend to all the minor personal matters that develop in connection with a group of employees. Actually the administrative assistant is directly charged with all the items under the preceding three points, and he has the assistance of the district clerk. However, the district manager is ultimately responsible, and much of his time must be devoted to supply and personnel matters.

4a. Public relations: No single item of public relations takes much of the district employees' time, but in sum public relations represent a sizable part of district administration. Conversations with ranchers are probably the most time-consuming phase of public relations for the district manager. During the course of work in the offices of various grazing districts in connection with this study, I several times listened to conversations between a district manager and ranchers from the district. In many cases as soon as the rancher had stated his problem or his interest in some matter of range management or adjudication, the nature of the problem and its solution were readily apparent even to an inexperienced outsider like myself. Nevertheless, the district manager would listen patiently while the rancher reviewed the entire history of his relationship with the district and with neighboring ranchers from the first hearings preliminary to the organization of the district down to the date of the conversation. Such conversations occupy a great many hours of a district manager's time during the course of a year. Another public relations activity requiring some time is the preparation of press releases for the local newspapers. Occasionally district managers conduct field excursions through their districts for educational purposes. They may address 4-H Clubs, make radio broadcasts, or help with an exhibit at the county fair. They must attend state Department of Agriculture meetings, irrigation development planning meetings, hearings on wildlife management problems, and so on; a page could be filled with a list of the meetings that a district manager may find it necessary to attend in the course of a year or two. Finally, the district manager must deal with the congressman from his district. Permittees sometimes write to the congressman asking him to act in their behalf vis-à-vis the BLM. The organization is sensitive to congressional opinion, and consequently each inquiry from a congressman is answered carefully, fully, and with great attention to accuracy and documentation.

4*b*. Relations with grazing district advisory board: To operate effectively, a district manager must maintain good relationships with his district advisory board. The Taylor Act requires only that he consult with the local board, but most district managers administer the district in cooperation with the advisory board, trying, on most questions, to reach a unanimous agreement of all concerned. To have the board meetings run smoothly may require previous consultation with influential members of the board, discussions with ranchers who will appear at the board meetings, preparation of an agenda, and arrangement of a time and place suitable for all. The difficulties that may be encountered are aptly illustrated by a letter written to his supervisor by a district manager in one of the Middle Rocky Mountain Basin districts.

Date

Dear Mr. [Supervisor],

. . . . You will note that at this meeting very little work of value was accomplished. The reason for this is two or three of the Advisors were called away from their livestock at times when they could not handily leave, and appeared at the meeting with a chip on their shoulder. In addition, the delegates from —— were resentful that the meeting was called in [elsewhere], and the Chairman especially did all in his power to hurry the meeting to a close without taking time enough properly to consider and act upon the matters which were brought up. . . .

(Signed) District Manager

On many matters individual members of the advisory board act as liaison between the district manager and the ranchers. Moreover, if the board is sympathetic to a new program or policy, it can do much to persuade the local ranchers of its merits. Formal and informal discussions with the district board members takes time, but it is time well invested.

5. Grazing lease fiscal administration: In some districts grazing licenses are issued on an annual basis, in others all licenses run for ten years, and still other districts issue leases for a variety of time periods but none for longer than ten years. The fiscal aspects of all leases are subject to modifications from year to year. Most of the annual variations arise from the practice of taking non-use. A rancher, it will be recalled, does not pay a fee for a.u.m.'s of grazing not actually used; thus his total annual grazing fee will rise or fall depending on whether he decreases or increases his quantity of non-use. Changes in leases also result from the sale of base properties and their associated grazing permtis. A rancher's permit may be increased as a result of purchase or decreased as a result of sale; an entirely new permit will be required for a purchaser not already holding one. Other changes in the size of permits may result from leasing of base properties and permits.

Clerks can do nearly all of the work involved in determining the size of grazing fees, issuing bills for fees, and recording collections, but the district manager or one of the range managers is responsible for the accuracy and promptness of the assessments and collections. In cases of transfer he must see that new and valid permits are issued. If new private land is being submitted as base property for a purchased grazing permit, it is necessary to ascertain from records in the county courthouse whether the applicant is actually the owner of the land. If the applicant has merely leased a base property, the district manager must decide whether he will permit a temporary arrangement of this nature.

6. Adjudication of grazing leases and allotments: The process of adjudicating grazing leases and allotments has been going on steadily since the grazing districts were formed and the first permits issued. Range use adjudication is a major task of many district managers and their range managers. New problems of adjudication are constantly arising as a result of base property sales and transfers of grazing permits. If a permit is transferred in its entirety and the new owner uses it in precisely the same way as his predecessor, no problem arises; but if he wishes to change periods of use or livestock numbers, or to change from one type of livestock to another, adjudication may be necessary to mesh this new use

with previous practices of other permittees who are entitled to joint use of the allotment.

7. Reports to higher administrative levels: The offices of the BLM in Wyoming are local branches of a federal bureaucracy which extends back through the state office in Cheyenne and the area office in Denver to the headquarters of the bureau in the Department of Interior Building, Washington, D.C. The regulations and operating procedures of the bureau necessitate numerous and detailed reports from local offices to the higher echelons of administration. These reports are of two kinds: routine reports, usually on an annual basis, relating to the normal functions of the local office; and special reports pertaining to some study or compilation being made on a state basis in Cheyenne, an area basis in Denver, or on a national basis. For these various reports the clerical staff can furnish the necessary statistical or stenographic help but commonly the district manager or his assistant must initiate the report, make sure it is properly compiled, perhaps actually compose the final summary, and assume responsibility for its accuracy and promptness.

8. Range inspection: The reader may have noted that all duties of the technical staff discussed thus far pertain to office functions, not to the physical management of the range lands. So heavy is the load of office administrative work that in the smaller districts with limited staff, the technical staff may spend much more time on office administration than it does on physical observation and action in the field. One of the two principal objectives of Taylor Act administration is to stabilize forage, soil, and moisture conditions on the federal government's land, and thus one of the ultimate criteria of the success or failure of the whole administrative effort is whether or not these conditions are improving, remaining constant, or degenerating. Rational administrative actions and policies to improve these conditions on federal range lands can result only from sound and accurate knowledge concerning the physical condition of those lands. Moreover, actual range condition is the test of administrative success, and range inspection is the primary method of ascertaining range condition.[26]

Range inspection may be formal or informal. Most of it is informal. In the course of their travels over the district, members of the technical staff

[26] One of the most commendable aspects of Taylor land administration is the pressure by the upper echelons of BLM supervision for field activity on the part of the district technical personnel. A district manager who gets a reputation as an office manager who rarely goes into the field to view the range, the improvements, and the problem areas will quickly find himself in bad repute with the state, area, and national supervisors.

commonly make visual inspections of the range lands that can be seen from the road or trail. Inspection of this sort cannot help but be haphazard and superficial in most ways, but for some conditions it is effective. During the growing season the amount of new growth can be rather accurately assessed by an experienced range man, thus providing a rough guide to desirable changes in the rate of stocking for that season. Severe damage to the range vegetation or any notable increase in the erosion rate on an area can usually be detected by this kind of superficial inspection. Even from a considerable distance a range manager will note an area where severe overgrazing has sharply impaired the forage. Still more apparent are new burns, new gullies, or rapidly enlarging gullies. Long-term trends in vegetation or water conditions, however, are difficult to perceive. A major weakness of this superficial, incidental type of inspection is the fact that it is not based on knowledge of critical areas, areas of unusually heavy use, or other rational criteria; but instead is tied to travel routes that are related to other and often irrelevant considerations.

Formal, planned, systematic survey of range conditions is rare. Much federal range land has been suveyed only once; some of it, indeed, has never been surveyed, and very little has been surveyed more than twice. Intensive, reliable, and objective methods of range survey are available but are seldom used because of their high cost.

Nor is there much intensive inspection by BLM officials of the grazing trailing, and herding practices on the district. Trespass investigation is rarely done except on specific complaint by a rancher, usually the trespassed party. The only time BLM personnel in the Middle Rock Mountain basins are specifically and exclusively assigned to range-use inspection is during the fall and spring livestock migrations. Violations of rules pertaining to trailing and the location of bedding grounds for sheep are ordinarily discovered and investigated only upon report by one of the district ranchers.

In some instances a few acres of timber have been logged from the federal lands of a grazing district, and the district technicians had no knowledge of it until months later. Sometimes they have been able to find out who did the cutting; in other cases not. Given the number of technicians, the size of the districts under their administration, the number of duties they are obliged to perform, the equipment at their disposal, and the prevailing views of range managers concerning the intensity of inspection that is feasible, it is easy to understand why most range inspection is superficial, haphazard, and inadequate.

9. Range maintenance and improvement: All technical members of a

grazing district staff engage in range maintenance and improvement work except the range conservationists, who devote their time (except for emergency work) to soil and moisture conservation. Up to the present, range improvement work by BLM technicians has been aimed principally at enhancing the utility of the range. The principal activities have been well-drilling, reservoir construction, truck trail construction, and fence-building.

Unless funds for range improvement work are periodically increased, the rate of new construction tends to fall because of the BLM's obligation to provide maintenance both for projects constructed by the bureau itself and for those constructed by the ranchers under Section-4 permits.

A minor amount of work is done on numerous other aspects of range maintenance and development. A few man hours or days per year, for example, must be devoted to fighting range fires. Ordinarily such fires will burn themselves out fairly promptly, but in three situations they may cause extensive damage. Range vegetation containing a large percentage of dry annual weeds will produce a hot fire that will completely destroy all plant life over an extensive area. A fire driven by a strong wind in an area of thick brush is likely to devastate a large area before burning itself out. And a fire starting near the bottom of a long, steep slope may burn over the entire slope before dying out. Whenever a range fire is reported to the district office, the BLM staff must hastily load tools and equipment and hurry to the scene of the fire, which occasionally may be as much as forty or fifty miles from the office. In recent years most range fires on the BLM lands of the Middle Rocky Mountain basins have not been especially serious, but in some districts fire control problems are not negligible.

In a few areas concentrations of poisonous plants occasionally become a sufficient menace to livestock so that BLM personnel must either spray the affected areas or fence them off. Other kinds of range maintenance or improvement activity include: construction of pack trails, corrals, cattle guards, and water storage tanks; range reseeding; allotment boundary marking; rodent and insect control; improvement of springs; and assistance to ranchers who are carrying on range improvement projects.

10. Soil and moisture conservation: Range conservationists are assigned almost exclusively to soil and moisture conservation. Their duties are to control water on the land and prevent soil erosion, but there is some overlap with range improvement work. For instance, a flood detention dam, if large enough, may create a source of stock water. Water-spreaders, diversion dams and ditches, contour furrowing, and similar devices

and practices may increase forage production by inducing a greater retention of moisture on the land. Reservoirs are usually considered to be soil- and moisture-controlling devices as well as range improvements. Soil and moisture men in general tend to concentrate their work on specific projects and to work intensively on a single project until it is completed. A common practice is to select the area of most severe soil erosion and silt-production in the district and then to draft and execute plans for remedying the situation. Generally such operations are time consuming, and as a consequence soil and moisture work advances rather slowly. In recent years the activities of BLM conservationists have been focused primarily on watersheds, this being the approach to water control currently in vogue.

Soil and moisture conservation as now practiced by the BLM suffers from: (1) the inadequate control that the bureau exercises over grazing intensity, and (2), especially in the past, inadequate inspection and maintenance of completed projects. One Middle Rocky Mountain regional soil and moisture maintenance report a few years ago stated that "approximately one-third of all projects examined needed maintenance repair in some degree." According to another report, "some completed projects have not been inspected for years, and others have never been inspected." It is current practice to develop definite inspection and maintenance plans at the same time construction plans are being made—still another example of the significant recent improvement in the Taylor districts as a result of the steady increases in size of staff. Inspection of completed projects is more frequent, and in many districts all *major* projects are now inspected at least once a year.

One aspect of Taylor Act administration remains undescribed and unanalyzed—the *Federal Range Code*. This code contains the specific rules and operating directives for management, administration, and policing of the Taylor grazing districts. It consists of a large number of discrete, detailed items—definitions, rules, policy statements, and specific procedures. To treat the code in all its details and ramifications would necessitate a disproportionately long and perhaps tiresome section. Although the code is of major importance, it will be more economical to consider the relevant items in connection with the operation of the Taylor Act and the *Federal Range Code* in the various basins of the Middle Rocky Mountain region. To the latter subject we may now turn.

Part Two

TAYLOR ACT ADMINISTRATION IN THE MIDDLE ROCKY MOUNTAIN BASINS

Chapter Five

THE MIDDLE ROCKY
MOUNTAIN BASINS

The Middle Rocky Mountain basins are essentially a vast, high, arid pasture occupying approximately the southwestern two-thirds of Wyoming. The regional relationships are indicated in Figure 9. The Middle Rocky Mountain basins are a part of the Intermountain West. They lie at the extreme eastern margin of the region. Their eastern boundary is the crest of the easternmost ranges of the Middle Rockies. The Great Plains lie just to the east and north. The southern basins of the group are traversed by one of the world's major land transportation routes—the Overland Route of the Union Pacific Railroad and U.S. Highway 30. The presence of this important east-west route has had a profound influence on the economic structure of the Middle Rocky Mountain basins, though its direct influence on land utilization has been small. A high proportion of the working population in the towns and cities along the route are engaged in some occupation related directly or indirectly to the transportation lines.

The Northern and Southern Rockies do not lie in a straight longitudinal line; the Northen Rockies (see Fig. 9) are offset to the west. The easternmost ranges of the Northern Rockies are at least a hundred miles farther west than the westernmost ranges of the Southern Rockies. Between these mountain masses lies a middle zone, the Middle Rockies, where the sequence of geological events did not produce an unbroken mountain mass. Instead the region consists of scattered and discontinuous mountain ranges of different heights and oriented in various directions, although the general trend of the Rocky Mountain uplift is clearly revealed, forming a reverse curve of aligned mountains from northwest to southeast across Wyoming. Interspersed with, surrounding, and separating these mountain ranges are a series of basins, more or less interconnected. Often the floors of these basins are rough and broken, though in places they are remarkably smooth. From the Great Plains to the east every one of the basins can be entered without crossing any major topographic barrier, although in some cases there is only a single narrow opening. On the western margin of the region no such openings exist; here the mountain barrier is complete. While no basin is completely encircled, each one is partially inclosed by ranges of the Rockies, and some are almost completely inclosed. Some of the encircling ranges are truly high mountains, while others are relatively low.

The Middle Rocky Mountain region has always been a refractory problem to those who have tried to fit the area into some larger system of regions. It is clearly not a mountainous area of the same order as the Southern or Northern Rockies; but it does contain numerous and extensive mountain ranges. It is not a plains area like the Great Plains (though it has some characteristics quite similar to those of the Great Plains), since each of the basin floors is flanked by two or more mountain ranges. It is not a plateau. It is not a humid region—the basin floors are dry and in some places truly arid. But neither is it an arid region as a whole, since extensive areas in the mountains and in the highest basins have fairly

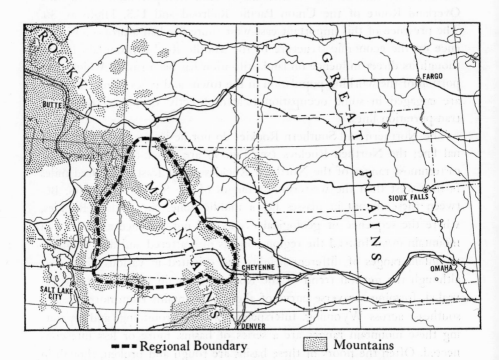

■ ■ ■ Regional Boundary   ▧ Mountains

Fig. 9.—Regional Setting of the Middle Rocky Mountain Basins

abundant moisture. The component parts of the landscape are not the differentiating factor for the region; it is the way these components are arranged. The unique physical character of the region derives from the close juxtaposition, the intermingling, of mountains of various shapes, sizes, and orientations with the numerous topographic basins that lie between and around them.

The Middle Rocky Mountain basins are an especially suitable region in which to study the operations and problems of the range livestock industry. Most of the land is used for range grazing and for no other purpose. Almost all of the ranches are located on the floors of the basins, but their operations extend outward to the divides of the bordering mountains and no further. Thus, so far as land use and range management are concerned, each basin is a functional unit. Unlike the situation in many western areas there is relatively little overlap of range use among the different areas. The ranchers of each basin have been able to work out their range use patterns independently. Each basin has had a somewhat different history of range use. Each major basin contains a grazing district. Because the basins are discrete, self-contained land use units, they are favorable for comparative studies.

The Middle Rocky Mountain region is high country. Most of it lies a mile or more above sea level. Even the lowest areas, on the floor of the Big Horn Basin, attain nearly 4,000 feet in elevation. The summits of the highest mountain ranges exceed 10,000 feet in elevation over extensive areas. Because of its high elevation and its location in the interior of the continent between 41° and 45° north latitude, the region is one of cool summers and long, cold winters. Winds blow vigorously and often. The floors of the basins are semiarid or arid, but the mountains, even the lowest, are humid. Their greater humidity can be ascribed in part to greater rainfall and in part to lower evaporation rates.

Almost all the land of the region is used exclusively for grazing. Although all the higher mountain ranges have extensive coniferous forests, lumbering is a minor occupation. Scattered along the perennial streams of the region are small patches of irrigated land, but the acreage under irrigation is only a tiny fraction of the total land area.

Population is sparse in all parts of the Middle Rocky Mountain basins. The mountain ranges are almost completely uninhabited. Extensive sections of the region are never visited except occasionally by a sheepherder and his flock, a cowboy with a herd of cattle, or, for a few days each year, by hunters. With the exception of the cities along the Union Pacific Railroad not a single town in the region has attained a population of five thousand. It is a wide land with few people; aside from roads, the impress of man is not easily observed in most parts of the region. Only in scattered urban places or in the narrow irrigated areas has the landscape been noticeably modified by human use.

Agriculture is the principal support of the population, and range livestock ranching is almost the exclusive form of agriculture. Even the irrigated land is devoted largely to the production of feed for livestock.

Scattered through the basins are oil fields of various sizes. Coal is mined in the southern basins. Agriculture, coal and petroleum extraction, tourism, and transportation—the latter largely associated with the Union Pacific Railroad and U.S. Highway 30—furnish most of the basic employment in the region.

Physical Geography

THE PRINCIPAL MOUNTAINS AND BASINS

Just south of Yellowstone Park in northwestern Wyoming is a broad knot of mountains. Nevin Fenneman has described the northern ranges of the Middle Rocky Mountains as radiating out "sheaf-like" from this knot.[1] The major lineaments of the terrain can be grasped most clearly and quickly by reference to Figure 10.

The Absaroka Mountains extend northward from the knot along the eastern margin of Yellowstone Park, eventually merging with the Beartooth Range in extreme southern Montana. They also extend southeastward as the Shoshone Mountains until they combine with the Owl Creek and Bridger Mountains, which swing east around the southern edge of the Big Horn Basin, and merge into the huge north-south arc of the semi-isolated Big Horn Mountains. The latter, with their northern extension, Sheep Mountain (or Pryor Mountains), recurve to within a few miles of the Beartooth Range. Inclosed within this nearly complete ellipse of mountains is the northernmost of the five major basins of the Middle Rockies—the Big Horn Basin—covering several thousand square miles in north central Wyoming.

Trending straight southeast for nearly a hundred miles from the mountain knot south of Yellowstone Park is the rugged, high Wind River Range. It gradually drops in elevation near its southeastern end, but the uplift continues eastward in a series of discontinuous and much lower mountains.

Between the mountain chains just described and the Owl Creek and

[1] N. M. Fenneman, *Physiography of Western United States* (New York: McGraw-Hill, 1931), p. 166.

Bridger Mountains to the north are two separate drainage basins referred to commonly, and on Figure 10, as the Wind River and Shoshone basins. However, the divide between them is extremely inconspicuous and low while at the same time they are bordered on three sides by conspicuous mountain ranges, so they are here treated as a single basin—the Shoshone–Wind River Basin.

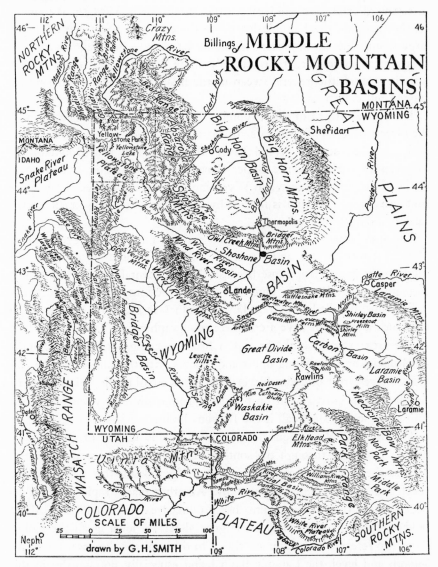

Fig. 10.—Physiography of the Middle Rockies. (Drawn by Guy-Harold Smith for *Physiography of Western United States*, by N. M. Fenneman [New York: McGraw-Hill Book Co.], by permission.)

From the mountain knot south of Yellowstone another chain of mountains extends southward along the Wyoming-Utah boundary, the barren, rugged, picturesque Grand Tetons. Farther south and east are the Mountains of Western Wyoming. The latter gradually decline in elevation toward the south until they merge into the more subdued surface of southwestern Wyoming. The entire area south of the Wind River Range and its eastward extensions and between the Mountains of Western Wyoming on the west and the Laramie Range on the east is in some ways a single large basin, with no important mountain barriers to interrupt its surface. It is sometimes referred to as the Wyoming Basin. A few minor uplifts, however, break the general sweep of the basin and produce some rather rugged hill country.

The western third of the Wyoming Basin lies in the drainage basin of the Green River. We shall refer to the northern part of the Green River drainage (between the Wind River Mountains and the Mountains of Western Wyoming) as the Upper Green River Basin. The southern part of the Green River drainage in Wyoming is called the Bridger Basin. The southern rim of the latter is formed by the Uinta Mountains in the northeastern shoulder of Utah.

The area between the Bridger Basin and the Laramie Basin is made up of several topographic and structural basins. It cannot be considered a single basin in the true sense because the continental divide runs almost through the middle of it. One of its major sections, through which the divide runs, is called the Great Divide Basin (see Fig. 10). Moreover, on the south it does not have a complete topographic rim. The level surface of the area extends south through a broad opening between the Southern Rockies and the Uinta uplift and merges with the surface of the plateaus of western Colorado. Nevertheless, it is a basin in its relationship to the mountains bordering it on the north and south. Solely for identification purposes we shall call it the Rawlins Basin.

The floors of the various basins exhibit a wide variety of terrain conditions. Scattered through the southern basins are several minor uplifts—such as the Rock Springs Dome in the Bridger Basin—that produce bold relief and rough, rugged topography. At other places rapid erosion, especially near the major streams, has produced extensive badlands. Many bold escarpments tower above the general terrain level in all the basins. They are referred to locally as "rims." In other places the basin floors are smooth and level, the Laramie Basin being especially noteworthy in this respect.

CLIMATIC FACTORS

Changes in altitude produce roughly a thousand times as great an effect on temperature as do equal changes in latitude. Ascending a mile in elevation produces about the same degree of change as traveling one thousand miles poleward. Similarly, a decrease in elevation of 2,500 feet brings about the change in temperature that would require an equatorward movement of 500 miles. Thus, despite the fact that the Middle Rocky Mountain basins extend over four degrees of latitude, altitudinal differences, not latitudinal differences, produce the important temperature contrasts within the region. For example, the Big Horn Basin, although the northernmost, is the warmest of all the Middle Rocky Mountain basins, because it lies at the lowest elevation. Precipitation is also more closely correlated with altitude than with any other factor, though the amount of precipitation on the basin floors varies somewhat with their relationship to the surrounding mountains. The lowest precipitation of the entire region is found in the low northeastern section of the Big Horn Basin.

Temperatures in the Middle Rocky Mountain basins are cool in summer and cold in winter, although the sensible temperature in winter is somewhat ameliorated by the comparative dryness of the air and the fairly abundant sunshine.

Winters in the higher parts of the mountain ranges are severe. The higher sections of the Wind River, Big Horn, and Salt ranges have average temperatures in January of less than 10° F.[2] The few weather records that are available indicate that most January nights in these mountains have minima below 0° F. and that sometimes for several consecutive days the temperature will stay 20°, 30°, even 40° below 0° F. Combined with high winds and much snowfall these temperatures discourage occupance of the mountains during the long winter season except at a few scattered logging camps.

The lower parts of the basins generally average 20° F. or higher during January except for the Upper Green River Basin, which averages at least 6° colder. Cold waves drive the minimum temperatures of all the basins down to —25° F. almost every winter, and occasional extremes of —40° and —50° F. are observed.

Midsummer average temperatures are quite high considering the altitude of the region. In the warmer parts of the basins average July tem-

[2] All data on weather taken from various publications of the U.S. Weather Bureau unless otherwise specifically noted.

peratures are in excess of 70° F. and even in the mountains they exceed 60° F. But occasionally the basins experience unusually low minima. Every one of these basins except the Big Horn Basin has a good possibility of frost during every month in the year, and the mountain areas are almost certain to have frosts even in July. Snowstorms covering the ground to a depth of several inches have occurred on the floors of the basins as late as the first week in June.

SOILS

Most soils of all the basins are residual desert soils that take their color from the underlying parent material; consequently a wide range of color is encountered in all the basins. The dominant colors are gray, brown, red, and pink. Over broad areas the surface layers are slightly fluffy in appearance and the surface itself has a thin and delicate crust. The surface layers are low in organic matter. The deeper soil horizons contain concentrations of lime or gypsum. Subsoils are dense, and in many places a calcium layer forms a hardpan.

Extensive areas are characterized by poor soils, derived from saline shales, having relatively fine textures and poor drainage. Salts tend to be concentrated at or near the surface by evaporation. Many of these soils are so alkaline that they will support only salt-tolerant vegetation, and water supplies in such an area may be so saline as to be unusable for domestic purposes, for irrigation, or as stock water.

Besides the residual soils the basin floors exhibit extensive areas of two kinds of alluvial soils: those found on the bottom lands of the streams and others located on stream terraces or on alluvial fans at the base of mountain slopes and of the higher rims or "cuestas." The soils of the alluvial fans and terraces generally occur in areas of somewhat greater rainfall, lower evaporation, and slightly heavier vegetation than is true of the areas where most residual soils are found. As a result they are generally of darker color than the residual soils—usually dark brown or dark gray. Although the alluvial materials from which they are derived are very loose and open (gravelly and sandy), these soils exhibit a well-defined calcium layer at a foot or two in depth, and in some cases a hardpan may even be formed. The soils developed on the river bottom lands vary so much in character that generalization is difficult. Many are sandy or silty loams underlain by coarser alluvial material at a depth of two feet or more. However, gravels, sands, and clays are common. The fresh alluvium of the river bottoms is generally quite salty.

The mountains contain extensive areas with little or no soil or with a rough, thin, stony covering best described as mantle rock. But sizable areas exhibit true soils. In general, the mountain soils are mildly acid. Soils of timbered areas are light in color, while grass- and brush-covered soils are darker. The best mountain soils are found in the mountain meadows.

VEGETATION

An altitudinal zonation of plant life is strongly marked in the Middle Rocky Mountain basins. The vegetation of the basin floors has been classified in various ways, but all authorities agree that it falls under the general heading of desert shrub. The basin floors are part of a vast series of dry lands in the northwestern quarter of the United States that are often characterized as cool sagebrush deserts. They present an almost identical view anywhere over tens of thousands of square miles in central and western Wyoming. It is the widespread homogeneity of vegetation and landforms which causes so many travelers to find these basins dispiritingly monotonous and uninteresting. The appearance of the basin vegetation differs only slightly from season to season—the predominant color is a greenish gray. In spring and early summer the plant life is at its freshest and greenest. If growth is rapid, the brighter green of the new shoots increases the color in the landscape. Most of the time, however, the masses of shrubs and brush present a dusty, drab, gray-green appearance and at a little distance seem to form a mat of vegetation stretching to the horizon.

Various species of sagebrush dominate the vegetation in most areas; but other kinds of bushy, woody, and semiwoody plants make up a sizable part of the vegetation complement. At the lower elevations grass does not grow very well, although it is sufficiently prevalent to constitute a major source of livestock feed. At higher elevations the relative proportion of grass increases, and it often becomes the principal source of forage. The density of vegetation in this arid or semiarid region is very low as compared with the vegetation stands of humid lands. The grasses of a good pasture in a humid area may easily cover as much as 90 per cent of the land surface, whereas a range area in the Middle Rockies is considered extremely heavily vegetated and highly productive if as much as 40 per cent of the surface is covered by grasses, forbs, and shrubs. Range lands that attain a 40 per cent ground cover are relatively scarce; most have much lower vegetation densities.

The vegetation of the basin floors adjusts itself to and reflects soil and moisture conditions. The better stands of sagebrush occupy the more fertile soils. Where more moisture is available—particularly on low terraces or river bottom lands—vegetation stands are commonly heavier than average, although in many situations the vegetation is sparse because of severe overgrazing. In areas with highly alkaline soils, salt-tolerant plants such as salt sage, seepweed, and greasewood become prominent. Where a particularly sandy, steeply sloping, or rocky area produces unusually dry conditions, plants adapted to these conditions (such as rabbit brush) become dominant.

As elevation increases along the sides of the bordering mountains, the character of the vegetation changes; plant associations are adapted to the cooler and more humid conditions of the mountains. Grasses become more prominent; for example, needlegrass, bluegrass, and blue grama grass. Extensive woodlands of widely spaced junipers are found at intermediate elevations and generally are poor grazing areas. At elevations of 8,000 feet or higher are extremely thick stands of conifers—fir, Engelmann spruce, blue spruce, and lodgepole pine. There is almost no understory or grass, and such areas are nearly useless for grazing. Where forests are absent in the higher areas vigorous stands of grass may form a dense sod over broad areas.

The Pattern of Population and Settlement

The Middle Rocky Mountain basins measure about 65,000 square miles in area and are occupied by slightly less than 150,000 persons, a density of less than three persons per square mile. Population distribution is illustrated in Figure 11. Between a fifth and a fourth of the entire population is found in just three cities—Laramie, Rawlins, and Rock Springs—spaced at roughly equal intervals along the Union Pacific and U.S. Highway 30.

The agricultural population is located exclusively on irrigated lands. In this dry region such lands, scattered along the perennial streams and at the base of the mountains are, perforce, the only areas of cultivation. Ranch headquarters are located on irrigated land where feed can be raised to supply the livestock during the part of the year that they are unable to subsist from the uncultivated native pastures of the range lands. The open range lands are almost uninhabited.

Scattered through the areas of irrigated land are the market towns—the commercial centers for the ranchers and farmers of the region. The number and size of towns in an irrigated district is roughly proportional to the acreage and productivity of the district.

The generalized picture of settlement that emerges is one of islands of irrigated land in a sea of range land; the irrigated land divided into comparatively small agricultural units. Each irrigated area has a moderately dense population living on ranchsteads or in a minor market town or two. There is a net of rural roads, telephone, power, and pipe lines, and irrigation structures and channels. At the edge of the irrigated areas the foregoing features all disappear except for a few main roads, power lines, telephone lines, pipelines, and the minor roads and trails of the ranchers.

The largest areas of irrigated land and the most favorable climate are found in the Big Horn Basin, which supports the largest population—more than 40,000 persons. The central part of the Shoshone–Wind River Basin supports about 20,000 persons. Another conspicuous population grouping is found on irrigated lands in the extreme southwestern corner of Wyoming. The remainder of the population in the region (approximately 50,000 persons) is widely scattered.

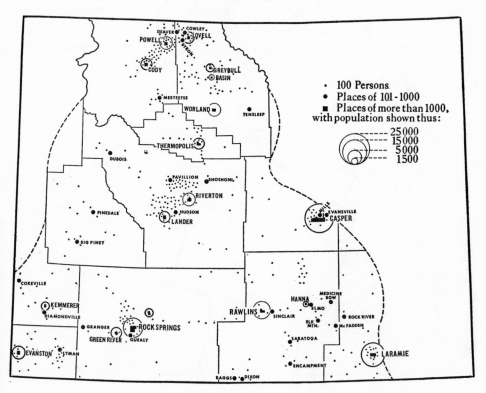

Fig. 11.—Distribution of Population in the Middle Rocky Mountain Basins, 1950

The Economic Structure

Specialized agriculture, mining, transportation, and recreation are the major economic supports of the Middle Rocky Mountain basins. The general distribution of economic activities is sketched in Figure 12. It indicates clearly the overwhelming proportion of land that is devoted to range grazing. It overstresses the extent of irrigation because only a part of the land is irrigated in the areas indicated as irrigated districts.

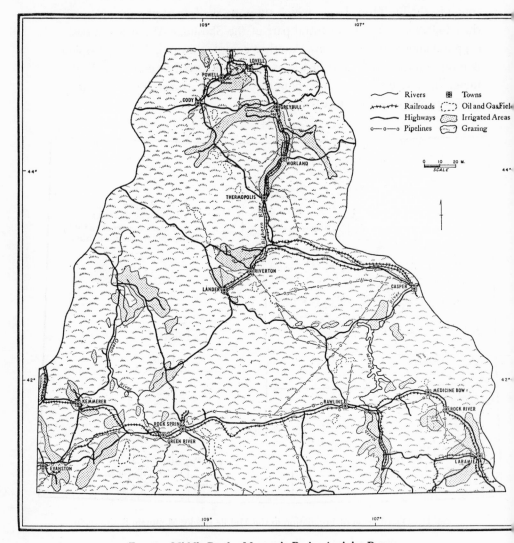

FIG. 12.—Middle Rocky Mountain Basins Activity Patterns

AGRICULTURE

The region's agriculture is almost completely commercialized. Subsistence farming (production of crops and livestock for use by the farm family) is almost non-existent. Whether on the small farm or ranch or the vast expanses of some big cattle spread, production is for the commercial market; even the small hay and grain farmer who owns few livestock produces to sell, not to use. Summers are generally too short and cool for most of the common fruits and vegetables to be grown.

Three-fourths of the regional agricultural income results from the sale of cattle, calves, sheep, lambs, and wool, and over much of the region the entire agricultural income is derived from these sources.

Approximately 5,500 farms or ranches utilize the irrigated lands and range lands of the region. The number of agricultural units has been decreasing for more than thirty-five years, and the average size has been increasing—a trend consistent with that of the United States as a whole. Data are not available specifically for the ranches of the Middle Rocky Mountain basins, but for Wyoming as a whole the average size of farm and ranch has doubled since 1930. Sheep ranches average much larger in size than do cattle ranches in the region.

Sales of cattle account for more than half the regional farm income. Cattle numbers have been surprisingly stable since the early 1940's at approximately a half-million cattle and calves. Something of the general regional carrying capacity may be judged from the fact that the region is somewhat larger than Wisconsin or Illinois but has little more than a tenth as many cattle as either of these humid states.

The region supports far more sheep—about 1.2 million—than cattle, but since five sheep are considered equivalent to one cow, sheep are only about half as important as cattle in recent years. For the past fifteen years sheep numbers have been declining sharply, though irregularly. At the low point in 1950 the region had only half as many sheep as it had supported eight years earlier. Since that time, numbers have fluctuated, but have not increased 10 per cent over the low point and amount to less than two-thirds of the 1942 high.

For decades horse numbers have been declining swiftly and steadily until today there are somewhat less than 35,000 horses left in the region. Numbers have declined almost a fourth since 1954. Other types of livestock are of scant importance. About 18,000 hogs and 225,000 chickens are kept on ranches in the region.

The last two decades have brought widespread changes in the marketing of the region's livestock. The steady and rapid growth of Pacific Coast population has extended the agricultural hinterland of that area to the Middle Rocky Mountain region. From the western part of the region a large proportion of the livestock, both sheep and cattle, moves west to the large stockyards at Ogden, Utah or on to California markets. But the Laramie Basin and the Shoshone Basin in the eastern part of the region are still firmly tied to eastern markets. The central part of the region is not oriented strongly either way: some stock moves east and some moves west. The pattern described is by no means hard and fast; livestock from the eastern part of the region sometimes moves to western markets and stock from the western basins will frequently move east. The marketing pattern of eastbound livestock has changed considerably in recent times. Formerly most cattle went to Chicago and other markets east of the Great Plains. Now, most of the cattle from southern and central Wyoming go to Denver. The largest market for cattle moving farther east is now Omaha, but several other markets—Sioux City, St. Paul, Waterloo, Kansas City, and Chicago—all receive some.

Hay is incomparably the most important crop. Both wild hay and cultivated hay (principally alfalfa) are utilized. About a quarter-million acres of wild hay are harvested every year and only a few thousand acres less of alfalfa. In the Big Horn Basin and the Shoshone–Wind River Basin nearly thirty times more alfalfa is produced than wild hay. Elsewhere in the region wild hay tonnage exceeds that of alfalfa.

A little more than 20,000 acres are ordinarily in wheat, about half of which is winter wheat in the southern Rawlins district. Oats and barley are more important than wheat. Of the more than 50,000 acres of each harvested in most years, the Shoshone–Wind River and Big Horn basins produce about three-fourths. Dry beans and sugar beets are of importance on the irrigated lands of the Shoshone–Wind River and Big Horn basins, but nowhere else in the region.

MINERALS AND MINING

Mineral production is of increasing importance. Twenty years ago agricultural production brought nearly half again as much income to Wyoming as did mineral production; a decade later the two were about equal. Since that time mineral income has been rising so rapidly that it now far exceeds agricultural income, and the margin is steadily widening. We need not concern ourselves at length with mineral production in this study of grazing land; but the rapid rise of minerals and mineral income in the economy of the region during recent years is of major significance in policy questions concerning the public lands.

Petroleum production is by far the most important mineral industry, since more than three-fourths of all mineral income in the region is derived from oil. Coal is declining in importance. For decades the main producing area for coal was the Bridger Basin, but in recent years most of the mines have closed and production has plummeted. The only other important producing district was the Rawlins Basin. Recent years have seen an important development of uranium mining in the southern Shoshone–Wind River Basin. Other mineral production worthy of note includes (1) by-product sulfur from oil in the Big Horn Basin, (2) sodium carbonate in quantity in the Bridger Basin, and (3) gypsum and cement in the Laramie Basin.

TOURISM

Quantitative information on the contribution of recreation and tourism to the Wyoming economy is unavailable, but it surely is large. U.S. Highway 30 carries extremely heavy tourist traffic during the summer season. The segment of this highway from Laramie to Evanston, Wyoming, is marked by numerous motels, hotels, restaurants, service stations, and garages, as well as specialty shops and other retail establishments, all deriving a substantial part of their income from the tourist trade. The oldest and one of the most popular of the national parks, Yellowstone Park, is located in the northwestern corner of Wyoming. Many of the millions of visitors to this park drive through the Middle Rocky Mountain basins for two or three hundred miles in going to or from the park. A high percentage of them spend one or more nights at tourist facilities in the towns and villages along the major highways leading to the park. The Jackson Hole country and the Grand Teton Mountains are other major tourist attractions. The higher parts of all the major mountain chains—the Absaroka, Big Horn, Wind River and Medicine Bow ranges, and the Mountains of Western Wyoming—are included in national forests. All of these offer mountain scenery, opportunities for camping, fishing, hunting, riding, pack train trips, hiking, nature study, photography, and other recreational activities. They attract many visitors, who often stay for longer periods than the average tourist, with resultant greater expenditures within the state.

The Middle Rocky Mountain basins support a substantial wildlife population, which attracts large numbers of out-of-state hunters and fishermen. In 1957 the number of non-resident antelope hunters alone exceeded 12,000. Hunters attracted by antelope, deer, elk, bear, mountain sheep, and upland game birds, and fishermen drawn by the excellent mountain lake fishing undoubtedly make substantial contributions to the regional income.

The Middle Rocky Mountain basins are also a major center of dude ranching. In 1957 dude ranches entertained at least 14,000 guests. Supplies, equipment, and services for so many guests are undoubtedly a major stimulus for the retail and wholesale business of the state.

The Wyoming tourist business is, however, highly seasonal. Traffic on the major through highways shows a sharp peak in July and August. Recreational use of the national parks and national forests is also largely confined to these two months, as is the peak of the dude ranch trade. Fishing and hunting extend the recreation season for about three months, although all hunting and fishing business is minor compared to the summer tourist trade. For five months from December through April the tourist business is confined almost entirely to services furnished to through traffic along Highway 30. Despite its seasonal nature, however, recreation is a basic industry of the Middle Rocky Mountain basins.

One of the greatest handicaps of the Middle Rocky Mountain basins is the unattractiveness of the region to twentieth-century Americans. To most it is a harsh, barren, windy, dusty, empty, and monotonous land. To many it is a desert, the climate much too rigorous. One professional man of the Middle Rockies basins with whom I became acquainted had spent his entire adult life in or immediately adjacent to the region. When he retired, within twenty minutes of the time he walked out of his office for the last time, he was in his car, driving to the West Coast, intending never to return. Many persons who live in the region, however, find it stimulating and attractive.

Chapter Six

THE SHOSHONE–WIND RIVER BASIN

The comparative studies of the Middle Rocky Mountain basins are introduced by a consideration of the Shoshone–Wind River Basin. In some ways it is the most complex and variegated of all the basins. It exhibits the greatest variety of land management problems and land tenure situations, and one of the more intricate range use patterns. It will, therefore, serve well to introduce most of the relevant matters in Taylor land management. A brief sketch of the general geography of the basin will be followed by somewhat more detailed descriptions of the natural landscape of the basin, the land tenure pattern, and the range grazing arrangements in the area. The rest of the chapter will treat the management of the federal lands administered by the local grazing district, the organization of the district, the allotment system, and the principal land management problems.

General Geography of the Basin

The Shoshone–Wind River Basin is in simplest terms a westward extension of the Great Plains; a great re-entrant into the Middle Rockies between the Big Horn Mountains and the Laramie Mountains in the center of Wyoming. No clear physiographic, climatic, soils, or vegetation boundary marks a western edge of the Great Plains. A low discontinuous ridge running from the end of the Laramie Mountains to the southern end of the Big Horns has been eroded into a few low hills and minor buttes which some physiographers have designated as the western boundary of the Great Plains, but these hills and buttes are insignificant interruptions in the broad sweep of the plains. An essentially unmodified plains type of environment extends westward into the Middle Rockies nearly a hundred miles. At its eastern broad end it is about sixty-five miles across from north to south. It narrows regularly toward the west until it terminates in the vicinity of the village of Dubois near the head of the Wind River Valley.

The Shoshone–Wind River topographic basin is three separate drainage basins. The western part of the basin is drained by the Wind River; the eastern section (part of which drains into the Platte and part into the Yellowstone) is referred to as the Shoshone Basin. The southern portion of the Shoshone Basin is drained by the Sweetwater River, which rises in the Wind River Mountains and flows east through some high country called the Sweetwater Plateau to join the North Platte in the southeastern corner of the basin (see Fig. 10). The entire area lies within the Missouri River drainage system.

In general the central basin areas are characterized by comparatively gentle slopes and small local relief (Plate VI). The western part of the basin has extensive areas of rugged relief and badlands; the badlands along the upper course of the Wind River are brilliantly colored, rugged, and spectacular. In general, relief increases around the rim of the basin floor near the base of the mountains. Here are badlands, buttes, mesas, hogbacks, coves, cliffs, and canyons. Plate VII shows a ranch lying at the base of one of the hogbacks flanking the Wind River Mountains and indicates

TABLE 2
TEMPERATURE DATA—WIND RIVER BASIN*

Station	Average January Maximum	Average January Minimum	Average July Maximum	Average July Minimum	Annual Mean Temperature
Lander........	31.6° F.	5.6° F.	84.5° F.	52.5° F.	43.1° F.
Riverton......	29.3	− .3	87.0	51.7	42.3
Dubois........	31.6	9.2	77.4	41.0	39.0
Casper........	36.4	16.3	87.6	55.5	47.2

* All climatic data are from various publications of the U.S. Weather Bureau.

the degree of roughness in some of the border lands of the basin. The lowest parts of the basin are slightly less than 5,000 feet in elevation. Extensive sections of the basin floor lie above 6,000 feet, and the base of the mountains is roughly 7,000 feet in elevation. It is high country.

The climate of the basin is perhaps not as severe as might be expected from its altitude, its continental location, and the absence of protection by mountains on the east. Summer temperatures range from cool to warm; winter temperatures are chilly to extremely cold. Temperature data are summarized in Table 2.

In winter the basin experiences periods of extreme cold and protracted and intense blizzards. Sometimes these severe conditions may last for several days. Temperatures of −20° F., −30° F., and even −40° F. occur from time to time during the winter season. Intense blizzards, commonly accompanied by high winds and below-freezing temperatures, often occur as late as April and May, and snowfalls are not unusual in June, particularly at higher elevations. These severe winter conditions constitute the single greatest natural hazard to the livestock industry of the basin. Perhaps in no other basin of the Middle Rockies do extreme cold, high winds, and blizzards exact so great a toll from the livestock industry as in the Shoshone–Wind River Basin.

The basin is arid to semiarid. The driest areas have a mean rainfall of less than ten inches annually, but most of the basin floor has slightly higher rainfall; approximately twelve or thirteen inches annually. Rainfall increases steadily with altitude, and the wettest parts of the mountains have thirty inches or more of precipitation. Nearly all the flows in the major streams of the basin are derived from the more humid areas in the higher, mountainous rim lands. Precipitation is quite variable, although it is comparatively rare to get a month without any. Occasionally one part or another of the basin experiences torrential rainfall; an inch to four or five inches may fall in a period of a few hours.

Vegetation has the general altitudinal zonation previously noted as being characteristic of all the Middle Rocky Mountain basins. The composition of the vegetation is also similar to that encountered in the other basins. Low-growing, widely spaced saltbushes of various species occur in the driest and saltiest soils. Where moisture conditions are just slightly better, shadscale enters the plant association. In the better areas on the basin floor big sagebrush is the largest and most visible vegetation component, but from the standpoint of grazing, the grasses are more important. Winterfat (a desirable forage species) occupies non-alkaline dry areas, and greasewood occupies its usual sites in areas of high alkaline content with water comparatively near the surface.

The higher basin areas and the mountain foothills exhibit a mixture of shrubs such as sagebrush and mountain mahogany together with sedges, flowering plants, weeds, and a number of bunch grasses such as bluegrasses, wheat grass, and June grass. Above the foothill zone is a forest zone made up of brush, aspen, and the various species of needle-leaved trees commonly found in the intermediate mountain areas of the Middle Rockies. Generally, this zone produces little forage. In some sections junipers dominate the plant association, and in such areas grazing is particularly sparse.

In the high mountain valleys and meadows grasses dominate the vegetation, but are associated with flowering plants, sedges, and weeds.

Like all the Middle Rocky Mountain basins the Shoshone–Wind River Basin is quite sparsely settled (Fig. 11). One concentration occurs just west of the center of the basin; the towns of Lander and Riverton and a cluster of rural population adjacent to each of the towns. The remainder of the population of the basin (not much more than an additional 2,000 persons) is found in three general locations: A sparse, scattered population is located at the southeastern edge of the basin along the base of the Green, Ferris, and Granite Mountains where small supplies of water have attracted a few scattered ranch headquarters. A similar (but more discontinuous) line of population is found along the northeastern edge of the basin at the foot of the Big Horn and Owl Creek Mountains. The third minor population group is scattered along the course of the Wind River, a source of irrigation water. The distribution of population reflects in part the economic activities supporting the population—range livestock ranching, irrigation farming, petroleum recovery and refining, and tourism.

The well-watered southeast end of the Wind River Range is drained by three small streams that unite after they reach the basin floor to form the Popo Agie River. The waters from these streams have been diverted for irrigation and have given rise to a cluster of irrigated farms and ranches. Roughly 35,000 acres are irrigated. Many of these irrigated fields are the base property of range livestock ranches. Lander (population 3,000) is the local market town for the district.

The principal stream of the western part of the basin, the Wind River, can be diverted for irrigation at various points along its length. Small private developments grew up along the Wind and along some of its north bank tributaries. The Riverton Project of the Bureau of Reclamation brought 35,000 acres of land under irrigation, to bring the Wind River totals to approximately 68,000 acres. The market town of the irrigation district is Riverton (population 4,200).

In the irrigation districts around Lander hay and small grains occupy almost all the irrigated lands. The production from the irrigated lands is fed to livestock, although some wheat is sold for cash. In the Riverton irrigation area, sugar beets, dried beans, and a little alfalfa seed are produced in addition to hay and grain. The tiny patches of irrigated land associated with the headquarters of various scattered ranches elsewhere in the basin produce almost nothing but grass for livestock feed.

The important transportation routes in the Shoshone–Wind River Basin are shown on Figure 12. The eastern section of the basin has rail transportation; two lines run west from Casper. The basin contains a few fine, wide, hard-surfaced main highways. One runs along the north edge of the basin; another along the southern margin. The secondary road network is rudimentary. The best developed secondary roads are gravel, and the remainder consist of little more than scraped or rutted tracks running across the floor of the basin or leading back to isolated ranches in the mountain foothills.

Land Tenure

The Shoshone–Wind River Basin has the most variegated (but not the most complex) land tenure pattern of any of the Middle Rocky Mountain basins. Public domain lands, both within and without grazing districts, national forest land, Indian lands, private lands, state lands, Bureau of Reclamation reserved lands, and military reserved lands, occupy part of the area of the basin. The eastern boundary of the basin coincides with a land tenure boundary. East of the basin, where the Great Plains open out, the land is largely in private ownership.

In the eastern half of the basin the lower lands are largely vacant public domain land, but are not included in the grazing district. There is, however, a very considerable admixture of privately owned land distributed along stream channels on the floor of the basin, at the foot of the surrounding mountains where small streams emerge onto the basin floor, and in the areas of intermediate elevation where good spring-fall range is available. At the base of the Ferris and Green Mountains in the southeastern section of the basin considerable areas are made up largely of private land. Along the northeastern margin of the basin and extending back into the Owl Creek Mountains are smaller areas of private land, some of which are small irrigated meadows and others simply high-grade, humid, middle-altitude grazing lands. Much of the private land in this area was patented under the Stockraising Homestead Act. The principal stream of the northeastern section of the basin, Badwater Creek, flows east-west at the foot of the Owl Creek Mountains into the Wind River. Lands along the creek that can be irrigated to produce hay are solidly in private hands and support the headquarters of a string of ranches. The Sweetwater River in the souteastern portion of the basin flows eastward into the North Platte River and is bordered by a similar narrow ribbon of private land. The proportion of privately owned land rises also around the southeastern nose of the Wind River Mountains where numerous small perennial streams emerge onto the basin floor. State lands are distributed in the usual pattern of two sections per township, although in some areas the pattern is somewhat more erratic, because of land-trading activities of an earlier date.

Private land dominates the tenure pattern completely in the vicinity of Lander and in the Riverton irrigation project.

A large section on the northwestern flank of the Wind River Mountains and their foothills is occupied by the Wind River or Shoshone Indian Reservation. It extends northward completely across the Wind River Basin, covers the entire western section of the Owl Creek Range, and reaches north into the Big Horn Basin. It surrounds the Riverton irrigation district on the south, west, and north. Most of the reservation lands belong to the Indians either individually, jointly as tribal lands, or as lands owned jointly by certain groups.

The lands of the upper end of the Wind River Basin are somewhat less than half vacant public domain land and slightly more than half private land. This country is so high and receives so much rainfall during the summer season that it is, for the most part, high-grade grazing land; consequently, ranchers of the area brought as much of it as possible into private ownership. Only a little of the private land is irrigated; most of it is grazing land. The usual pattern of state land has been almost completely obliterated in the upper section as a result of land-exchange which has concentrated the state lands into larger contiguous holdings.

Some of the surrounding mountains show a high proportion of land in private ownership. The bordering Owl Creek Mountains on the north are more than half in private ownership, and in the higher parts the percentage is greater. The Green and Ferris Mountains on the southeastern margin, however, are almost completely undivided public domain except for a narrow strip or two along the principal creeks.

The central section of the northeast slope of the Wind River Mountains is occupied by the Wind River Indian Reservation which extends all the way to the crest of the range. The rest of the northeast slope together with the extreme western end of the Wind River Valley and the south end of the Absaroka Range is included in the Shoshone National Forest. A very extensive rectangular area of federal land in the southeastern section of the basin is occupied by the Casper Gunnery Range. It was set aside during World War II for military purposes. Livestock still graze it under license from the BLM. During its early days ranchers grazing stock on the area were fearful of stock losses from the military explosives, but no cattle have ever been lost.

Historical Development

The Shoshone–Wind River Basin was explored and utilized nearly as early as any part of the Middle or Northern Rocky Mountain area. Because there were no mountains intervening between this basin and the East and because it could easily be reached by following the North Platte River, it was entered, exploited, and sparsely settled very early. South Pass, a low and easy pass lying between the southeastern end of the Wind River Mountains and the Antelope Hills just to the east, was discovered very early (1812) and was one of the most important passes along the routes to the West. Trappers' rendezvous were held near the Popo Agie River during the era of the "mountain men" and fur trade (1820–50). Semipermanent settlers operated ranches or way-stations along the Sweetwater River to serve and supply the wagon trains heading for Oregon or California and to furnish a few animals for the soldiers and trappers at the forts along the trail a few miles to the east.

The earliest permanent settlers in the basin entered the area around Lander in 1867; the possibilities of irrigation, the good grass, the adjacent spring-fall range of the lower Wind River Mountains, and timber along the stream banks were the principal inducements to settlement. Almost contemporaneously some minor gold workings were being exploited in South Pass, and in 1869 a fort was established in the same general Lander area of the basin.

Although settlement began fairly early, expansion came very slowly and much later. Fremont County was not organized until 1884. Settlers did not occupy the north rim of the basin floor until 1890, and the high, western end was settled even later. Settlement has continued to the present. After World War I there was some homesteading by veterans, and since then a slow increase in farm acreage has resulted from increases in the acreage of irrigated land, largely under the leadership of the federal government. The railroad did not reach the center of the basin until 1906.

District Administration

The federal government owns and administers through the BLM 2 million acres of range lands within a grazing district in the Shoshone–Wind River Basin. The district headquarters are located at Lander.[1] Each graz-

[1] Prior to 1957 the Lander office administered a greater acreage than any other BLM office. Not only did it administer the land currently in Wyoming District 2, but the Lander office staff also had charge of more than 2.5 million acres of Section-15 lands scattered across the western Great Plains from North Dakota to Kansas. During the late 1940's there were periods when this entire area was administered by a single district grazier and clerk. As the BLM's fortunes improved, the staff of the Lander office increased rapidly. By the mid-1950's, 15 to 20 persons were at times working out of the Lander office. During the big reorganization of the bureau in the mid-1950's the considerable acreages of Section-15 lands in Montana and the Dakotas were transferred to the Montana office at Billings, which formerly had been the regional headquarters for Wyoming and Montana. Early in 1957 all the remaining Section-15 lands in the Great Plains were put under the jurisdiction of a new office opened in Casper.

The office in Casper now administers 2.4 million acres of Section-15 lands. The office is operated by nine employees. They lease the land through 1,997 leases, all except 41 in Wyoming. A total of 150,000 head of cattle and 475,000 sheep are grazing on these lands; but only 290,000 a.u.m.'s of grazing are involved. Two large live-ing district has a name and a number; the district at Lander is Wyoming District 2. The office now has ten permanent employees. The personnel of the Lander office consists of the following: a district manager; two range managers, whose principal duties are range administration, adjudication, regulation, and management; two range conservationists, who are more directly concerned with the so-called soil and moisture program, the management of water on the range lands; a forester, whose principal concern is the tree-covered lands or range improvement and soil and moisture work involving tree or shrub planting or control; an administrative assistant, who handles such matters as reports to the state and area offices, payroll, and all other paper work matters relating to administration of the office; two clerk-stenographers; an operator general, who drives and cares for trucks, bulldozers, patrols, and any other mechanical equipment attached to the office.

These ten BLM employees administer a district that embraces more than four thousand square miles. It is seventy miles from Lander to the westernmost lands in the district. The lands of the district are widely scattered, large areas are difficult of access, and the tenure pattern is complex. Scores of ranchers hold permits. A total of 38,000 cattle and 90,000 sheep graze on the district at various seasons in the year in a grazing pattern of maximum complexity.

The Taylor Grazing Lessees

The grazing lessees of Wyoming District 2 are a most heterogeneous group—cattle ranchers, sheep ranchers, and ranchers who graze both types

stock companies each lease more than 50,000 acres of these Section-15 lands, and several others lease more than 25,000 acres.

The district office—it is now referred to as Wyoming Grazing District 6—has three major administrative problems. In the area at the eastern entrance of the Shoshone–Wind River Basin, between the north end of the Laramie Mountains and the southern end of the Big Horns, the heavy seasonal movements of stock between the mountains and the plains have caused much trouble with the stock driveways. At present the plan is to fence long sections of the driveway to see if the problems cannot be ameliorated by that means. The administration of a very large number of tiny isolated tracts is difficult, particularly when private properties or state-leased lands change hands. To solve this problem permanently the Casper office is pushing isolated tract sales. Consequently, the Casper office has far more isolated tract sales than any other office in Wyoming—150 to 200 sales per year. The arrangement of such sales is clearly a major function of the Casper office, although many of the details of appraisal, classification, and sale are handled by the state office of the BLM in Cheyenne. The affairs of the Casper office touch only tangentially on the field of this study, as only the extreme westernmost Section-15 lands administered from Casper are located in the Middle Rocky Mountain basins. Hence the administration of those lands will receive no further consideration.

of stock. Some lessees are urban dwellers; some live on isolated, lonely ranches. Some ranches are extremely large, other operations are tiny. Some lessees have far flung, complex grazing patterns; others have compact and simple range operations.

In most Taylor grazing districts a relatively few large operators use a large proportion of the total a.u.m.'s of grazing on the district lands. Wyoming District 2 reveals the typical distribution. The thirteen largest operators in Wyoming District 2 use 44 per cent of all the range forage, while the 43 per cent of the district ranchers at the lower end of the size scale use *less than 2 per cent* of the total a.u.m.'s in the district. In all consideration of the grazing administration of the Taylor lands this wide range in size of ranches and permits constitutes an important aspect of the problem.

The kind of ranching operation which might be termed the standard type (the type with which most people are acquainted) is a large ranch, owner-operated, and focused on a rural ranchstead. Such ranches use a considerable share of the forage resources of all the Middle Rocky Mountain basins. The operators of those ranches are constantly faced with complex problems of land tenure, range management, and grazing operations. There follows a study of one of these large ranches. Once the nature of the problems involved and the general methods of solving them are made clear from the analysis of one large ranching operation a more general treatment of the problems will be more meaningful.

A Large Ranch in an Area of Complex Land Tenure

The ranch of R. W. Spratt and Sons of Lost Cabin, Wyoming, is large, but it is not among the largest in the Intermountain West, or, for that matter, even in the Middle Rocky Mountain basins. It is, however, a substantial property. More than 90,000 acres are utilized to support a cow herd in excess of 1,800 head, but more than this number could be handled.

The property of the R. W. Spratt and Sons Ranch is an oddly shaped piece of real estate spread over part of the south flank of the Owl Creek Mountains, extending from the crest of the mountains to the basin floor. The ranchstead and the irrigated lands are strung out along Badwater Creek. All the various kinds of seasonal range are found within the ranch borders. The outline of the ranch, the drainage pattern, and the principal features of the land tenure pattern are shown in Figure 13.

The ranchstead is more impressive than that of most western ranches, even very large ones. The main house of the ranch is a particularly imposing structure (Plate VIII). It has a broad expanse of lawn surrounding

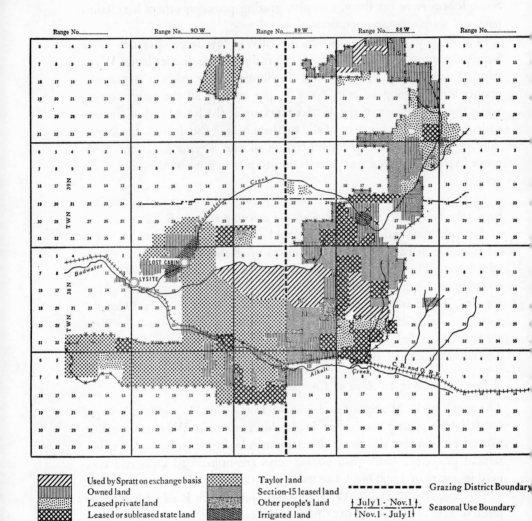

FIG. 13.—R. W. Spratt and Sons Ranch Land Tenure Pattern

the house—an unusual sight on an active western livestock ranch. It is occupied by one of the sons and his family. In addition there is a small
bungalow used by Mr. and Mrs. Spratt, Sr.

Immediately adjacent to the ranchstead is a large pumping station on a
pipeline that carries oil from the oil fields of north central Wyoming to
the refineries at Casper (see Fig. 12). The land is leased from the ranch.
As the ranchstead is the site of the former hamlet of Lost Cabin, there is
a small former retail store building now used for storage and a few
houses occupied by workers at the pumping station and employees of the
ranch.

Running both northeast and southwest from the ranchstead is an ex-·
tensive area of irrigated land along the banks of Badwater Creek, from
which comes the irrigation water. In Figure 13, it can be seen that just
up the creek, where it re-enters the ranch property, there is another section of irrigated land on the site of a ranchstead of another former ranch
property which has been incorporated into the Spratt ranch.

The dimensions of the ranch can be read from the map. Its longest dimension, from the southwest corner to the northeast corner, is a little
more than 28 miles. Most of the land within the ranch boundaries lies on
the floor of the basin. Running east-west across the center of the map
(Fig. 13) is a dashed line representing the main seasonal grazing use
boundary. North of the line is the range used from July 1 to November
1—mountain land lying on the south flank of the Owl Creek Mountains.
The much larger area south of the line is used as winter and spring range
from November 1 to July 1 of the following year. Most of the land south
of the line lies on the comparatively flat floor of the basin, but in the
southeastern section there is a long, low nose of the Owl Creeks that extends nearly to the Burlington tracks and is used largely in late fall or in
spring.

The ranch is actively managed by R. W. Spratt and his two sons. To
operate the ranch requires seven regular workers, including the two sons.
Each employee is paid $225 per month, is furnished with a house rent-
free, his electrical bill is paid, his family is supplied with free milk, and
he has an irrigable garden area. Employees who wish to do so are permitted to run a few head of their own cattle on the ranch. At the time of
the field study of the Spratt ranch one employee was running 30 head of
his own cattle along with the Spratt herds. The owners encourage this
practice because they believe that it makes better employees. Seven former employees of the ranch now have ranches of their own.

The calf crop on the Spratt ranch is usually about 80 per cent or a little lower. During the year of the study approximately 400 of the 1,835 ranch cows on the ranch were without calves. About 200 of those cows were sold. During the spring, summer, and early fall, in addition to the 1,650 remaining cows, the ranch supported roughly 1,450 calves and about 700 yearlings. About 600 of the yearlings were steers and were sold that fall; the remainder were heifers, replacements for the cow herd. Approximately half the calves were sold in the fall. Thus the total marketings from the Spratt ranch that year were: 200 cull cows, 600 yearling steers, and approximately 700 calves.

At that time it was not the practice of the Spratt ranch to carry any of the yearling steers over the second winter; they were all sold in the fall. Ordinarily more than half of the calves were sold in the fall also. Two considerations were responsible for these marketing practices. First, the Spratts seemed to have more range than they had cattle to use it and they were in the process of building up their cow herd. Second, it was difficult and expensive to carry calves through the winter. Cows could be "roughed" through the winter mostly on range forage supplemented by a little hay, grain, and cottonseed cake. Calves, however, needed to receive liberal supplies of hay, grain, and cake from Christmas until nearly May 1. This entailed a good deal of work and extra expense. It appeared that the Spratts had insufficient livestock, that they were aware of the situation, and were striving to increase the size of their cow herd.

The ranch supports some additional livestock. On the ranch are approximately 45 bulls, which were not raised by the Spratts but were purchased from ranches in Montana. Approximately 50 horses for use by the riders with the herds are kept, as well as 20 milk cows, a few hogs, and a flock of chickens for use by the families on the ranch.

We might regard the Spratt ranch as a factory for the production of beef animals and examine the source of the raw materials and the markets for the finished product. Livestock are the sole item for sale; the quantities for one year have been noted above. The principal raw materials are feed and water for the herds. There are two sources of water—Badwater Creek and four pumped wells strategically scattered over the range lands of the ranch.

Much the largest source of feed is range forage supplied from the range lands of the ranch. The other major source of feed originating within the boundaries of the ranch is the hay produced on the irrigated meadows during the summer and stored in haystacks until the winter season. Hay introduces the crucial element of flexibility into the feeding operations. If the hay is needed the winter after it is cut, it is available; but if the winter is mild and the range open and in good condition, the cattle can be kept on the range, and most of the hay saved until the following winter. Hay kept over until a second winter loses some of its nutritional quality but is still a valuable source of feed. If in the second winter it appears desirable to reduce somewhat the supply of stored hay, large amounts of hay can be fed and the cattle will finish the winter in excellent condition. If the winter is unusually severe, or if drought on the range or prolonged blizzards or deep snow make lengthy feeding necessary, all the available hay will be used. Under unusual conditions the Spratts may find it necessary to buy small amounts of hay.

Some raw materials must be purchased. Grain is the largest single item for the Spratts, who buy about 150 tons per year at a total cost of $10,000 to $12,000. This grain is purchased directly from the farmers in the irrigated area around Riverton or from the elevator in Riverton, which buys grain from the Riverton district irrigation farmers. This practice exemplifies the point made in the first section of this volume concerning the variety of means by which irrigated lands and range lands can be integrated. One way to achieve such integration would be for the Spratts to raise their own grain, produce less hay, and reduce the size of their range herd. The a.u.m.'s of range forage freed by the Spratts to balance their operation could be assigned to irrigation farmers of the Riverton district who would then feed their hay and grain to their own livestock and thus have less grain for sale. Another form of integration is the one that, in fact, exists at present, that is, the Spratts purchase grain from irrigation farmers and use their irrigated land exclusively for grass production.

Cottonseed cake is another purchased feed. About 1,800 sacks of cake, purchased in Denver and Omaha, are fed per winter. A highly concentrated cake is fed to calves, a less concentrated mixture to the mature cattle on the range. About 9 tons of salt are purchased in Casper for the stock each year.

Another major item of import for ranch operations is fencing materials. In relation to the number of acres involved, however, this is a comparatively small item, and such purchases occur sporadically.

The yearly round of operations on the Spratt ranch is similar to that found on cattle ranches in the range areas throughout the Intermountain West. The calves are born in spring on the floor of the basin in areas comparatively near the ranchstead. About the first day of May the herds begin to move into the lowest foothills of the Owl Creek Mountains; that is, on the low, southern end of the long nose that runs out from the mountains along the eastern border of the Spratt holdings. The riders in charge of the cattle drift them higher into the mountains as summer progresses. Most of midsummer is spent in the highest parts of the ranch along the northern margin. In late summer and early autumn the cattle are herded back to lower elevations, finally returning to the basin floor at the onset of the first of the winter's storms. The calves and yearlings to be sold are sent to market sometime in the fall; the calves to be wintered are brought into the ranchstead in early winter and remain there until spring. The main cow herd, tended by the riders, grazes the floor of the basin throughout the winter, except when deep snow or severe drought make it necessary to feed hay. From time to time, sick or unusually poor cows are brought into the ranchstead for special care and feeding for a period. With the arrival of spring and the new calf crop, the yearly cycle begins again.

The map of the Spratt ranch (Fig. 13) shows that the borders of the ranch form an irregularly shaped area and embrace a complex land tenure pattern. An explanation of how the ranch came into its present size, shape, and pattern of land ownership will throw considerable light on numerous aspects of present-day livestock ranching in the Middle Rocky Mountain basins.

For many years Mr. R. W. Spratt operated a ranch, considerably smaller than his present one, on the eastern margin of the Big Horn Basin. As his two sons grew older, he decided to buy a new and larger ranch, partly because of some unsatisfactory aspects in the operation of his former ranch and partly to provide greater opportunities for profitable activities for himself and his sons. Once he had made the decision to purchase a new ranch, he had available to him several different ways of acquiring the new property. He could have (1) purchased a large operating ranch of the size desired, (2) assembled several small contiguous ranches into one large operating unit, or (3) purchased several moderate size ranches not very widely separated and managed them as units of a larger operation.

In such a situation the easiest way is simply to purchase a large ranch of the desired type. However, the number of large ranches for sale over a reasonable period of time in any particular region is not very large, and, moreover, a large well-integrated ranch is precisely the type of ranch property that many urban investors are looking for. Consequently, the price is generally so high that the rate of return on the investment (even with highly efficient management) is apt to be quite low.

To buy several contiguous small ranches and unite them into a single large one is extremely difficult to do in a short period of time, as not all the ranches will be for sale at the same period for a reasonable price. Buying several medium or small size non-contiguous ranches is not much less difficult. Even if such a purchase is successful, however, the purchaser becomes the owner and manager of several individual ranches, although to some extent the operations of the various ranches can be made to complement each other.

A large proportion of urban ranch-property investors are highly conscious of the geographical setting of a ranch. To many such investors a clear, rippling trout stream running through the property greatly enhances the desirability of a ranch. A view of distant mountains, opportunities for big game hunting, interesting trails for riding, pleasant climate, accessibility to cities and to main transportation lines are matters of major concern and considerably enhance the desirability and price of ranch properties thus situated.

When Mr. Spratt was looking for a new ranch property, an enormous sheep ranch centering on the ranchstead at Lost Cabin was for sale. It was not an easy property to dispose of because it had none of the desirable characteristics just mentioned. Moreover, it was a sheep ranch; far less attractive than a cattle ranch in the eyes of most urban investors. It was a vast sprawling property made up of a congeries of types of holdings, grazing rights, leases, and use exchanges. It completely surrounded some smaller ranches, and some of its boundaries were indeterminate. Finally, the sheer size of the ranch was so great that the number of investors financially capable of purchasing it was comparatively small. Consequently, the owner decided to sell off the ranch in parts instead of to a single investor, and thereby increased the number of potential purchasers and also the possibility of obtaining a greater net return from the sale of individual pieces than he could from the sale of the property as a unit.[2]

[2] It is my strong impression that this is the history of most ranch properties in the Intermountain West. Most ranches tend to grow larger; some ranches stay the same size; few get smaller. Ranchers enlarge the size of their operations by purchasing additional private lands, by buying leases on state lands, by purchase of Taylor leases, by use exchange, and by other methods. Ranches that pass from one owner to another either by inheritance or by purchase exhibit this tendency. The ranch will continue to grow, by accretion of adjacent properties, through two or three generations or through two or three ownership transfers by sale. And then the ranch disappears. Instead of selling it as a unit, the owner markets it in parcels, mostly or entirely to adjacent ranchers. This piecemeal marketing of a large ranch with its grazing rights and base properties often leads to serious complications in the adjudication of range rights and use. It may be years before the situation settles down again. As stated above, this picture of the history of western ranches represents only the impression gained by non-systematic interviews and field observation. An intensive study of the ownership history of western grazing lands and ranches would be of great value in increasing our understanding of western land management.

Such was the situation when Mr. Spratt entered into negotiations to purchase part of this large ranch as the nucleus of his present ranch property. During the negotiations he had to keep certain important considerations in mind. He intended to change the grazing use from sheep to cattle, and the carrying capacity of many kinds of range is not the same for sheep as for cattle. A range with a great predominance of browse would support far more sheep than cattle in terms of animal unit months. For cattle it was necessary to insure a supply of water on all parts of the range. Also the ratio of irrigated land to range land needed to be higher on a cattle ranch than it had been for the sheep operation. There were additional considerations. It was desirable to have a balance of seasonal ranges —summer, spring-fall, and winter. Finally, it was necessary to spell out with precision what Taylor rights were attached to each piece of private property that was being purchased, exactly how many a.u.m.'s of use were attached to each piece of private property, on precisely what pieces of public land the grazing rights could be used, and the exact date each year that they were to be used.

After buying the nucleus of the ranch, Mr. Spratt purchased two small adjacent ranches to gain irrigated hay land, sources of water for parts of the range lands, and, finally, additional range rights.

The results of these transactions are shown on the map of land tenure of the Spratt ranch (Fig. 13). It can be seen from the legend that the pattern of land tenure and use is a complicated one. But since the map fails to indicate the full complexity of the land tenure pattern within the boundaries of the ranch, it can best be illustrated by a list of all the different kinds of land status actually found in or immediately adjacent to the Spratt ranch.

1. Private land owned by Spratt having "demand rights" on the public domain; "demand rights" means that grazing leases, rights, or privileges on the public domain or Taylor grazing lands have these privately owned lands of Spratt's as their base property. Some private lands do not carry demand rights or, expressed differently, are not base property for grazing rights on Taylor grazing lands.
2. Private land owned by Spratt not having demand rights on the public domain.
3. Private lands of which Spratt is the lessee having demand rights.
4. Private lands of which Spratt is the lessor having demand rights.
5. Private lands of which Spratt is the lessee not having demand rights.
6. Private lands of which Spratt is the lessor not having demand rights.
7. Private lands owned by another rancher, entirely surrounded by Spratt property, but used solely by the owner, and to which Spratt must provide trailing privileges.
8. Private lands owned by another rancher, entirely surrounded by Spratt prop-

erty but used by Spratt in exchange for use of Spratt property located else-where. This land may or may not have demand rights.

9. Private land owned by Spratt, not contiguous to the rest of his property, and used on an exchange basis by another rancher.

10. State lands leased directly from the state by Spratt and having demand rights on the public domain.

11. State lands leased directly from the state by Spratt but not having demand rights on the public domain.

12. State lands of which Spratt is the sublessee and having demand rights.

13. State lands of which Spratt is the sublessor and having demand rights.

14. State lands of which Spratt is the sublessee, but not having demand rights.

15. State lands of which Spratt is the sublessor, but not having demand rights.

16. Taylor grazing (public domain) lands lying within Wyoming Grazing District 2, attached to the base properties described above, and for which a grazing fee is paid.

17. Public domain (Taylor grazing) lands lying outside of Grazing District 2 (Section-15 lands), within the boundaries of the Spratt ranch, and used by the Spratt ranch, leased to the Spratt ranch, and for which a different fee is paid, and not carrying a base property requirement.

18. Same as 17 except leased to another rancher and used by Spratt on an exchange basis.

19. Same as 17 except lying outside the operating border of the Spratt ranch and used on an exchange basis by another rancher.

The pattern of land tenure status on the Spratt ranch is not much more complicated than that found elsewhere in the West wherever the land tenure pattern is relatively complex. It is true that the Spratt ranch happens to straddle the edge of a grazing district which adds types 17, 18, and 19. Most ranches have either type 16 or types 17, 18, and 19 but not both. Many ranches, however, have national forest grazing allotments, and various kinds of joint grazing arrangements on their Taylor land. The Spratt ranch has no national forest allotment and an almost negligible amount of joint public domain use.

It has been shown previously that the Taylor grazing rights of a large ranch constitute a whole series of interlocking agreements with other ranchers. When the large pre-existing ranch was broken up, certain parts of the complex of rights and agreements were assigned to the Spratt purchase. Some of these arrangements, agreements, understandings, and assignments were not made sufficiently precise and explicit at the time of the sale. As a result, either real or manufactured misunderstandings have developed in the minds of the various purchasers of the old ranch property or their neighbors, and there is imperfect agreement concerning the assignment of grazing rights in parts of the range in the vicinity of the Spratt ranch.

Other actual or potential difficulties are partly related to the tenure pattern. By no means all of the periphery of the Spratt ranch is fenced. Along the northern section of the eastern boundary of the Spratt properties, for example, there is a stretch in the excellent summer range that has no fence. This boundary is carefully ridden by two riders, to prevent Spratt's livestock from trespassing on adjacent properties and to prevent trespass on his. Neighboring ranchers take similar precautions, but trespass is not wholly avoided.

Near the northwest corner of the ranch property is an east-west vertical ridge too steep for cattle to climb (Plate IX). Several hundred acres of Spratt's land lie north of this ridge. To reach the area north of the ridge the cattle must detour around the end of the ridge, which for various reasons is impractical. Consequently, Spratt never makes use of this land; it is used by one of the neighboring ranchers to the north. Mr. Spratt has tried to make arrangements for exchange use of this land, and he has also tried to sell the land north of the ridge, but he has been unsuccessful in both cases because his bargaining position is so weak. It is an excellent example of the close interrelationships between natural land conditions, property lines, land use, and the market for grazing lands.

The views of Mr. Spratt regarding the whole western ranching situation—and his own situation in particular—are instructive in several ways. In general, Mr. Spratt seems to find his relationships with the Bureau of Land Management and the personnel of Wyoming Grazing District 2 satisfactory. Although he did not say so explicitly, it was my impression that he believes Section-15 lands should be sold to the current lessees. Because he is a decisive, independent, and self-confident person, his greatest dissatisfaction with the administration of the Taylor Grazing Act is the vague, haphazard, and indecisive status of some range allotment problems that affect his operations. One has the feeling that he would probably prefer to have the matters settled adversely to his interests, rather than to have them continue indefinitely in their present disputed and ambiguous state. He is not, however, actively dissatisfied.

He is outspoken in his antagonism to the Forest Service even though, it will be recalled, he has no forest allotment. He says that one of his principal reasons for selling his former ranch in the Big Horn Basin was his strong feeling of insecurity of tenure in his grazing permit on the Big Horn National Forest. He asserts further that he was led to believe that a transfer cut of 10 per cent would be made when he sold his property, but upon application of the new owner for a new permit, the transfer cut turned out to be 20 per cent of the a.u.m.'s. Spratt felt obliged to return $3,000 of the purchase price of the base properties because the forest permit was not as large as anticipated. The source of much of the widespread rancher antagonism to the Forest Service is the damage to the pocketbook when cuts reduce the capitalized value of the subsidy involved in the generally underpriced forage resources of the national forests.

Spratt is firmly convinced that the Forest Service attitude is inimical to the rancher. He feels that it is their aim to turn the national forests into "playgrounds." When it was suggested to him that perhaps this might not be such a bad idea, at least in a less extreme form, his response indicated that he was aware of this viewpoint and regarded it as a typical ignorant urban attitude. He feels such action would be a grave injustice to the ranchers and a blow to the economy of the West and the nation.

Oddly enough, Mr. Spratt seemed most preoccupied with and most defensive about two range management problems which one might suppose would be relatively minor ones. He consistently refused to discuss range grazing fees on the federal lands, which was the only aspect of his operations that he did refuse to comment upon and discuss. On the other hand, he seemed anxious to convince me that ranchers were taking a satisfactory point of view toward wildlife management problems. He explained that nearly all ranchers were ardent hunters and fishermen and consequently could be expected to take a highly favorable attitude toward wildlife propagation. Moreover, ranchers were among the most active members of the local rod and gun clubs and the Isaac Walton League. The local wildlife conservation groups he regards as being sensible folk who are favorably disposed toward the ranchers and their handling of the wildlife problem; but he also feels that the national organizations have fallen under the control of unwise leadership.

Most range livestock ranchers in the Intermountain West must face problems similar to those of Spratt. Each rancher must effect some combination of private, state, and federal lands into a combination of seasonal forage sources to supply the ranch livestock throughout the yearly cycle. The character of the solutions to this problem is related to differences in the local land tenure pattern, to local physical land conditions, to the kinds of solutions developed by other local ranchers, and to the policy and organization of the two major federal bureaus charged with administering the nationally owned grazing lands.

Most ranchers, however, do not operate large-scale ranches like the Spratt ranch. On the contrary, their operations are small, their economic arrangements are highly variegated, and their range use practices are shifting and complex. To give a more definite and precise concept of the small permittees operating in the Middle Rock Mountain basins, it will be useful to make some very brief sketches of a number of small operations found in Wyoming Grazing District 2.

A CROSS-SECTON OF SMALL LESSEES

ALT is a full-time rancher whose ranchstead is located in a tiny, isolated private irrigation development. He owns 156 acres of irrigated, cultivated land that he normally puts entirely into hay and pasture. This produces an average of a little less than 1 ton of hay per acre, all of which he feeds to his own stock. He leases 200 acres of state range land and, in partnership with another operator, he owns an additional 324 acres of range land. He has a permit to graze 200 head of cattle on Taylor grazing land from November 1 to April 30 and another permit to graze 30 head from May 1 to November 30. The rest of the year his cattle are on his small acreage of dry range land, or are grazing on his irrigated pasture, or are being fed hay. He has no national forest permit. It is clear that such a rancher is a small operator (only 200 mature cattle in his herd) with an operation so small as to furnish him only a fair income.

WJ ran about 1,000 sheep and 35 head of cattle on the public domain for part of the year from the organization of Grazing District 2 in 1936 until 1951. He had an irrigated farm of 255 acres which he planted entirely in hay and grain, most of which he used for feeding his livestock. In 1951 he sold all his livestock but not his Taylor permit on which he took non-use for a few years. He then brought cattle and since then has changed his allotment use from predominantly sheep to exclusively cattle. His operations illustrate the wide flexibility which the BLM must somehow maintain in its administration. Here is a man who in less than five years changed from sheep use, to non-use, to cattle use.

WD is a small irrigation farmer. For a number of years he ran 80 sheep on Taylor land for six months each year and kept them on his irrigated land the balance of the year. In 1950 he leased a small acreage of private land carrying demand rights on the public domain and grazed 30 head of cattle for four months according to the demand rights of the leased private land. He was informed by the BLM that he could not continue the practice unless he bought the land instead of leasing it. He bought part of the land. All the federal land he uses is immediately adjacent to his privately owned irrigated property. He is a full-time irrigation farmer and obviously has a substandard income.

RN is a semiretired former urban dweller who has a small 118-acre farm in an irrigated district near Lander. Only 42 acres are actually irrigated and are kept in hay and grain to feed his livestock. In addition, he rents 50 acres of flood irrigated hay or pasture land. He owns no range land, nor does he lease any state land. He has a permit to graze 30 head of cattle on the Shoshone National Forest from June 15 to September 30; a total of 105 a.u.m.'s. He also has a Taylor permit to graze 65 head of cattle and 10 horses entirely on public land immediately adjacent to his irrigated farm from May 1 to October 15. His range grazing totals about 460 a.u.m.'s, and so the rest of the year he must supply his stock on his irrigated farm. An operation of this size obviously is not highly profitable.

HNJ is a part-time rancher, who did not purchase his "outfit" until 1949. He owns a 160-acre farm of which 130 acres are irrigated and used entirely for raising hay for his 23 head of cattle and 5 horses. He has a permit to graze 35 head of cattle entirely on the public domain from May 1 to September 30 in an allotment with several other small users and one large operator, all of whose cattle are herded in common. He manages and works on the ranch in the summer, but works winters in a factory several hundred miles away.

CAW owns a large, high-altitude, isolated ranch in the southern section of the basin. He has 640 acres of land under irrigation, which he devotes entirely to hay and pasture. He has extensive holdings of private range land and also leases state land and private land from other owners. These are scattered throughout his Taylor allotment and are calculated to furnish approximately a third of the forage on the allotment. Thus his livestock are assumed to be on the public domain lands 68 per cent of the time they are on the allotment. He has one permit to graze 225 head of cattle on one allotment from May 1 to June 15, but he pays for 230 a.u.m.'s ($225 \times 1.5 \times .68 = 230$). On June 16 he takes 100 head off his Taylor allotment and puts them onto the Shoshone National Forest, where they remain until September 15. The remainder stay on the Taylor allotment on the basin floor. On September 16, the 100 head go back onto the Taylor allotment from the national forest, and the entire 225 head remain there until October 31. From November 1 until May 1 they are kept on lands adjacent to the ranchstead and are fed hay and cake. CAW is not a full-time rancher. Although he is the active manager of his ranch, he also holds a well-paid job that requires his absence from the ranch for considerable periods. He is an example of a widely prevalent type of Taylor grazing lessee; an urbanite whose principal economic interests are elsewhere, but who is the owner and active manager of a ranch.

A number of important points emerge from the examples just presented. A large proportion of all Taylor permittees are relatively small operators who use only a minor amount of the total forage produced in a district.

Many of them are in highly straitened financial circumstances and have substandard incomes. A large proportion of Taylor permittees are part-time operators, some of them because their ranch holdings will not furnish them a minimum income and they must earn extra money from outside work, such as driving school buses, working on the highways, or working in town or other employment. Other part-time ranchers are men whose principal sources of income are derived from other occupations, and their ranching operations are simply investments. They may be very active managers of their ranching operation, spending several hours a week on the range and irrigated land; or they may be almost completely inactive, relying on a professional ranch manager to handle all details of running the operation. Many of the large ranches of the West are owned by such urban investors. In many cases in the Middle Rocky basins these large ranching operations were inherited by their present owners who retain them partly as investments and partly for the prestige which in the West accrues to the owners of ranching operations.

Grazing Pattern in the Shoshone–Wind River Basin

The pattern of range land utilization in the Shoshone–Wind River Basin is extremely complex. Each rancher large or small must graze his cattle or sheep on those range lands and during those seasons that his Taylor permits or forest permits stipulate, and he must somehow balance his use of his privately owned range land, his state land leases, and his irrigated land into year-round operation. Since each rancher acts independently, enlarging or decreasing the scale of his operations, buying or selling leases, and changing the type of livestock he raises, the result is a constantly shifting and changing pattern of range land use and allocation, and an extraordinarily complex pattern of seasonal and areal livestock movement and range allotment. Only the most general outlines of district use of the range can be described. The most prevalent annual cycle followed by the greatest number of livestock in the district[3] is similar to that described for the Spratt ranch—an annual migration from the basin floor to the surrounding mountain lands and back to the basin floor. In the northeastern part of the basin a few large ranchers trail their stock from the basin floor to the foothill lands of the Big Horn Mountains in the spring, on to the Big Horn National Forest in summer, and thence back to the basin floor, where they spend the winter on privately owned lands, state land, and Section-15 lands.

[3] But, undoubtedly, not the practice of a majority of the ranchers in the Shoshone–Wind River Basin.

In the southeastern portion of the basin, where ranchsteads are scattered along the Sweetwater River and its tributaries, there is no use of national forest lands. Some ranchers use the basin floor in winter, spring, and fall and then go to the Rattlesnake, Ferris, and Green Mountains in the summer. Other ranchers operate throughout the year at lower altitudes, on private lands, state lands, and Section-15 lands on the floor of the basin.

The lowest (central) section of the eastern end of the basin is winter range for sheep that summer in the mountains both to the south and north. There is sporadic cattle use in early and late winter and, since the development of water sources in the area, extensive use by cattle in the summer (Plate X). Water development thus has various effects. A reservoir may make certain range areas available to cattle which they previously were unable to use, and thus may result in more effective use of forage. However, it may also make the range accessible to livestock at all seasons of the year and thus raise grazing pressure to a level so high that it depresses forage-production.

The situation is somewhat similar in the north central section of the basin. The Owl Creek Mountains (or Bridger Mountains, as the eastern extension of the Owl Creeks is sometimes called) do not contain any national forest lands; hence, the seasonal and areal operations of most ranchers in this area are quite similar to the procedure described for Spratt.

In the south central part of the basin, in the vicinity of Lander, and in the central part of the basin, the range allotment and use situation is even more complex. Some ranchers use the basin floor almost exclusively; some have national forest permits on the Shoshone and Bridger National Forests; some trail across the basin to the north and summer in the Owl Creek Range.

Problems of Range Land Administration

The yearly round of administrative duties occupies the major portion of the district staff's time. Until the recent increases in the size of the staff, the yearly cycle of administrative duties absorbed all the staff energies. But the administration of the range is not an end in itself; it is done for the purposes set forth in the Taylor Act: to stabilize the western range livestock industry and to protect the federal lands against injury.

ALLOCATING RANGE USE

Unquestionably the most difficult and time-consuming problem of district management is the allocation of range use. It is a never-ending process, because the status of the individual ranchers in the district is constantly changing and changes in the ranchers' circumstances necessitate changes in the district grazing pattern.

Two mutually exclusive methods of range allocation are widely utilized in the Middle Rocky Mountain basins and are of importance in administration in the Shoshone–Wind River Basin. One scheme is joint use or "in common" use of an allotment by several permittees. A lessee with a large permit will have a large number of cattle or sheep on the allotment; a rancher with a small permit will have only a few animals on the allotment ranges. The various ranchers using the allotment in common may have their stock on the range at different times or at the same time; some will have cattle, some may have sheep; and each rancher's stock may be on the range for different lengths of time. Most ranchers' stock may graze all areas within the allotment; others may be confined to part of the allotment. The common allotment has certain advantages, the greatest of which is flexibility. The exigencies of weather may make parts of the range less usable at certain times in the year, or from one year to another. On a common allotment all forage is open to all permitted stock, and all animals may use any water source within the allotment. And it makes expensive fencing unnecessary.

The common allotment also has numerous serious disadvantages. Trespass is much more difficult to detect and prove because the trespassing animals must be identified and counted. With a very large common allotment a rancher's cattle may be so scattered over a large area that it is difficult or impossible to prove that he is grazing more than his permitted numbers. The greatest difficulties arise in connection with the physical management and improvement of the range. To take any action usually requires the acquiescence or active support of all the permittees on the allotment. To put up a fence requires everyone's approval. To drill a well or build a reservoir may necessitate the agreement of every single permittee to pay his proportionate share of the cost. The same universal agreement and co-operation are needed for construction of truck trails, a corral, or for range seeding. Range management measures may also demand a complete agreement that is usually difficult to attain. If a particular piece of range is known to be especially good early in the spring, a race between the permittees will ensue each spring to see who can reach and utilize that particular piece of forage first. Common use tends to incite useless and even harmful competition for forage. No one spares the range, no one saves forage; permittees turn out excessive numbers of stock, or enter the allotment a few days early; each operates on the theory that what forage he doesn't use will inevitably be used by one of the other permittees. Consequently, all permittees tend to use the full value of their permits every year regardless of weather and range conditions or forage production.

The numerous difficulties in the management and use of common allotments have caused most western livestock ranchers and the majority of BLM technicians to favor the alternative allocation scheme—individual Taylor grazing allotments. The individual allotment is just what the name implies—a piece of range land within a grazing district allotted for use by just one permittee. An individual allotment need not be fenced and some are not, but most permittees having individual allotments prefer to have them fenced against trespass. A fenced individual allotment is operated and managed much like a piece of privately owned range land, except that the permittee pays a grazing fee for his use of the federal range, and the number of stock that he can turn onto his allotment is stipulated in his license. In numerous instances in the various Wyoming grazing districts, permittees with individual allotments use them almost exactly as if they were private property; that is, they turn out about as many stock as they wish at any time. This use is difficult to prove and some BLM technicians deny it, but much evidence convinces me that in scores of circumstances it is the case. Such use is not necessarily bad, however, and is often a positive contribution to conservative range management. When a rancher has no competition for the forage and when he knows he will have sole use of the allotment for the indefinite future, he may choose to graze his allotment very conservatively, stocking it lightly, using it only at the proper seasons, and trying to restore forage productivity. In many cases he will be willing to make investments in drift fences for better cattle control, in additional water sources, and perhaps even in range reseeding. Contrariwise, other permittees abuse their private allotments by spotty grazing, overgrazing, and use at improper seasons, just as some landowners do with their private lands. The use of individual allotments exhibits most of the characteristics, both good and bad, of private ownership.

Individual allotments, however, have caused many difficulties in range administration and adjudication in the Shoshone—Wind River Basin. During the 1940's and 50's, ranchers came into the BLM office in Lander and requested individual allotments. After lengthy negotiations with the other permittees in the same general area, outlines for an individual allotment were agreed upon and the allotment assigned. Normally the permittee promptly fenced his allotment. The assignment of individual allotments proceeded most rapidly during the late 1940's. and extensive sections of the range were fenced into individual allotments. The new fences caused some trouble in the Wind River District.

Land sales, unusually numerous in the Shoshone–Wind River Basin, always complicate range allocation, adjudication, and management, particularly when new units are being formed or when ranches are enlarging. During and after the 1941–45 war period, these processes of ranch enlargement were going on actively. Following most such purchases, the rancher wanted to add his newly acquired rights to his existing individual allotment; but, to obtain additional forage, the area of any allotment had to be increased. If the allotment were surrounded by other allotments in which the rancher had no claim, prolonged and difficult negotiations, exchanges of claims, and trading of various rights with respect to areas that could be used and time when they could be used, and perhaps actual exchanges of state land leases or deeded land might be necessary in order to make it possible for a rancher to enlarge the size of his allotment.

When numerous ranches shift from sheep to cattle, they introduce a second source of difficulty in range allocation. Some range is satisfactory for sheep but less well adapted for cattle and thus a shift from sheep to cattle may necessitate a decrease in the number of a.u.m.'s of grazing permitted. Frequent changing of allotment boundaries tends to keep range allocation in a constant turmoil with attendant disagreements, animosities, and general dissatisfaction. The necessity of having water sources within each cattle allotment is also of importance in the shift from sheep to cattle.

The steady shift from sheep to cattle ranching in the Shoshone–Wind River Basin is shown in Table 3. In 1939 the Wind River District licensed 19,400 cattle and 198,000 sheep. Since then the number of cattle has more than doubled and the number of sheep has dropped to less than half the 1939 total; 39,500 cattle and 88,000 sheep were licensed in 1958.[4] These extensive changes have necessitated recurrent changes of allotment boundaries, changes in rated carrying capacity, and the other unfortunate effects on range management just described.

This history points up one of the major weaknesses of Taylor Act administration. When there is flux and change within the western range livestock industry, range allocation and range grazing arrangements are likely to break down. In most areas in the Middle Rocky Mountain basins the range is allocated and used under a whole series of interlocking informal and formal agreements, land exchanges, lease exchanges, and simi-

---

[4] The district licensed 1,600 horses in 1939; in 1958 only 500 were permitted on the district lands.

lar types of mutually advantageous arrangements. However, these are disrupted during a period of active ranch property sales, and range allocation, adjudication, and management become confused. When the disturbances are numerous, range use conditions may become nearly as competitive and anarchic as they were prior to the Taylor Act.

Attaining a satisfactory allocation of range resources among the various claimants is not always sufficient to insure good range management. In many cases, as pointed out in Part I, the original leases permitted more livestock to be grazed than the range will support. This was true in the Shoshone–Wind River Basin. A second major activity of the BLM district technicians is the reduction of these permitted numbers.

TABLE 3

RELATIVE PROPORTION OF CATTLE AND SHEEP USING WYOMING GRAZING DISTRICT 2 IN TERMS OF STANDARD ANIMAL UNITS,* 1937–57

Year	Cattle	Sheep
1937......	16,000	43,000
1939......	18,000	36,000
1942......	20,000	44,000
1945......	31,000	30,000
1948......	34,000	23,000
1951......	39,000	21,000
1954......	37,000	22,000
1957......	38,000	18,000

* One cow is considered the equivalant of five sheep. Thus, in 1937, there were 16,000 cattle on the range at some time during the year and 215,000 sheep (43,000 × 5 = 215,000).

REDUCING GRAZING PRESSURE

Section 161.6 (e) (5) of the *Federal Range Code* for grazing districts provides that "In the event of range depletion resulting from drought or other causes, the grazing privileges that may be exercised under any license or permit may be reduced in whole or in part, and for such period of time as may be necessary." This passage is clear authorization to the field personnel of the BLM to make reductions in livestock numbers whenever range conditions seem to warrant it. The authority is used with the utmost circumspection. A cut in range numbers is seldom officially proposed unless it has the unqualified approval of the grazing district advisory board, and it is rarely made unless there is almost universal approbation from the permittees concerned. The total number of official reductions is much smaller than the number of unofficial reductions of the types previously described, that is, reductions by official non-use and reductions by paying the fee but not using all the a.u.m.'s paid for. Taylor grazing permittees oppose official cuts and reductions for three reasons. First, Taylor grazing permits of maximum size give the permittees the maximum amount of flexibility in their operations. Occasionally, for some reasons relating to ranch management, they may wish to carry, for a season or two, the full number of stock to which their permit entitles them, even though they are fully aware that the range could not support these numbers very long. Second, a large permit allows them to increase numbers to take full advantage of any abnormally large range forage production during a year or series of years of unusually heavy precipitation. Their third and most important reason for opposing reductions in their licensed numbers relates to the effect of cuts on the capitalized value of the rancher's total ranch property. The capitalized value of a Taylor grazing permit is most commonly expressed in the sales price of the commensurate property on which it is based.[5]

A Taylor grazing permittee who rarely grazes more than two-thirds of his permitted numbers will commonly oppose unrelentingly any cut in the size of his permit because of the effect of the reduction on the capitalized value of his grazing permit or his base property. When he comes to sell his permit, the rancher will sell all the a.u.m.'s to which his permit entitles him.[6]

Occasionally the BLM will move to bring about reductions on parts of districts despite rancher opposition. During 1957 the Wind River Grazing District Office in Lander initiated such a move. Along with some other smaller cuts in other parts of the district, the BLM proposed a 42.8 per cent cut on a grazing unit (the McGraw Flat Unit) south of Lander. The federal government owns less than half the land in the unit; it is used by numerous permittees, and much government land is immediately adjacent to private lands. The BLM believes that over a long period the unit does not produce enough forage to support the permitted numbers. The permittees think so, too.

On October 24, 1957 the *Wyoming State Journal* of Lander, Wyoming, under the headline "BLM Planning Grazing Cut on McGraw Flat; Ranchers Fighting It," carried the following account:

[5] Unlike national forest permits which are usually tied to a base property, Taylor grazing permits can be purchased and transferred to another suitable base property, hence their value is not always embedded in the value of a piece of real property.

[6] And the purchaser will try to use all the a.u.m.'s he purchased, with all the deleterious effects on range use and management in the vicinity that we have previously noted, unless he happens to purchase an individual allotment.

The Bureau of Land Management plans to cut cattle grazing permits 42.8 per cent on McGraw Flat unit.

But the proposal is stirring opposition of ranchers using that area south of Lander.

A protest meeting at the National Guard Armory Monday afternoon was attended by 42 stockmen. It was called by the Southern Fremont Cattle Growers Association.

Ed Mudge, president of the association, said "They [the BLM] say there's not enough feed up there. Why, there's more feed left up there this year than grew the three years before.[7] About 1,500 cattle came off this fall, all nice and fat."

"That 42.8 per cent is misleading," said Rex Colton range manager here for the BLM.

"Actually, we're just bringing the figures down to what we've been selling all the time. There's been a great deal of non-use."

"This isn't just happening in Lander," Colton said, "It's going on all over the West. We're just bringing licensed use of the ranges to carrying capacity and giving ranchers a firmer basis so they'll know what they have coming."

By that latter statement, Colton meant the BLM has been giving only one-year licenses in the past few years so it now is in a position to offer 10-year permits.

"Some of those at the meeting thought maybe the wildlife people were behind this. Others wondered if eastern capital is trying to get the cows off the range. No, it's our own program."

"Ranchers can protest to the BLM Advisory Board, then take it to an examiner for the Department of Interior, appeal to the BLM Director, then Secretary of the Interior and then go to the courts," Colton said.

As a first step, the ranchers meeting Monday went on record in opposition to the proposed cut and retained W. A. Smith of Smith and Nicholas to represent them legally.

Mudge said that ranchers were entitled to take their stock up May 1 but most of them held off until the middle or end of May. "Now they're trying to take a month away from us," he said.

"They'll never give it back—the government never does."

He said the new plan would mean ranchers couldn't take their cattle up before June 1.

"Look what this'll do to the community," Mudge said. "We sure shouldn't have much trouble getting the businessmen to sign a petition for us, should we?"

Colton disputed any suggestion it will hurt the economy of the area.

"It won't either upset the whole economy of the town," he said. "We're merely getting rid of the non-use. Why, several outfits haven't used their permits for several years, some for financial reasons, others because they didn't think the feed was up there.

"And with the 10-year permits, we're putting things on a more solid basis instead of just a year-to-year basis like it is now. The bankers will think more of it this way, I'm sure."

[7] The reference is to the three severe drought years that preceded the 1957 grazing season.

Colton said that less than half of the land on McGraw Flat is government owned and that most of the privately-owned land is used for sheep.

"They say there's no reason for a reduction this year, but the records show that our moisture was more than double the average. We're looking at the long-time picture.

"The original range survey was made in 1941 and 1942. We've been rechecking it this summer.

"But that 1941 survey was never actually put into effect. And the picture has changed a lot since then. There used to be some big sheep outfits in that area. Now there are cattle. The grazing season has increased. And there are many cattle being grazed on other's land.

"That 42.8 per cent cut isn't bad as it sounds. If a man owns his own land there, he isn't affected at all.

"The federal government owns very little water, mostly ridge tops and dry hills. The water and most of the feed is on private land.

"I grant that this may hurt a lot of small ranchers who already are in financial straits but in the long run it will be better for the whole area generally."

This story is a near-perfect illustration of the issues and the tactics involved in such controversies. The bureau is trying to cut the permitted use to bring it in line with the long-term range forage-production. Some small ranchers, however, have been using the full number of their permits. Since grazing reductions are across-the-board reductions, these small ranchers will lose part of their actual range use, but the rest will lose only their non-use, at least during most years. In refutation the president of the cattle growers association cites the good range conditions that prevailed at the end of the previous grazing season as evidence that a cut is not necessary, although he knows that it was a season of abnormally heavy rainfall. Had range conditions been poor the argument would have been that the government was making its cuts on the basis of a very poor year instead of the long-range average. The ranchers retain an attorney.[8] There are the usual statements that the cut will effect the business community adversely. There are the usual rumors that the wildlife interests or "eastern capital" are trying to get the cattle off the range. The BLM emphasizes that the reduction largely effects non-use, that it may make possible ten-year permits, and that the ranchers have the right of appeal. No one mentions the national interest; possibly no one thinks about it.

About a month later, on November 19, the same paper carried the following short report:

[8] The practice of hiring an attorney by both individual ranchers and by livestock groups to represent them in discussions and actions with the BLM is an intriguing aspect of BLM-rancher relationships. The contravening power of the ranchers versus the BLM is political power, not legal. Do the ranchers not know this; or do they just feel more comfortable after retaining an attorney? Perhaps the attorney is retained simply as a spokesman for the ranchers.

Ranchers Map Plans to Fight Cut by BLM

An open meeting will be held Thursday night at the National Guard Armory to discuss plans to protest the cut in grazing on the McGraw Flats and Lyons Valley as ordered by the Bureau of Land Management.

The meeting is called by the Southern Fremont Cattle Growers Association.

Ed Anesi said "We want to get together to fight this cut before its made final on December 3. We'll point out what a 42 per cent cut on McGraw Flat and 33 per cent cut on Lyons Valley will do to the income and tax collections."

Anesi especially urged Lander businessmen to attend. The meeting will begin at 8 o'clock.

The action taken consisted of mobilizing political pressure against the reduction and devising a plan to postpone action. The ranchers contacted the U.S. senators from Wyoming, state senators, officials of the national livestock associations; they talked with one of the Wyoming members of the National Grazing Advisory Board Council, and he apparently discussed the matter with the director of the BLM. They adopted one of the most commonplace (but perhaps also most effective) tactical devices in the field of public affairs to postpone action: They called for a survey.

An article appearing in the *Wyoming State Journal* of March 13, 1958 states:

District Range Manager Rex Colton told county stockmen Tuesday that the proposed cuts in grazing permits would not be made this year.

He said that the usual quota of permits would be issued.

The announcement was made at the regular meeting of the Fremont County Cattle Growers Association.

Following a few details concerning the association meeting the article continues:

Talk of an independent range survey to see if government grazing permits cuts are really needed highlighted the meeting.

Although no definite action was taken, the way was cleared for permittees in the disputed area to push such a project.

In response to a letter from Randall Van Patten, President of the Lower Popo Agie Cattle Growers Association, the College of Agriculture at the University offered to conduct the survey.

BLM Willing

Rex Colton, district range manager, pledged the cooperation of the BLM. He said the only reservation might be a limitation of funds to aid the survey.

Mr. Colton and others emphasized the fact that the program would take close cooperation between the BLM, the individual cattle grower, the Natural Resources Board [an agency of the state of Wyoming] and the University.

It was also pointed out that the survey would be most valuable if taken over a period of years, to indicate a trend in range conditions.

The account of that portion of the meeting dealing with the grazing reductions ends with a report of some advice from an officer of the state livestock association.

Bryan Patrick, President of the Wyoming Stockgrowers Association, emphatically urged the cattlemen to take swift and decisive steps.

"There's been a definite trend among all government agencies to cut [grazing rights]. You people should get at it. Don't leave it to the government agencies."

The "it" in the last two sentences of the quotation refers to an independent survey; a survey which, presumably, would be more apt to obtain results satisfactory to the ranchers than would a survey by the BLM.

It was perhaps clearly implied in the preceeding discussion that the proposed cuts in grazing use were cancelled because of political pressure by the affected lessees. The Wyoming State office of the Bureau of Land Management insists[9] that the cuts were not cancelled, but simply postponed so that the adjustments could be made in conformance with an impending change in the Federal Range Code, and thereby not jeopardize the rights of the ranchers in case they wished to appeal the local decision to higher echelons of the BLM and the Department of Interior. Since there is much to be said on both sides of the issue even indefinite postponement would not necessarily indicate that the bureau had simply reacted to pressure.

It is impossible to forecast what will eventually be done about the reductions on McGraw Flat, Lyons Valley, and the other areas within the Wind River District where cuts have been planned. We can be certain that the question of reductions will not be decided on the basis of the range survey. If the BLM can devise some procedure for making the reductions that will meet with the approval of the grazing district advisory board and a top-heavy majority of the ranchers within the affected units, reductions will probably be made. If, however, the ranchers are sufficiently strongly opposed so that they will directly and through their state and national livestock associations bring sufficient pressure to bear on their U.S. senators so that the senators will be really offended if the BLM acts to make the proposed reductions, the reductions will not be made. The BLM is extremely sensitive to political pressure. They offend no one by responding to political pressure from western interests.

[9] Personal letter dated June 17, 1958.

RANGE CODE ENFORCEMENT

A considerable variety of range rule violations are possible: illegal fencing, improper care of fires, improper sheep bedding practices are just a few of them. In the actual administration of grazing districts, however, two range violations—trailing violations and trespass—exceed all others in importance. In the Shoshone–Wind River Basin trailing problems are relatively unimportant, but trespass is a problem.

Trespass has occurred repeatedly in various sections of the Shoshone–Wind River Basin in the past. It is attributable to the unstable range conditions resulting from the shift from sheep to cattle, to the numerous sales of land and Taylor grazing rights, and to the unsatisfactory financial position of many livestock ranchers, particularly some of the smaller ranchers, examples of whose operations were described previously. With inadequate land resources to support their small herds these ranchers are apt to turn to trespass as a way of increasing their forage supply. In the Shoshone–Wind River Basin this is particularly true in the range lands adjacent to the widely distributed, narrow areas of irrigated land and small farms. Some trespass, however, is accidental or results from carelessness in handling the stock.

Four types of trespass may be recognized. The first is use of federal lands by livestock belonging to a rancher who is not a Taylor district permittee. A second type of trespass results when stock of a district permittee graze on an allotment other than the one on which they are permitted. Trespass on federal lands also occurs when a permittee turns more livestock onto his allotment than his lease stipulates, and lastly when livestock are turned onto an allotment at the wrong season or before opening dates and after closing dates.

Under current conditions trespass is commonly difficult to detect, hard to prove, and difficult to punish. If trespass is observed and reported by another rancher but not by BLM personnel, the offending rancher can insist that the trespassing livestock were not his. If they were actually observed and inspected by BLM technicians, he can plead that the stock got onto the range through an accidently opened gate or that his sheep were grazing outside of his allotment because his inexperienced herder was confused about where the boundary line was located. He can also assert that though his stock was in trespass when observed, they were in trespass for only a very short time until he discovered the trespass, rounded up his stock, and returned them to his own lands.

Punishment is mild, and many ranchers know this. If a BLM official discovers trespass when it is occurring, he may simply tell the offender to remove his stock, and it it is done promptly, the matter is dropped. If evidence of past trespass is uncovered, a BLM official may inform the offending rancher that his trespass is known, and exhort him not to allow the offense to be repeated. If some official notice is taken of the trespass, a common practice is to get an agreement or understanding with the rancher before any official action is taken, in order to avoid a protracted legal procedure and to avoid making the rancher actively hostile to the bureau. The usual procedure is simply to write the rancher a warning letter.

In a particularly flagrant case of trespass the district grazier may estimate how many animal unit months of forage were used by the trespassing livestock and demand that the owner pay a trespass fee for the forage used. The rancher offers the district grazier a settlement supposedly based on the current private lease rates for the amount of forage used. It therefore varies both by location and by season. The offer is relayed to the state superintendent of the BLM, who decides either to accept or reject the offer. Since the fee for the forage is generally no more than the minimum private lease rates, the rancher may not object to paying the fee. If for some reason, however, he does not want to pay, he can appeal the case through a series of administrative levels to the Secretary of Interior, a procedure which may take several years. Thereafter he has the right to appeal to the courts if he wishes.

There are some difficulties in determining exactly what the rate for private range land leases is at any time because the value of forage on any particular piece of land depends upon so many factors. Consequently the ratio of federal trespass fees to private grazing fees is a matter of considerable disagreement even among those persons best acquainted with the situation. Some BLM officials and ranchers maintain that trespass charges are equal to the current rate for private range, while other officials and ranchers maintain with equal assurance that trespass charges are no more than half the private lease rate. Since no one insists that they are punitive, they seem to me to be a positive incitement to trespass; a rancher might conclude that it was worthwhile to gamble on getting some free forage by trespass, since the worst that could happen to him would be to pay approximately the same price for the feed that he would otherwise have to pay to some private landowner.

Probably trespass charges have almost no effect on trespass activity. When a rancher's stock are in trespass on the federal range, they are either in trespass on the rancher's own allotment or on some other rancher's allotment. Probably the desire to get along with the neighboring ranchers and to avoid retaliation by them is the most effective force in preventing trespass.

Only a small percentage of all trespass cases are officially recognized as trespass or even possible trespass. This is partly reveled by the bureau's own figures. In the Wind River District official figures for 1951 list less than 2,500 a.u.m.'s of trespass grazing, other than by wild horses. For 1954 the comparable figure is 1,500 a.u.m.'s, and for 1957 the figure is 2,700 a.u.m.'s. It is quite possible that the actual trespass figures were two, three, even five times the official figures, but the Wind River District's trespass figures are more realistic than those of some other districts.

It might be argued that Section 2 of the Taylor Act gives the Secretary of Interior the right to levy fines up to $500 for repeated violations of the range code, but this is possible only if the violation is "wilful." It is difficult to discover a violation of the range rules, it is still more difficult to prove the violation, it is extremely difficult to prove that it was "wilful." It is almost unheard of for a rancher to be so fined.

The impotency of BLM officials to enforce legally the range rules and agreements against trespass on the lands that the federal government has placed in their custody is disgraceful. Because of the political weakness of the bureau and the weak enforcement clauses in the Taylor Grazing Act, it is difficult for the BLM unaided to control a recalcitrant rancher. In theory it is possible for the BLM to revoke the range permits of ranchers who are repeatedly in trespass; in reality, permits are rarely revoked even under the most extreme provocation.

The file of one of the permittees on Wyoming Grazing District 2 illustrates this point. This permittee had a lease to run both cattle and horses on an allotment made up of his private land interspersed with public domain lands. He had over a dozen proven cases of trespass against him. His livestock was almost continuously in trespass. He kept both branded and unbranded stock. When BLM officials counted an excessive number of stock on the allotment he would either assert that the unbranded stock was not his or that the stock had been on certain of his own private lands which were not included in the allotment. He, of course, refused to go onto the range with the BLM officials and would then deny their findings in the ways mentioned. It would have been possible, according to the *Federal Range Code*, for the BLM to round up the unbranded horses and cattle and remove them from the range. However, Wyoming law requires that before such cattle can be sold they must be advertised—the advertisement describes the stock and tells where they were found—and held for thirty days. When the BLM was asked why they did not round up the unbranded cattle, they asserted that they had no facilities or personnel for keeping the stock for thirty days. When the permittee sold his branded stock he would round up his unbranded stock, brand them, and then purchase more unbranded stock to run in trespass.

He falsely represented that he had leased some private land carrying demand rights. When the fraud was discovered he simply paid the grazing fees on the trespass which he had been justifying by his fraudulent statements. He finally attacked a BLM man attempting to count the livestock on his allotment. He refused to pay the assessments on earlier cases of trespass and appealed the cases through the whole series of appeals to the Secretary of Interior. When the case was finally decided against him, he simply paid the normal fees for the cattle in trespass. He repeatedly trespassed his stock on some of the very best portions of his neighbor's allotments. After several years of constant trespass and difficulty, with several unsettled trespass counts standing against him, and with an assault action pending against him, he retained precisely the same range permit that he had held for more than a decade.[10] What is necessary to cause a rancher's permit to be cancelled is indeed something to contemplate.

MAINTAINING FLEXIBILITY OF RANGE USE

On the basis of the BLM's annual figures concerning total amount of grazing permitted or actually used, it has been asserted that federal management of the public domain lands results in great rigidity in their use. Regardless of either economic conditions or weather, it is explained, the rancher rigidly adheres to the terms of his unvarying annual grazing permit, and any annual or cyclic variations in his scale of operations must be absorbed by his private and state lands. There is, in fact, notable flexibility in federal range use that the annual grazing figures conceal. Flexibility of range use intensity is one of the *strongest* points of BLM administration, because it is necessary for proper range management and because it is highly important to the economics of individual ranch operation. Ranchers may decide to liquidate part of their herd during periods of high prices, or to build up herd numbers during periods of

[10] In reviewing an early draft of this section the state supervisor in Wyoming commented that an incident of this type he would "seriously doubt could be repeated nowadays." Letter, June 17, 1958. He is almost certainly right. Moreover, the case cited is an extreme one. But the real question is whether or not less flagrant cases can be handled successfully.

low or rising prices. A rancher may need money and wish to realize on his accumulated livestock numbers, or he may wish to shift from one type of livestock to another with a concomitant decrease in numbers during the changeover. Ranges vary from year to year in their forage-production. All of these circumstances require increases or decreases in the rate of stocking.

Official figures for total numbers of a.u.m.'s of grazing on Wyoming District 2, as shown by the district annual reports, are shown in Table 4. It indicates variations of more than 20 per cent in the period of record even if we ignore the 1939 figure that probably represents an error in reporting. Moreover, these are total quantities and reveal nothing about the increases and decreases in range use on the individual ranches that may just balance each other.

TABLE 4

TOTAL NUMBER OF A.U.M.'S OF RANGE
USE, WYOMING DISTRICT 2

Year	A.u.m.'s of Range Use
1937	227,000
1939	221,000
1942	313,700
1945	313,500
1948	299,000
1951	283,500
1954	283,700
1957	261,700

Other factors cause the published figures to conceal the amount of variability. First, many ranchers pay their full permit fee but use only part of it. This is feasible because the fee is such a small portion of their total costs. Even today a rancher who pays his full fee but uses only half of the a.u.m.'s he is permitted is paying only 38 cents per a.u.m. for those he is actually using. In unusual circumstances a rancher may use only a third or a fourth of the a.u.m.'s he pays for. It can be seen that a major element of flexibility is largely concealed because grazing district statistics are based on the paid permits.

Second, any rancher can graze fewer livestock than his permit entitles by asking to "take non-use." If he askes to take non-use, he does not pay grazing fees for the number of animal unit months of grazing which he refrains from using. He can thereby reduce the size of his grazing operations almost immediately. To increase the size of his operation he again makes use of his entire permit. Official figures conceal the extent of this flexibility in range use because a large number of such changes simply cancel each other; increased non-use by one rancher is counterbalanced by decreased non-use by another. Occasionally, severe drought or widespread livestock sales will cause some variation in an entire district, but just as the district figures conceal numerous changes in individual ranch operations, so the regional or national figures conceal variations in district figures.

Third, numerous completely informal and unofficial variations in use are never revealed in the official figures, and may not even be known to the district BLM personnel. In the fall, for example, if the weather is good and a wet summer has produced an abundance of forage, a rancher may keep his cattle on his allotment from a few days to a few weeks later than the terms of his permit stipulate. A cold spring may cause him to turn his cattle onto his allotment three weeks later than his permit allows. Perhaps in neither case will he report this substantial variation to the district office. Unofficial underuse exists in substantial amounts. There is less unofficial overuse because in joint use of grazing allotments the other allotment lessees will probably report any cases of unofficial overstocking. It is to their interest to do so.

CONTROLLING WATER

Water-production from most of the public domain lands in the Shoshone–Wind River Basin is of relatively little importance. The very highest Taylor lands—in the Owl Creek, Ferris, Green, and Rattlesnake Mountains—contribute some runoff; but most streams that originate on public domain lands are intermittent streams. Taylor grazing lands furnish little water to the Missouri River system to which they are tributary, except during the occasional periods of heavy rainfall, when most of the basin streams do contribute a little runoff and large quantities of silt to the stream system. The water is relatively unimportant, but the amount of silt transported by streams in flood is extremely large. Moreover, raw stream banks and adjacent badlands on the public domain furnish silt to the perennial streams that originate in the wetter mountain and foothill areas. Until recently the silt contributed to the Bighorn River by the basin lands was of importance mostly to the irrigation farmers further downstream whose canals and other structures silted up rapidly. However, completion of Boysen Dam in the Wind River Canyon by the Bureau of Reclamation at a cost of $30 million has made the extension of the life of this expensive reservoir by controlling silt-production a matter of major economic concern.

Controlling sediment movement is, however, complex and difficult. One of the areas of greatest silt-production lies very close to the Boysen Reservoir. It is an area of badlands with an extremely sparse vegetation cover (Plate XI) that extends eastward for approximately twenty-five miles along the southern base of the Owl Creek Mountains just east of the upper end of the Boysen Pool. Whenever a major storm occurs substantial quantities of sediment are washed into Boysen Reservoir. Farther from the reservoir but also abundant silt-producers are the spectacular badlands along the upper course of the Wind River. Both of these areas discharged silt in their natural state; thus, to prevent sediment-production from these lands it will be necessary to induce and maintain some new and artificial condition. Whether or not this can be done at some reasonable cost is largely unknown. Research is needed to find plants that will anchor the soil, or to design inexpensive structures to prevent or greatly slow the rate of sediment movement. Livestock grazing should be prohibited. It would be a negligible loss because these lands provide almost no forage for the current graziers.

Prior to the building of Boysen Dam no recommendations for sediment-control research would have been justified, because relatively little benefit would have been derived from the expenditure. Certain types of water- and sediment-control measures increase forage productivity, but these slight benefits are quite inadequate to justify the considerable expense of an aggressive research and action program to design effective water- and sediment-control measures. However, if the life of the $30 million Boysen structure could be extended only a decade by such a research program, rather considerable expenditures would be thoroughly justified.

Over many sections of the Shoshone–Wind River Basin an occasional intense storm produces runoff that enters the drainage system and transports large amounts of silt. If the water can be retained on the land, sediment movement is virtually halted. The value of both the sediment control and the additional forage produced is, however, very small, sufficient to justify only minimal expenses for water management and control. Some research work along these lines has gone forward. For example, in the south central part of the basin, an extensive series of water-holding and spreading dikes (one of which is shown in Plate XII) and some tree plantings were installed to prevent water and sediment movement out of a draw and to increase forage-production slightly. The greater production of forage behind the low dikes is clearly apparent in Plate XII by the darker areas just to the right of the structure. The system portrayed in the photo is wholly uneconomic; benefit-cost analysis shows costs several times the maximum benefits. The Soil Conservation Service of the Department of Agriculture has carried on similar experiments elsewhere in the basin as has the Indian Service on the reservation lands, but all of these experimental works have been so expensive and elaborate that the costs are sometimes tens of times the highest possible benefits that accrue from them. Research might discover simple and cheap methods of achieving water- and silt-control on these lands, but long experience in many parts of the world with this problem makes it appear doubtful that a major improvement in the benefit-cost relations could be achieved.

INCREASING RANGE FORAGE PRODUCTION AND
  EFFICIENCY IN HARVESTING

The most important present function of the Middle Rocky Mountain basin public domain lands is production of range forage, which can be increased in a variety of ways. Reseeding the range with better grasses increases productivity, at least for a time. Brush-removal and water-spreading may also increase forage yield. Where ranges are overstocked, a decrease in the intensity of use will increase the forage yield, though improvement may come slowly. Proper adjustment of the season and period of range grazing also may increase forage production.

Not much is being done to increase forage production and not much is known about what should be done. In the Shoshone–Wind River Basin relatively little land has been reseeded by the Bureau of Land Management or by the permittees. Various circumstances contribute to this situation. Relatively little is known about the practice of range reseeding. To most of the ranchers and the BLM technicians in the Middle Rocky Mountain basins the results of reseeding are still rather mysterious.[11] Sometimes it succeeds, sometimes it fails. Because it is a gamble, both groups prefer to expend the available funds on other range investments from which the return is more sure. Little is known about the relationships between site factors (soil, drainage, exposure) and the growth potential of various types of grasses normally used in range reseeding. The BLM itself has done no research on range reseeding in the Shoshone–Wind River Basin.

In recent years the administrative and operating bureaus have been

11 In commenting on early drafts of this study some BLM technicians reacted sharply to these statements and asserted categorically that they were false. They insisted that their knowledge was adequate and that additional research was unnecessary. My own views are based on considerable observation and discussion so I have not changed my statements; but these exceptions to them should be noted and weighed.

instructed not to carry on research, but funds never had been available to make such investigations. About a half-dozen experimental plots, selected with respect to altitude—on the basin floor, on the Sweetwater plateau, and near the crest of the Owl Creek Mountains—were operated for a time by the Forest Service (see Plate XIII). They have since been discontinued. Some of them involved reseeding. Other plots were designed to investigate the results of various methods of brush removal—fire, bulldozing, chemicals. These few Forest Service plots represent the entire research effort of the federal government with respect to range reseeding and brush removal to increase forage-production on millions of acres of its land in the Shoshone–Wind River Basin. The only experiments with water-spreading to increase forage yield are the few already described in the discussion of water and sediment control.

Forage-production can often be improved by decreasing grazing pressure. Decreases in the rate of stocking to increase forage-production are difficult, and in the past few reductions were made. Since the mid-fifties, however, the situation has improved markedly. Prior to that time the staff of the district office was so small that all the available manpower was needed to handle the annual round of duties necessary just to keep the district operating. With the recent substantial increases in personnel, manpower has become available to make the surveys necessary to determine what lands need stock reductions, to make new range management plans, and to carry out the protracted negotiations with the ranchers that are necessary to bring the new plan into effect. As a result, however, substantial reductions in numbers of permitted stock have been made in several places in the Shoshone–Wind River Basin. A substantial fraction of many reductions consisted of permitted numbers on which the rancher regularly took non-use; but this also represented progress, because it eliminated one important latent source of range use instability.

Difficulties in determining the degree of overgrazing have resulted in the past, partly from insufficient manpower in the district offices but also from inadequate large-scale methods of range survey. There is not currently available any reliable, accurate, and objective way of making rapid surveys of either range condition or trends in range condition.[12] Ranges

[12] One widely used method (one which some range managers assert is reliable and accurate) is to determine the increase or decrease in numbers of certain key species of plants on widely scattered sample plots. The BLM in the Middle Rocky Mountain basins uses a method called after its inventor the Deming two-phase method. Many technicians in the region feel that it is highly reliable and "completely satisfactory." It is moderately expensive to use. For a thorough review of the current state of range evaluation see an article by E. J. Dyksterhuis in the *Botanical Review*, XXIV (1958), 253–372.

in very poor condition can be recognized quickly and easily by experienced range managers and examiners, and the same is true for excellent ranges. For all other conditions, however, the decision is much more difficult, as evidenced by the differences of opinion regularly arising over questions of range condition, and by the lack of objective evidence cited to substantiate judgments on range condition. Evaluating trends in range condition is probably even more difficult, as it involves all the problems of judging range conditions but also requires judgments about previous conditions of the range. I observed two extensive range trend and condition surveys, and the procedures are such as to engender little confidence in the reliability and objectivity of the results. The surveyors drove along the roads and trails observing the vegetation and occasionally on a rise that gave a view of the range they stopped, got out, and surveyed the country in all directions. From time to time they looked in and around some of the shrubs and identified a few of the grasses, then looked for five seconds at the area within a few yards to see whether they identified other similar grasses. From time to time they made remarks such as: "This range is in really fine shape"; "Man, there's lots of good feed here; there's plenty of feed"; "This range is in much better shape than it was when I was here ten years ago," and similar remarks. When asked how they knew the range was highly productive the examiners often had fairly specific answers and evidence, though some answers were vague and highly subjective. With respect to range trends, however, the answers were wholly unconvincing. When asked if they could really remember what the range looked like a decade ago, the surveyors were willing to admit that they had only a vague, subjective memory of its general appearance at that time. It was also clear to all concerned that no measurable evidence was being presented to substantiate the subjective judgments concerning range condition trends.[13]

The preceeding discussion should not be interpreted to mean either that the range examiners were wrong in their judgments concerning range conditions and trends, or that no methods are available for objective determination of range condition trends. As a result of years of experience the range surveyors may very well have been entirely correct in their judgments, but the chronic disagreement among independent range examiners and the lack of objective evidence clearly make such procedures unsatisfactory for effective range administration.

[13] Here again the increase in available manpower in the district offices has resulted in the beginnings of a marked improvement in range survey procedures. Today so-called "write-up sheets" are used that carry a written description and explanation of the observations. These sheets are and will be available to the next examiner.

In 1955 and 1956 the BLM began making range trend estimates in all the Middle Rocky Mountain basins by means of transect studies. These transects are surveyed strips about a foot wide and of various lengths. At equal intervals along the length of the transect a tiny sample, commonly a square foot, is taken. Each plant within the sample is identified and the proportion of the sample area covered by the plant is closely estimated. At regular intervals (about once in five years is the common practice of the BLM) these sample areas are resurveyed. From changes in the density and composition of the samples a reliable estimate of the changes and trends in the vegetation can be made. However, the work is very detailed, it is expensive, and the results obtained from a transect cannot usually be extrapolated to areas very far removed from the transect. Moreover, changes in the long-range trend of range vegetation occur very slowly, and may be concealed by short-term changes in precipitation, moisture conditions, and grazing intensity. Such transects must be maintained and surveyed for rather lengthy periods before results begin to repay the investment. Most of the transects of the BLM in the Middle Rocky Mountain basins are only a few years old. Every effort should be made to keep them in operation for a long period without interruptions in the observations. Although they are expensive, these studies may prove a good investment, because they may furnish the first satisfactory data on range conditions and trends on which to base management decisions. The lack of such data handicaps the bureau in its operations now.

Inefficient harvesting of range forage by the livestock will cut the yield from an area as effectively as will low forage-production. Effective harvesting is largely a matter of proper livestock distribution over the range during the proper seasons and in the proper numbers. Satisfactory sheep distribution is assured if competent herders are available and have been properly instructed, because sheep are always herded and their movements controlled thoroughly. Moreover, under some circumstances sheep need few or no sources of water on the range. The problem is more complex with cattle, which often are not herded and tend to utilize the range in a very spotty fashion. A more even distribution can be achieved by proper location of salt, fences, and particularly, sources of water. Even when cattle are herded, they are not grazed more than four miles from a source of water; consequently, effective range forage harvesting by cattle largely depends upon a proper distribution of water supplies.

Extensive sections of the Wind River District needed water development to increase their utility, and water-development work has been a major phase of the Wind River District's work program. One example of their work is shown in Plate X.

Two additional problems of Taylor land administration in the Shoshone–Wind River Basin are by no means of equal importance to those previously discussed, but each of them will probably increase in importance. They are minerals prospecting and exploitation and recreational use of the public lands.

MINERALS PROSPECTING AND EXPLOITATION
ON THE PUBLIC DOMAIN

Mineral land leasing on the public domain is handled by the Bureau of Land Management, and from the standpoint of revenue mineral-production is of major importance to the bureau. The bureau has no control over prospecting for minerals. The lands of the basin are being actively explored for oil and uranium. Most forms of mineral exploration offer little interference with other functions of the land, but geophysical prospecting for oil sometimes interferes with grazing use. Bulldozers are used to make lanes along which the geophysical prospecting crews can haul and set up their equipment. In the Shoshone–Wind River Basin ranchers complained that geophysical companies destroyed excessive quantities of forage in their prospecting activities. Active production from an oil field ordinarily interferes slightly (but not seriously) with grazing use of the land. The areas adversely affected are usually relatively small. It commonly destroys the land's recreational value temporarily. Other kinds of mineral-production ordinarily supersede and prevent all other functions of the land, but mines of various sorts occupy only very small acreages in the Lander district.

It is possible that the lanes of destroyed vegetation with their modified environments and decreased plant competition may serve as avenues for the spread of noxious and poisonous plants. Halogeten, a highly poisonous, exotic plant, may spread along such lanes, but little is known on the subject.

In some of the southern sections of the Shoshone Basin mineral prospecting has been done by digging shallow pits. These pits were not filled in by the prospectors; consequently, they constitute a minor hazard to grazing stock and to range travel by truck, auto, or horse.

RECREATIONAL USE

Current recreational use of the public domain lands of the Shoshone–Wind River Basin is for big game hunting, fishing in the creeks in the areas of highest altitude, and camping. The latter is unimportant—only a few hundred man-days per year. The major recreational land use in the region is on the national forest lands at higher elevations, where fishing, vacationing, pack train trips, and camping are of considerable importance. There is a concentration of dude ranches in the Dubois area, and these ranches use the public domain for such recreational purposes as riding or rifle target practice. The major recreational use of the public domain lands of the Shoshone–Wind River Basin is hunting mule deer and antelope—a recreational activity that has grown large enough to be economically significant for the area. Approximately 2,500 hunters, a third of them non-residents, took 600 mule deer and 2,000 antelope from the area in 1957. The One Shot Antelope Hunt conducted from headquarters in Lander is now an important event in the yearly round of activities of that city.[14]

Recreational use of the public lands of the Shoshone–Wind River Basin constitutes a minor economic asset to the area and increases the amenities of life in the region. No reliable data on its importance exist, and it would be difficult to determine. One of the main routes to Jackson Hole and Yellowstone Park passes through Lander and much of the tourist business is related solely to this transit function. A large part of the local recreational activity relates to the national forest lands rather than to the public domain lands.

Although the Grazing District Advisory Board has a wildlife representative, the BLM and the board take only a minor part in wildlife management on the public domain lands. Wildlife management on the basin ranges is handled by the Wyoming Game Commission—a state agency.

No classification useful for recreational purposes has been made of the Taylor grazing lands of the Shoshone–Wind River Basin. Such a classification would require an assessment of the characteristics of the land in terms of suitability for various kinds of recreational purposes. Perhaps a few of the very choicest locations may be used for cabin sites and camp sites, but for the foreseeable future the greatest recreational contribution to be made by the basin range lands will be to furnish forage for big game.

[14] The businessmen of Lander strongly support the antelope hunt not only because it brings increased business during the hunt but also because of the widepread interest in the hunt. Every effort is made to get expert riflemen to enter, especially ones who are widely known personalities in other fields of endeavor.

Chapter Seven

THE RAWLINS DISTRICT

All of southern Wyoming west of the Laramie Mountains may be considered either one vast basin or a number of small basins separated only by low divides or minor uplifts. The Rawlins district is the eastern half of this area. It includes all the land administered from the BLM's Rawlins office. The major topographic relationships are shown in Figure 10. The district is bounded by mountains on three sides; on the east by the Laramie Mountains; on the north by the line of the Ferris, Green, and Shirley Mountains; and on the south by two ranges of the Southern Rockies, the Medicine Bow Range and the Park Range projecting northward into the basin lands. Adjacent to these ranges are two areas known in Wyoming as "mountain valleys." Between the Laramie and the Medicine Bow Range lies a high area, drained by the Laramie River, which we will call the upper end of the Laramie Basin. The valley between the Medicine Bow and Park ranges, drained by the North Platte River, is called Saratoga Valley. Each is a re-entrant of the basin lands into the Southern Rockies. The remainder of the district consists of five "basins"—the Washakie Basin in the southwest along the Colorado border; the Great Divide Basin, an area of internal drainage in the northwestern part of the district; the Shirley Basin in the extreme northeast, hemmed in by the Laramie and Shirley Mountains; the Carbon Basin lying south and southwest of the Shirley Basin; and the Laramie Basin in the southeastern corner of the district.

Most of the Rawlins district is uninhabited (see Fig. 11). Rural population, extremely sparse everywhere, is centered on scattered ranches at the base of the southern Rocky Mountains or along the principal streams. The greatest number are in Saratoga Valley, where land can be irrigated from the North Platte River. In the entire district only a few other places are inhabited. A few ranches are located in the Shirley Basin. The Medicine Bow River flows west across the Carbon Basin to join the North Platte and ranches are strung out along the Medicine Bow floodplain. A few ranches are located near the base of the Ferris and Green Mountains. The remainder of the district is uninhabited except along the Union Pacific Railroad. The district has two dominant cities—Laramie (17,000), the central city of the Laramie Basin, and Rawlins (7,500), which serves the rest of the district. Both cities are stations on the Union Pacific Railroad, although this fact is now less important than formerly. Laramie is the site of the University of Wyoming, of major importance to the economic life of the city. The other major function of Laramie is as a market town for the Laramie Basin.

Rawlins is the urban center for all of south central Wyoming. Despite its comparatively small size, its tributary area is large. The closest cities of equal or greater size are Laramie, Casper, and Rock Springs—each more than a hundred miles away. Thus, in all directions the service area of Rawlins extends approximately fifty miles. Many of Rawlins' residents work in the oil fields to the north and east.

The Rawlins district contains 650 ranches, about equally divided between the Laramie Basin and the other part of the district. The number of ranches has decreased steadily for a quarter-century, while their average size has increased rapidly. The major form of agriculture is stock-raising. Carbon County is the leading sheep-raising county in Wyoming and the second in the nation. Carbon County ranches keep 275,000 stock sheep. In the Laramie Basin sheep are relatively unimportant—normally, less than 30,000. Despite the migratory character of Carbon County sheep ranching, a high proportion of all the sheep listed in Carbon County spend the entire year within the county. This is not the case in many western counties. The census lists sheep according to the location of the ranch headquarters. In many cases sheep recorded in a county spend part (perhaps most) of the year in a different county or even in a different state; but, substantial amounts of all seasonal sheep ranges are found within the Carbon County boundaries. Cattle ranches are much more numerous, and in general are smaller. The Laramie Basin supports about 43,000 head of cattle, the balance of the district about 58,000. Thus, in one of the major sheep-producing areas of the United States cattle exceed sheep in importance whether measured in terms of animal unit months of grazing or in relative value.

The number of horses in the district is declining; only 7,000 remain. Twenty years ago, this district supported one of the larger wild-horse populations in the United States. To many persons, particularly fiction readers, the wild horse is a romantic creature; but ranchers and range managers more prosaically view wild horses as animals that destroy an excessive quantity of forage by grazing and trailing without bringing any economic return. Consequently, sustained efforts by ranchers and horse hunters to round up the wild horses of the district have resulted in their virtual elimination.

Nearly 10,000 acres of winter wheat are produced in Carbon County each year. Wheat and hay are the only crops of any importance in the Rawlins district.

Many of the ranching operations, particularly the sheep operations, are carried on with an absolute minimum of permanent equipment such as barns, sheds, ranch houses, corrals, and the like. They present a primitive, rustic, and unimpressive appearance. This is less true of cattle ranches than of sheep ranches and in general is least true of cattle ranches with extensive irrigated meadows and hay fields.

Organization of the District

The public domain lands in all of the diverse basins in south central Wyoming are included in the management responsibilities of the Divide Grazing District or, as it is also designated, Wyoming Grazing District 3. The office of the BLM for the Divide District is in a one-story building in a residential section of Rawlins. Rawlins is located very near the center of the district; the intersection of diagonals drawn connecting the corners of the district would fall not more than a mile or two from the city. The district is large; the most remote parts are nearly ninety air miles from Rawlins and still farther by road. Moreover, in the western third of the district most of the land is accessible only by ranch roads, trails, or rutted tracks. The Rawlins office also manages 382,000 acres of Section-15 lands lying in and around the margins of the Laramie Basin. These lands are 65 to 130 miles from Rawlins and include many small blocks each covered by a separate lease.

The rapid improvement in the fortunes of the BLM during recent years and the concurrent increase in the intensity and systematization of federal range management are well exemplified by the Divide District. At the low point in the operations of the BLM and particularly the Division of Grazing, during the late 1940's, the district was administered by three persons—a district grazier, as he was called at that time, his assistant, and a clerk. By 1952 the staff had increased only to four. In 1955 the staff totaled seven and in 1958 twelve.

Table 5 indicates the acreage administered either directly or in association with Taylor grazing leases. The unreserved and unappropriated public domain lands grazed under regular Taylor leases within the Divide District total 3.6 million acres. Associated with and used with these Taylor lands within the district are 222,000 acres of other types of federal land holdings, 415,000 acres of state land, and 2,357,000 acres of private land. It is clear from Table 5 that the acreage of public domain grazed under Section-15 leases is relatively small, but the acreage of other types of federal land under such leases is substantial. These other federal lands are mostly reclamation withdrawals and federal wildlife refuges; unusually large acreages of both types of land are in the Rawlins district.

The total area of the Divide District proper is 6,646,000 acres. The BLM has issued permits to graze 45,000 cattle, 900 horses, and 435,000 sheep on these lands. The land and the forage are leased to 248 ranches, corporations, or associations, which are licensed to take 459,000 a.u.m.'s of grazing use.

Although several large ranching operations center in the Divide District, such large operations do not take as great a proportion of the total forage as in many Taylor districts. The general pattern of range permits

TABLE 5

LANDS ADMINISTERED DIRECTLY OR INDIRECTLY
BY BLM OFFICE–DIVIDE GRAZING DISTRICT
(Thousands of Acres)

	Public Domain	Other Federal	State	Private
Regular....	3,590	222	415	2,357
Section-15..	381	1,034	375	2,606
Total.......	3,980	1,258	792	4,964

is the common one found throughout the Middle Rockies. Cattle ranchers outnumber sheep ranchers nearly three to one, but the sheep ranching operations are much larger. More than a third of all permittees in the district are cattle ranchers grazing less than a hundred head of cattle. Two cattle ranches have permits for more than a thousand head. At least seventeen sheep ranchers have permits to graze more than 5000 sheep; but these seventeen ranchers, who make up about 8 per cent of the permittees in the district, use about a third of the total forage in the district. The Divide District has only a dozen ranches that combine both sheep and cattle operations. The largest carries 6,000 sheep and 1,500 cattle.

The number of animal units and the number of a.u.m.'s of use licensed in the Divide District in recent years are shown in Table 6. Such statistics mean little. They indicate only what they are labeled as showing—i.e., the total number *licensed*, nothing more. They show little about amount of range use. In most districts no one knows exactly how much actual use (as distinct from licensed use) there is.[1] All districts have some non-use.

[1] A conclusion sometimes stoutly contradicted by the BLM technicians; who assert that the figures represent the facts, but that in some cases the figures do need some interpretation.

Technicians in various districts hold different views about the amount of non-use and the accuracy of the non-use figures. In some districts it is asserted that the total use and non-use is very accurately known;[2] in other districts it is viewed merely as an estimate. In the Divide District in recent years non-use has arbitrarily been declared to be a third of actual range use, based on the ratio of known use to original permit figures. Since the amount of trespass is also only imperfectly known, the relation between licensed use and actual use cannot be accurately estimated.

It is certain that the Divide District carries excessive amounts of non-use. This is partly because the district is still only partially adjudicated. Out of a total of 290 permits in the district only 130 are ten-year permits, issued after a section of the range has been adjudicated. The number 130 represents a substantial recent increase, as only 99 term permits had been

TABLE 6

ANIMAL NUMBERS AND A.U.M.'S LICENSED
DIVIDE GRAZING DISTRICT (NOT
INCLUDING WILDLIFE)

Year	Animal Units (Sheep Numbers Divided by 5)	A.u.m.'s
1947........	103.5	464.7
1949........	103.3	470.4
1953........	113.9	539.6
1957........	116.0	459.0

issued at the end of 1957. It reflects one of the favorable results of the steady increase in number of employees in the districts. Adjudication still has a long way to go. In some parts of the district half the land has been finally adjudicated and is under term permits; in other areas only 10 per cent is adjudicated. Two big stumbling blocks stand in the way of final adjudication. A considerable acreage has never been inventoried. Until carrying capacity is known with fair accuracy, final lease adjustments cannot be made. Second, extensive sections of the Divide District are used at the wrong season, but it is exasperatingly difficult to effect changes.

Contributing to the unusually large amounts of non-use in the Divide District are a number of elderly sheep ranchers who are quite willing to utilize their leases at less than capacity. This extensive non-use tends to reduce grazing pressure on the range—some sections have no grazing intensity problems as a result—but it tends also to slow down final adjudication

[2] The personnel in District 5, for example, insisted that the estimates of use and non-use on their district were accurate.

because the ranchers object to parting with any of their rights even though they are not currently using them. Moreover, the non-use is a potential disruptive factor if the land should be sold and the new owner started to use his full lease.

In the Rawlins area, as elsewhere, the two parties most directly involved, the BLM and the area ranchers, are pushing toward individual allotments, although there is no unanimity of opinion in either camp. Some BLM technicians are not enthusiastic supporters of individual allotments, and some sheepmen are violently opposed to individual allotments. The weight of opinion in both groups, however, favors the individual allotment.

A third group with an active interest in the management of these lands, the sportsmen's clubs, are against all fenced allotments and thus against individual allotments, which are commonly fenced. The sportsmen claim that fences seriously interfere with the movements of migratory game animals. Under severe storm conditions big game animals pile up against fences and die, as they did in the area west of Rawlins during the severe blizzards of 1948–49. Such extreme conditions are unusual, and the effects of fences on elk, deer, and antelope under ordinary circumstances is more disputable. It is also true that the wildlife interests have little direct power locally, as the one wildlife representative on each district advisory board is only one of a dozen board members. In general, the influence of the sportsmen is in proportion to the amount of public commotion they can arouse and the indirect pressure thereby exerted on the advisory board and the BLM.

The nature of range land use, the land tenure pattern, and the problems of public land administration differ so sharply from one section of the district to another that it will be desirable to treat the district by sections.

Laramie Basin

The Laramie Basin, in the extreme southeastern corner of the Middle Rocky Mountain region, is not a homogeneous unit from the standpoint of range land administration. Its northern lower end, at an elevation of about 6,000 feet, is covered with desert shrub. The basin slopes upward toward the south, attaining an elevation of about 7,500 feet at its high southern end. This end of the basin, somewhat less than a thousand square miles in area, is flat to gently undulating, and, because it is high, it is humid and cool and as a consequence is grass-covered with almost no admixture of shrubs or brush (Plate XIV). When seen from the surrounding mountains the basin is an impressive sight—a vast, smooth, shallow, green bowl.

The principal stream of the basin is the Laramie River, which has a wide and flat floodplain. Extensive areas of this floodplain are irrigated, although much of the irrigation is early season flood irrigation, because most of the water rights to the basic flow are held by irrigation farmers far down stream along the Platte River. Many of the larger ranches of the region have their headquarters along the Laramie River.

The driest parts of the Laramie Basin receive about 10 or 11 inches of rain annually; some of the wettest parts, mostly near the base of the mountains in the southern section, receive as much as 17 or 18 inches. Annual variability of precipitation is considerable. The bordering mountains receive more rain, but the amounts are not startlingly higher. Both in the basin and in the mountains, summer precipitation is notably heavier than that of winter; much of it falls as intense summer showers. The winter precipitation of the mountains is of major importance, however, because it falls as snow and accumulates throughout the winter season. Much of it appears as runoff when thawing occurs in spring and early summer.

Winters are long and cold in the Laramie Basin, but extremely severe weather occurs only very irregularly. The average maximum temperature in January at Laramie is just above freezing; the average minimum is about 10° F. Daytime temperatures in summer are quite warm; average summer maximum at Laramie is about 75° F.

Vegetation exhibits a regular gradation from a nearly unmixed excellent grass stand in the high southern section to a typical desert shrub dominated largely by sage in the somewhat warmer and drier northern section.

Agriculture in the Laramie Basin is livestock ranching and almost nothing else. In the high southern section cattle-raising predominates; in the lower northern section sheep are relatively more conspicuous.

In the Rawlins district in general ranchsteads are relatively simple affairs—a ranch house, a few small buildings, some rough corrals; on a sheep ranch perhaps a shearing or lambing shed of slightly greater size. There is a wide variety in ranch sizes within the Laramie Basin.

The lands of the Laramie Basin, particularly the southern section, are a versatile range; that is, they can be used to good advantage throughout the year. A rancher can use the basin lands as winter range for either sheep or cattle, as completely satisfactory summer range because it is high enough to receive enough rain, and as excellent spring-fall range. Because of this year-round grazing potential, the basin has a great diversity of grazing practices, and stock are on the basin ranges throughout the year.

Although the Laramie Mountains stand at 8,000 or 9,000 feet elevation they are not rough and rugged. Most of the upland surface consists of rounded forms with moderate slopes covered with grass. Trees are sparse. It is excellent mountain grazing land, and, because it is good, it has been brought largely into private ownership. The northern section is higher, more rocky, rugged, and heavily forested. Much of it is included within the Medicine Bow National Forest. Laramie Basin ranchers use only a minor portion of the lands in the Laramie Range. Ranchers from east of the mountains own most of the mountain deeded land and have a majority of the forest permits.

The Medicine Bow Mountains to the west are higher, more rugged, much more extensively forested, and are included almost entirely in the Medicine Bow National Forest. Only at their north end has private land penetrated into the mountains at all, and even there it is widely scattered.

The map of land tenure in the Laramie Basin (Fig. 14) reveals the key facts affecting management of the federal lands. In the southern part of the basin, federal lands make up only a small proportion of all land and are widely scattered in tiny parcels—forty acres, eighties, quarter-sections, here and there an isolated section. Most of these pieces of federal land are entirely surrounded by private lands. The very highest lands at the extreme south end of the basin, however, are almost solidly public domain.

The federal lands of the Laramie Basin are utilized under Section-15 leases. Except for their duration and cost, Section-15 leases are very similar to private ones. The Bureau of Land Management computes the annual carrying capacity figures, which are changed into monetary values by using the current federal charge per a.u.m. within grazing districts. The annual rent on the lease is then expressed in terms of cents per acre instead of in terms of a.u.m.'s as is the practice within grazing districts. Section-15 lease rates average about 3 cents per acre per year. In the past no restrictions were made concerning the number of a.u.m.'s of use that might be taken from the lands under a Section-15 lease, again in contrast to the practice within grazing districts where the maximum amount of use is stipulated. In recent years, however, some Section-15 leases have stipulated number of a.u.m.'s and season. The leases run for ten years and are always renewed upon request.

In the Laramie Basin it would be impossible without a map to distinguish in the field the government sections under Section-15 leases from the adjacent private land. Normally the land is not fenced or in any other way separated from private acres. The Bureau of Land Management rarely inspects its Section-15 lands, unless they have some reason to suppose that the land is being severely abused. During the first twenty years of Taylor Act administration many Section-15 lands were inspected only

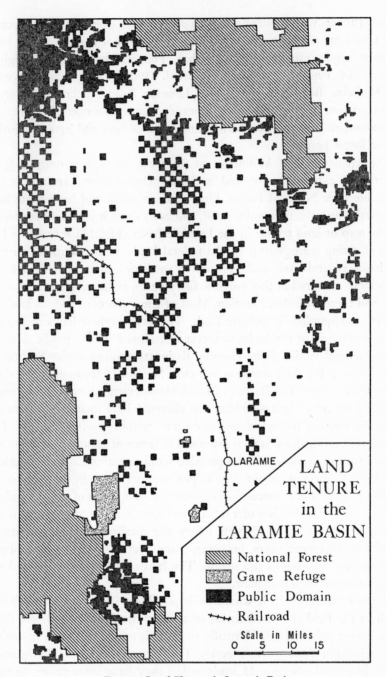

LAND
TENURE
in the
LARAMIE BASIN

National Forest
Game Refuge
Public Domain
Railroad

Scale in Miles
0   5   10   15

OLARAMIE

Fig. 14.—Land Tenure in Laramie Basin

once, if at all. In recent years the Rawlins district office has inspected all Section-15 lands before new leases are issued, which means that the lands are inspected at least once every ten years. Many Section-15 lands are cursorily inspected every three or four years.

The facts concerning the land and the ranching and tenure practices in the southern portion of Laramie Basin have been described in more detail perhaps than the amount of land warrants; but, these Section-15 lands of the southern Laramie Basin are of the highest interest because they expose various facets of the problems of federal land policy more clearly than almost any others. Here is an area of excellent range, where range land values are relatively high, where range land is sought after, where almost all the land has gone into private ownership. Why does the federal government own land in such an area? The answer is simple: it owns the land simply because it was never alienated. It was not retained for any purpose, it was not selected to be held; it is the land that no one patented. It was retained by accident, not by policy.

The people of the United States derive certain values from retaining ownership of these lands, although most of the values are potential rather than actual. The federal government receives a small rent, although far less than private lands of similar values bring. Viewed as federal income, it is trivial. The federal government retains title to whatever potential surface or mineral values the land may have. By retaining the land in federal ownership certain common-use values are retained. The Section-15 lands are open for hunting by any citizen who complies with the Wyoming game laws, although this is more a theoretical right than an exercised one. Probably few hunters ever consciously hunt on the federal range lands in the Laramie Basin; moreover, many of these lands would be inaccessible unless permission was obtained to cross the surrounding private lands. Anyone may prospect for minerals on the Section-15 lands; few do. They can be used by anyone for riding, hiking, picnicking, shooting, almost anything except grazing. Only the holder of the Section-15 lease has the grazing rights. All their values except grazing values are potential, not actual.

No values can be assigned to the government's stewardship of the land, because the government exerts no control over use of its land. Whatever value it has as a watershed, whatever is done to protect it against erosion or overgrazing could be derived equally well from private ownership because private ranchers are now controlling and managing the lands.

We may conclude that the lands now have little utility except as grazing land, that they bring little income to the federal establishment or the local governmental units, and at the same time constitute a minor administrative chore for the BLM. Although these lands have little present utility except for grazing, the government by retaining ownership holds the potential values for all the people at little or no cost.

Much of the low utility of the land is closely related to its fragmented and scattered arrangement. One way to increase its utility considerably would be to consolidate the federal holdings into larger blocks.

Shirley Basin

The lands of the Laramie Basin sweep uninterruptedly all the way to the northern tip of the Laramie Mountains. The northern end of these basin lands, however, is known as the Shirley Basin. The margins of the Shirley Basin are rough and broken, and the basin itself is less spacious and extensive than the Laramie. It is bordered on three sides by mountains: the Freezeout Hills to the southeast, the Ferris Mountains to the northwest, and the Laramie Mountains to the northeast and east (Fig. 10). Several small streams originate in the surrounding mountains and flow across the basin on narrow floodplains.

The organization of grazing in Shirley Basin is simple, because there are few ranching units within the basin and the various seasonal ranges are closely juxtaposed. A considerable part of the Shirley Basin is within a single allotment—the Sullivan Company ranch. It is the area marked "3" in the upper right corner of Figure 15. The boundaries of the allotment include the deeded land of the ranch as shown on Figure 15. Like most large ranching operations, it has grown from an initial small holding of 12,760 acres purchased by one of the brothers in the early 1930's. They gradually enlarged their holdings until 1948, when they made their first large expansion. The ranch has now grown to more than 200,000 acres. In the process of expansion several ranches have been consolidated, and today operations are directed from two major headquarters along Muddy Creek, the principal stream of the basin; they are indicated by X's on Figure 15. The owners have a mixed operation, normally running approximately 20,000 sheep and 500 cattle.

The ranch holdings are so compact that the operations are simplicity itself. The cattle spend the winter (from October 1 to April 30) on the extensive irrigated pastures surrounding the two ranchsteads. About May 1 they are simply turned out to wander the range until the end of September. For two months they stay on the basin lands, but about midsummer, when the heat and aridity increase, they wander to the higher

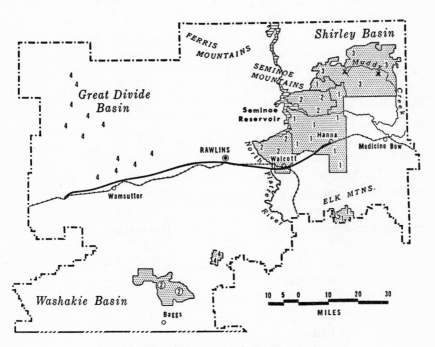

Fig. 15.—Selected Allotments in Divide District

ground around the west and north margins of the allotment. About October 1 they are rounded up and put back on the irrigated lands.

The numerous bands of sheep are kept on the lowest part of the range south of the ranchsteads during the winter, and they lamb in that area also. Later in the spring the sheep are brought into the western headquarters for shearing, after which the dry ewes, yearlings, and bucks are separated and taken to the lands at the extreme northeastern edge of the allotment that are high and moist enough so the sheep can stay all summer. Some of the other bands head northwest and spend the summer in the northwestern part of the allotment. One band moves off to the east. In fall all the bands are brought back to the vicinity of the eastern ranchstead, where the sheep to be sold are cut out and trailed straight south to the railroad at Medicine Bow. The rest of the sheep return to the winter ranges.

The tenure pattern of the Sullivan allotment is simple. The irrigated land is deeded land. In the northern part of the allotment all the other land is Taylor land. The winter range at the south is mixed public and private land. In general, the BLM regards the Sullivan allotment as a satisfactory one. Because it is compact there is little trouble with trespass, trailing is at a minimum, and livestock numbers and grazing intensity are easy to check. The district technicians, however, feel that the ranch has an inadequate amount of summer range and that the summer ranges on the allotment are grazed too heavily. They regularly urge the ranch proprietors to acquire additional summer range. The important point here, however, is the generally satisfactory operation that results from a large compact range unit.

The few other ranches in the Shirley Basin do not have such a neat operation. The area is extremely remote and difficult of access. The more distant parts of the basin are eighty or more miles from the district office at Rawlins and, consequently, the ranchers in that area long operated with a minimum of supervision. When a staff of more adequate size became available the district office was able to assign a man to part-time supervision of the Shirley Basin Unit: another management improvement resulting from recent expansion.

Checkerboard Lands

The map of land tenure in the Divide Basin (Fig. 16) shows part of a forty-mile-wide band of checkerboard lands that extend east-west across the entire district. North of the checkerboard strip all land is in federal ownership except for two sections of state land in each township. Southwest of the checkerboard lands the same solid pattern of Taylor lands is found, but in the southeast, in the area fringing the Medicine Bow National Forest, the land tenure pattern exhibits a high proportion of private land. Private land is also found along the principal streams—the North Platte, the Medicine Bow, and some of their tributaries.

A district manager once suggested that had Congress deliberately planned to construct a land tenure pattern as difficult as possible to administer it probably could not have devised anything worse than the checkerboard arrangement. Certainly the checkerboard pattern presents most perplexing administrative problems.

Prior to the enactment of the Taylor Grazing Act the sheep ranchers

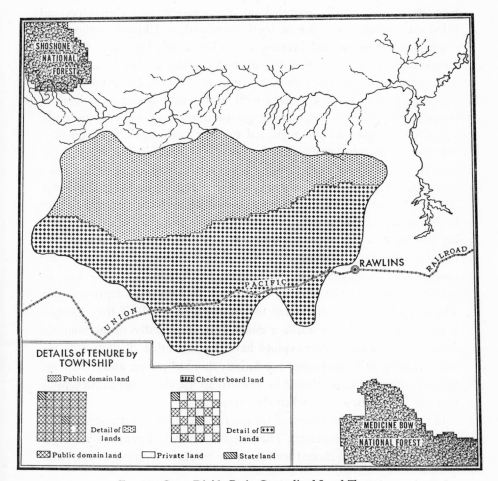

FIG. 16.—Great Divide Basin Generalized Land Tenure

of the district purchased or leased the Union Pacific Railroad lands and used them to control the alternate sections of public land. This control was possible because the alternate sections of federal land cannot be entered without trespassing on the adjacent private lands. The Rawlins district was an area in which competition for the range lands was very keen. The winter ranges of the basins are bordered both north and south by mountain pastures, but bands of sheep also trailed into the area from the Wind River Mountains to the northwest, from the Colorado Rockies to the south, and even from as far away as the Wasatch Mountains of eastern Utah. Moreover, the cattlemen from the numerous ranches around the mountain margins also tried to make use of these winter ranges. However, for a long period a closely knit group of large sheep ranchers in the Rawlins area informally parceled out the range among themselves and aided each other in the use of legal, extralegal, and illegal methods for organizing range use and keeping out other would-be users. Although competition for the ranges was sharp and continuous, the local ranchers achieved and maintained a modest degree of control. Consequently, the sheep ranchers of this area looked with an unfavorable eye on federal attempts to organize and regulate range use in the area, because the range was already organized and regulated to their satisfaction. Consequently, for many years the Rawlins district was one of the principal areas of opposition and antagonism to Grazing Service efforts to establish order and regulation on the federal lands in the district and in the West in general. The local ranchers had no desire to co-operate with the Grazing Service in the organization of the district. Rather, their attitude toward the Grazing Service was that of an adversary. It was common practice to discuss range management matters with the district manager only when the rancher was accompanied by his lawyer, and in some cases the rancher did not even enter the discussion but sent his lawyer to represent him. The sheep ranchers would agree to any regulation only if they thought it tactically advisable to make a concession. Repeatedly throughout the history of the district the sheepmen have reiterated that all allotments, use dates, trailing rules, and other regulations should be done away with and that the sheep ranchers should be allowed to use the range as they think best—go where they want when they want.[3]

In the original adjudication of the district the sheepmen came off much better than did the cattlemen. The sheep ranchers had previously bought up the deeded checkerboard land in order to obtain control of the alter-

[3] The last such formal recommendation was made as recently as 1956.

nate government sections, whereas the landholdings of the cattlemen had been confined largely to irrigated land. Having control of the checkerboard lands, the sheep ranchers tended to hold their stock out near the margins of the checkerboard strip as long as possible and not until midwinter bring them down closer to the railroad. In earlier times the railroad was the best means in winter for the rancher to travel out from Rawlins to see his herds. As long as the sheep were held near the margin of the checkerboard strip, cattle were not likely to move into the area in any numbers, and thus the cattle were always kept on the irrigated lands of the ranches throughout most of the winter. Consequently, when prior range use was being established, the sheepmen could prove that they had been using the higher lands outside the checkerboard strip about as much as the cattlemen and using the checkerboard lands far more. On the basis of prior use they had a notable advantage.

Moreover, during the early part of the adjudication process the sheepmen succeeded in establishing a ruling that gave them a great advantage in all subsequent negotiations, a ruling that the BLM personnel now regard as a serious mistake. The concept of base property is already familiar. It is now necessary to introduce the term "parallel lands," which refers to private range lands that are interspersed with and must be used simultaneously with federal range properties at certain periods in the year; that is, they are not considered as supporting the operator's livestock when the stock is not using the federal range. Parallel lands, thus, are not base property.

During the early adjudication period the sheep ranchers of the Rawlins district managed to have the privately owned checkerboard lands designated as base property rather than as parallel lands. In establishing claims to graze the federal range, it will be recalled, previous use of the federal range was one criterion for establishing priority; the second criterion was the operator's ability to support his livestock throughout the year. In the Rawlins district it was declared that the operator must be able to support his stock on his deeded lands for one hundred days a year. Most sheep operators kept their bands on the checkerboard lands for well over one hundred days a year, and half the checkerboard land was the sheep operator's deeded range land that had been declared base property. Hence, half of all the animal unit months of grazing on the checkerboard lands furnished so-called commensurability for claims to the federal range. The claims greatly exceeded the available forage, and when pro rata cuts were made the huge commensurability base established on the privately owned checkerboard lands enabled the sheep ranchers to obtain the lion's share of the grazing rights. Moreover, in the areas north and south of the checkerboard lands, where the competition between cattle and sheep for range had been most severe and where use had been most intense, the cuts had to be the greatest. Here the cattle operators were most severely hurt.

The BLM technicians have found it almost impossible to organize, manage, and regulate the checkerboard lands without the complete co-operation of the sheep ranchers, and, as pointed out previously, the ranchers in the Divide District were among the least co-operative. If the BLM were to allocate the federal range in a way that did not suit the adjacent private landowner or were to set up any other regulation not to the satisfaction of the deeded landowner, the rancher could fence off the area from effective access. If two or three ranchers were to combine forces, they could construct a barrier to these checkerboard lands stretching for miles, with access only by a few openings. State law requires that access must be granted to all range land, but a few narrow openings to a huge piece of property are sufficient to comply with the law. Moreover, by judicious construction of internal fences it would be possible to keep stock away from water sources, to force them to climb excessively steep slopes in order to reach certain areas, and to interpose other difficulties and obstacles. The government, as owner of the alternate sections, could do all of these same things, but presumably the national government would not indulge in such petty retaliatory measures. Moreover, the Department of Interior would not allow itself to become vulnerable to opprobrious attack and scorn by an antagonistic congressman by engaging in such maneuverings. Hence, checkerboard land holders are in an extremely strong position.

Overstocking of the federal ranges is extremely difficult to combat in checkerboard areas. Livestock operators cannot be held for trespass on the federal range except for the period when their stock is actually on federal lands.[4] In an area of alternately arranged landholdings such as the checkerboard lands it is extremely difficult, in this region of scarce property boundary markings, to prove that the stock are on federal lands, not deeded lands, and it is wholly impossible to establish any precise period of trespass.

These examples do not exhaust the list of difficulties encountered in checkerboard land administration. They serve to make clear why the Divide Grazing District is one of the most difficult districts to organize and regulate. The checkerboard lands, however, are not used in isolation;

---

[4] If cattle, however, are known to have been in an area half of which is federal land, they may be held to be in trespass on federal lands for half the time.

they are part of the entire management problem of the district that can best be taken up area by area.

Carbon Basin

Land management and use is fairly satisfactory in the Carbon Basin—the entire eastern part of the Divide Grazing District, roughly east of Rawlins and southwest of the Shirley Basin. In this area cattle ranchers had made extensive purchases of range land in the checkerboard area prior to the Taylor Act, partly to control access to water along the streams and partly because it was fairly high-grade grazing land; consequently, they were not required to take disproportionately large cuts during the adjudication process and have not used the non-checkerboard lands so intensively. Also a large part of the lands of the Carbon Basin have come under the management of a relatively few ranches, and large compact operations, as illustrated by the Spratt ranch and Sullivan Brothers ranch, usually tend to simplify the problems of regulating and managing the range.

The land in the eastern part of the Divide District within the area "1" on Figure 15 is largely either the property of the Palm Livestock Company or is Taylor land allotted to the company. The total area is greater than 225,000 acres, and the ranch supports more than 20,000 stock sheep. This huge property was put together very recently. The owner, a wheat farmer from the vicinity of Cheyenne, made his initial purchase in 1948 and expanded his operations to their present size in just ten years. The ranch operations are directly supervised by his three sons.

The sheep are wintered on the rectangular block of checkerboard lands in the center of the basin north and west of Hanna. In spring they are trailed to a big shearing shed on the railroad just west of Hanna, at one of the two major ranch headquarters. After shearing, the bands are made up for the summer, and the yearlings and dry ewes are taken off to the high lands at the extreme northern end of the allotment. The ewe bands drift south and lamb beyond the railroad, where the owners have made extensive water developments. The sheep continue to drift southward toward higher lands. With the arrival of full summer they have reached either the southern end of their big main block or the little block of land marked "1" along the southern margin of the district. Most of the bands summer in the Medicine Bow National Forest, but some spend the entire summer in the southern part of the district allotment. In the fall the sheep come off the forest and begin to drift slowly back to the checkerboard land. Some of the sheep to be sold are cut out and shipped as soon as they leave the forest, and the rest are shipped when the bands reach the railroad.

With a big, compact, individual allotment like this, trailing is held to a minimum, management is efficient, and administration is easy.

Long trailing is, however, a characteristic of sheep operations in the Divide District. A good example of such nomadic operations is furnished by another large ranching operation in the eastern section of the district—the Leo Sheep Company. The company normally has about 12,000 stock sheep. In the winter 9,500 of these sheep graze the checkerboard lands of the large allotment (marked "2" on Fig. 15) north and south of the railroad in the vicinity of Walcott; the other 2,500 winter near the circled "2" in the extreme southern part of the district, north of Baggs. In the spring after shearing, which is done at Walcott for the main bands, the bands are split up. Some trail north across the northwest corner of the Palm Livestock allotment to reach the area marked 2 just east of the Seminoe Reservoir. They utilize the southern part of the allotment during the early part of the season and spend the midsummer period along the margins of the Seminoe Mountains. Another band of 2,000 trails west along the main district trail adjacent to the railroad from Walcott all the way to Wamsutter and thence south to the circled 2, where they spend the summer in the higher lands immediately adjacent to the national forest. The rest of the sheep drift south through the main company allotment and into the Medicine Bow National Forest.

In the fall the sheep from the forest drift back onto the south end of the main allotment and thence north to the winter ranges near the railroad. The 2,000 sheep from the Baggs area follow their spring trail back through Wamsutter, east to the main allotment, and thence back north to the winter ranges near the railroad. The last band trails back from the north.

The activities of the Leo Sheep Company will probably be considerably modified in the next few years. The company has been notified that its allotments on the Medicine Bow Forest are to be severely cut. The owner has already started purchasing additional range rights within the district to replace the forest cuts, but for a period the company may ask for heavier use on their present BLM allotments.

The other lands of the Carbon Basin are operated in a manner similar to the two operations just described. Despite excessive trailing and seasonal migration in two directions, reasonably satisfactory range management is characteristic of this basin.

Washakie Basin

Only a geologist would call the Washakie Basin a basin, for it is actually an upland, highest in the center. It is called a basin because of its structure; that is, the underlying rocks dip toward the center of the area. Wherever the more resistant rocks reach the surface they form outward facing cliffs. Laney Rim and Cathedral Bluffs shown on Figure 10 are some of these outward facing scarps, but there are several rows of them ranged concentrically around the area. Where these cliffs have been severely eroded, badlands have been formed. The basin is unproductive. The moderately rough topography and the sandy, rocky, thin, droughty, and infertile soils combine with the low rainfall (about ten inches annually) to produce only a scanty, low-grade vegetation.

Checekerboard ranchers from the area around Wamsutter and ranchers located near the base of the mountains in the vicinity of Baggs are the principal users of this area. Several sheep bands come off the Medicine Bow and Routt National Forests, spend the fall in this area, and then drift north to the checkerboard lands for the winter. Sheep ranchers from Baggs use the area as both fall and winter range. The western part of the basin is used for cattle in spring, summer, and fall by ranchers from the adjacent Baggs area. One extremely large sheep-ranching operation trails more than 25,000 sheep from the Medicine Bow and Routt National Forests west completely across the Washakie Basin into the grazing district to the west. In recent years a group of sheep operators from the west have acquired extensive grazing rights along the western border of the Divide District, particularly in the Washakie Basin section.

The western margin of the Washakie Basin is the site of the principal soil and moisture operation of the Divide District. An area in the vicinity of Shell Creek is covered with a highly erosible soil. Its vegetation cover, probably none too sturdy in its original condition, has now been depleted by grazing, and the area is just on the verge of eroding severely. Moreover, there is no possibility that the area will recover unaided. As the quality of forage on this range has declined, grazing pressure has increased relative to the remaining quantity of vegetation, which has hastened the vegetation depletion. The objective of the BLM work in the Shell Creek area has been to retard the rate of water runoff and thereby prevent erosion and increase the vegetation density. To achieve these ends the district's soil and moisture funds have been used to construct 6,000 acres of water-spreaders (similar to that shown in Plate XII) to remove water from channels and spread it out over a larger area so that it will sink in instead of running off. The increased soil moisture in the water-spreading areas increases vegetation growth, in time increases the density of vegetation, heightens the resistance of the surface to erosion, and also improves forage-production. After this has taken effect the BLM can increase grazing pressure at some seasons, but will ask the ranchers to remove their stock from the area entirely during the months of May and June (the period when the grasses are making their most active growth) to rebuild the vegetation cover more rapidly.

Great Divide Basin

One of the more unusual features of the Middle Rocky Mountain basins is the Great Divide Basin—a 4,200-square-mile area of internal drainage located directly athwart the continental divide in the western part of the Divide District. From a range management standpoint it is of considerable interest, as it is an area of complex ranching practices and of excessive trailing.

One of the larger operations centering in the Great Divide Basin is that of Louis Larsen, who runs approximately 10,000 sheep. From the first of January until the end of March they graze in the large allotment (southern "4's" on Fig. 15) in the northeastern part of the basin and along the northern edge of the checkerboard strip. At the end of March the entire band trails south to the railroad for shearing. Thereupon the "bucks" and dry ewes are trailed all the way to the Green Mountains, which are located north of the northwest corner of the district. The rest of the sheep go south along the main trail to the lambing grounds—the small allotment marked "4," about 30 miles south of Rawlins. After lambing, about 4,100 sheep trail far south into the Routt National Forest near Steamboat Springs, Colorado, 50 to 60 miles south of the southern allotment. The rest of the sheep stay on the lambing grounds all summer. At the end of summer the forest bands return to the southern allotment, pick up the other bands there, and then all trail back north until they reach the area of solid public domain lands (northernmost 4's on Fig. 15) north of the northern allotment where they spend the rest of the year. At the beginning of the new year they return to their northern allotment to begin again the annual migratory cycle. Some of the sheep have trailed well in excess of 250 miles during the course of the year, and during the summer season the northern and southern bands are more than 175 miles apart.

The grazing pattern followed after returning from the forest is a direct outgrowth of the pre-Taylor grazing pattern. Prior to the passage of the act the sheep ranchers could control grazing on the checkerboard lands. Thus, the use pattern was to scramble for the forage on the public land beyond the checkerboard strip until it was gone, whereupon the checkerboard ranchers would retire onto their checkerboard lands; but only when they were more or less forced to by the disappearance of outside forage.

The federal lands of the Great Divide Basin are of special interest because they throw into sharp outline certain aspects of western public land policy. The two reasons invariably adduced for federal ownership of public domain land in the West are: (1) to protect the land's value as watershed and (2) to protect the land against accelerated erosion. These reasons, however, come to their test in the Great Divide Basin. Since it is an area of internal drainage, it has no watershed value, and it will have none in the foreseeable future. If the federal government is holding these lands to protect their watershed value, it may as well dispose of them. Some lands of the Great Divide Basin are mildly susceptible to erosion, but most of them are quite flat and rainfall is scanty, so that this is an area with relatively minor erosion problems.[5] Hence, the reasons commonly advanced for government ownership are not applicable in the Great Divide Basin. Certainly tens of millions of acres in the United States worth several times more per acre are more subject to erosion than those in the Great Divide Basin. If one of the functions of the federal government is to protect the nation's land against erosion by holding it in federal ownership, to be consistent, those other millions of acres susceptible to erosion should be purchased.

The public does have another interest in the Great Divide Basin. The basin is the range for the largest prong-horned antelope herd in the United States. The federal government owns most of the land in the basin, so the herd must derive most of its sustenance from government lands. Perhaps all the people would like to retain ownership of the range that supports this antelope herd, but this is an objective and a purpose served by the national wildlife refuges. If this is our national purpose, perhaps we should create another wildlife refuge in this area, but it would be impossible to create a refuge in the area of the checkerboard lands until the federal lands holdings had been consolidated.

The purpose of the foregoing discussion is not to recommend that the federal lands of the Great Divide Basin be sold nor to recommend that they be consolidated into a national wildlife refuge. It is intended to show that the pattern of federal land holdings in the Great Divide Basin is simply the result of historical accident, and that the federal establishment continues to hold these lands for reasons which do not apply in the Great Divide Basin. The implication is clear that a review of policy with respect to these lands is indicated.

[5] There is some wind erosion. The basin is sandy, and in this land of sparse vegetation winds produce live dunes, blowouts, and shifting sands.

*Economic Aspects of Range Forage Prices
  in the Divide District*

Total receipts from grazing in the Divide District were $72,000 in 1956, and about $76,000 in 1957. These receipts were not quite enough to cover the costs of materials, rent of machinery, rent of the district office, gasoline, and seeds that were utilized in the physical management of the district.[6] The salaries of the district technicians and all the costs of administering those parts of the state office concerned with grazing were paid out of general funds. Total costs were probably about $115,000. From a fiscal standpoint it would be better for the federal government just to forbid grazing on the federal lands. The policy which was supposed to prevail for nearly a decade from 1947 to 1957—that the government would charge for forage about what it cost to administer the Taylor Act—was clearly being given a special interpretation. Apparently by the mid-1950's it had been interpreted as meaning direct costs of managing a district, exclusive of employees salaries, and including none of the overhead costs at state and national administrative levels.

In the light of these facts it will be useful to examine some interesting comparisons of the leasing and pricing rates of federal forage and privately owned forage in the Divide District.

It was emphasized in Part I that pricing of range forage is a matter of considerable importance, but that it is extremely difficult to establish either the value or the price of a block of range forage. The current lease rate for Taylor forage is 19 cents per a.u.m. In 1957 the private checkerboard land on the floor of the basins of the Divide District sold for about $3.50 per acre if it carried rights to an adjacent section of federal range land. Most of this basin-floor land is so-called 6- to 10-acre land; that is, it takes 6 to 10 acres of such land to furnish an animal unit month of grazing. If 8 acres are taken as an average, it follows that two acres—a private acre and a federally owned acre—will furnish about a fourth of an a.u.m. of grazing. Four times that amount ($3.50 for each of the four private acres necessary) would result in a land cost of $14 per a.u.m. An interest rate of 5 per cent would produce an annual cost of 89 cents per a.u.m.—70 cents in interest plus the 19 cents of fee which would have to be paid for the forage on the federal land. But numerous complicating factors are involved: for example, the forage on the privately owned land is owned

[6] Figures taken from a special compilation made for the author by the BLM. Since some costs are compiled by the type of operation for the entire Wyoming area rather than by district, it is necessary to pro rate such costs for each district; hence district expenditure figures are only approximate.

in perpetuity, but the rights to the forage on the public lands are subject to whatever insecurities of tenure are inherent in the Taylor Grazing Act. Local taxes must be paid on the privately owned acres, but not on the federal land. Presumably the price represents a weighing of all these factors. Two large sales of range forage took place in the Divide District in 1957 at which prices were expressed directly in terms of a.u.m.'s; the price was $13, only slightly less than the estimated price in the previous case. Informed opinion in the district held that these were not abnormally high prices for government forage.[7] The current price for private grazing leases in the Divide District during 1957 ranged from $1.65 to $2.50 per a.u.m. The conclusion seems inescapable that government forage was being leased for only a third or a fourth of its minimum value.

Special Administrative Problems of the Divide District

The boundaries of the Divide District fail to coincide with the use pattern in several areas. For example, the district boundary lies north of the Ferris Mountains. Sheep from the checkerboard lands use the south flank and the crest of the Ferris Mountains for summer range, but the north flank of the mountains is grazed by cattle from the Sweetwater country to the north. Were the line drawn somewhat farther south, this spilling-over of cattle from District 2 into District 3 would not occur. A little further west the opposite situation occurs. Sheep from District 3 graze to the crest of the Antelope Hills and Green Mountains, but those areas are located in District 2. Hence, if the line there were drawn farther north, overlap could be avoided. The northwest corner of the district is used by sheep from three different districts. In the fall, sheep from the checkerboard areas of the Divide District make a big circular swing through that corner of the district to pick up whatever forage is available. In similar fashion sheep going from the Wind River Mountains to the basin lands of the district to the west make an elliptical swing through this same area. Also, in summer, cattle from the Sweetwater country drift south into this area; they can do so because water sources are available there. All this stock must be supervised and bills for the forage sent to ranchers in three districts.

Recreational use of land is of increasing importance in parts of this district. One such area is Saratoga Valley, which lies between the Medi-

[7] A sale made in the Divide District in late 1958 points up some of the difficulties involved in arriving at range forage prices. One large outfit split up its holdings when it was sold. The sale prices were expressed in a.u.m.'s, but the sale prices ranged from $7.50 per a.u.m. to $30 per a.u.m.

cine Bow Range and the northernmost extension of the Park Range (Fig. 10). Much of the valley floor is covered with sagebrush and other semi-desert types of shrub; but running through the middle of the valley is the North Platte River, bordered by willows, cottonwoods, and other shrubs and trees, and by irrigated meadows and hay fields. It is a clear, strongly flowing trout stream and has several attractive tributaries of the same character. As most of the floor of the valley is above 7,000 feet elevation, aspen and other open-forest trees come down the mountain foothills almost to the floor of the valley. It is an excellent hunting area. Deer are particularly numerous, upland bird shooting is fine, and elk, bear, and antelope live in areas nearby. These all indicate a very attractive recreation area, and many people agree that it is. Saratoga Valley is one of the centers of dude ranching in Wyoming, and the valley also has some strictly resort hotels offering riding, swimming, and fishing. A few ranches in the valley are owned by wealthy urbanites who operate the ranches to reduce the cost of owning the land which they retain mostly for recreational purposes.[8] On weekends during the summer and during the hunting season the valley is invaded by substantial numbers of visitors, the largest numbers coming from the Denver metropolitan area. Hunters, fishermen, campers, and picnickers use the public domain lands (among others) for recreational functions. Certain of the most favored BLM lands in Saratoga Valley are used regularly for camping and picnics, although they have no facilities for either activity. The BLM has no procedures, plans, or organization to manage recreational use of these public domain lands, the lands are not prepared and managed for recreational ue, and use of relatively low intensity tends to cause the condition of the lands to deteriorate for the very recreational uses for which they are most advantageous.

In a favored recreational area of this kind there is a brisk demand for land suitable for private recreational purposes. Among the other classes of land available for purchase are the public domain lands, and there is a steady stream of inquiries and actions, particularly by urban dwellers, to acquire title to public domain land for recreational purposes. Such applications are handled, under the provisions of the Small Tract Act, by the state office of the BLM. After the application has been received, state office personnel classify the land. If it is classified as most useful for recreational purposes, the application is processed, and eventually a small parcel of the land (two, five, or perhaps ten acres) is sold to the appli-

---

[8] The valley also has oil and gas possibilities, and that may be another reason for acquiring private properties.

cant for a very low price. Most of these applications are for the very best recreational lands in the valley; in effect, the very best recreational lands are being alienated on a piecemeal, *ad hoc,* unsystematic basis. Formally the district office has no part to play in this small tracts activity, but since the district technicians are the only BLM local representatives they may be asked to assist in locating the area precisely on the ground and on a map, or to furnish other information.

Wildlife also causes a problem in the same general area. Many different local land managers—including ranchers, Forest Service rangers, and BLM staff members—are convinced that deer have become so numerous in the north end of the Park Range and the adjacent foothill and basin areas that they are damaging the land. The federal land managers refer to the present deer-land ratio and its effects on the land as constituting "nearly a disaster area."[9] But control does not reside with federal officials; the length of the hunting season, the size of the individual hunter's bag, and other similar regulations are set by the Wyoming Game Commission. Thus in effect the successful management of the game populations of this area depends upon the co-operation of the three agencies involved—Forest Service, BLM, and state commission.

The Divide Grazing District administers a few "special" (non-grazing) leases and permits. In all the Middle Rocky Mountain basins such special leases are of minor concern, but they will become of steadily increasing importance with the continued growth of western population, commerce, and industry. The miscellaneous nature of these permits is indicated by those in force in the Divide District. The city of Rawlins leases 10 acres on which have been drilled water wells for part of the city water supply. The local gun club leases 200 acres to use as a shooting range. The Union Pacific Railroad leases 194 acres on which to put septic tanks, bunk houses, warehouse sheds, and other small structures. A total of 58 acres is leased for 21 different business sites. A free-use permit was granted to take 20,000 tons of sand and gravel for use in road construction. All leases and permits are in the vicinity of Rawlins or along the major highway and rail route.

The Divide District is unique among the five grazing districts in the Middle Rocky Mountain basins in that it has a major fire control problem. Parts of the district are sufficiently high to reach into the forest zones of the mountains. The district contains 290,000 acres of forest lands, of which 110,000 are considered to be light commercial forest. The principal commercial species is lodgepole pine. Two sections of the district have

---

[9] Internal memorandum, Divide Grazing District to state office.

particularly severe fire-control problems—the Shirley Mountains in the northeastern part of the district and Elk Mountain, the northernmost major peak of the Southern Rockies. To protect the latter the BLM has installed a fire lookout, manned by temporary employees during the summer season. However, during the dry period at the end of summer, when the fire hazard is at its annual peak, about a month is devoted by all technicians in the district office to fire-prevention and control work. On one occasion the Divide District had a really serious fire that burned for several weeks.

The timbered lands at the southern margin of the district are located adjacent to the Medicine Bow National Forest. Fire-control work, timber sales, and timber management are some of the principal functions of the Forest Service. It seems reasonable to raise the question whether these lands should not be transferred to the jurisdiction of the Forest Service.

Summary

The Rawlins district contains a variety of lands, tenure patterns, management practices, and administrative problems. In the southern Laramie Basin the high, humid, grassy, Section-15 federal lands are widely scattered, receive almost minimum supervision, and are rented by the federal government almost exactly as they would be by a private landlord. It was implied that there might be good reasons for the federal government to relinquish ownership, although the cost of retaining the lands is relatively small. Consolidation of federal holdings into larger solid blocks was also suggested.

Two large compact ranch operations in the eastern part of the district were shown to be efficient and easy to administer. Livestock of ranches in the western section of the district trail extraordinarily long distances, ranching operations are scattered, and these conditions have led to great difficulty of administration by the BLM. Many of the current grazing patterns arise directly from the pre-Taylor grazing pattern that grew out of private attempts to control range use. Grazing competition in the pre-Taylor period was intense in this area, but range allocation was solved in a manner satisfactory to the local ranchers; consequently they have always resisted attempts by the BLM to establish regulations on use of the open range. Their obduracy has made the process of adjudication so slow and difficult that much of the basin land is still in a fairly anarchic state of administration and regulation. Part of the difficulty results from the extreme complexity of checkerboard land administration, and again the implication is that consolidation of federal holdings into larger compact blocks would help to remedy the situation.

The situation in the Great Divide Basin is clearly a very special one that brings into focus some questions regarding the relationships between the public domain lands and the purposes for which they are being retained in federal ownership.

The next area to be considered is the Bridger Basin to the west of the Divide Grazing District. The physical characteristics of the Bridger Basin and many aspects of the land tenure pattern, seasonal migrations, and range use are very similar to those in the Divide District; but, because of some differences in the history of the development of range management and administration, range use conditions have taken a sharply divergent course.

Chapter Eight

THE BRIDGER BASIN

Few grazing districts in the West repay study more handsomely than does the Green River Grazing District (Wyoming District 4) that occupies the Bridger Basin. The basin exhibits a wide diversity of natural conditions and range use arrangements. Particularly it is notable because it was the scene of one of the most successful and interesting attempts to control range use by private methods and because these earlier attempts at control have greatly affected the methods of range administration by the BLM since the organization of the district under the Taylor Act.

General Geography

The main line of the Union Pacific Railroad runs east-west across the Bridger Basin. At the little village of Granger in the western part of the basin the line splits; the main line strikes west and southwest toward Ogden, Utah, while the Oregon Short Line leads west and northwest toward Idaho. U.S. Highway 30 parallels the rail line. At Granger the highway also splits; U.S. 30 North follows the Oregon Short Line, while 30 South parallels the main line.

These transportation lines have had an important influence on population distribution in the basin. If the lines did not exist, the pattern of distribution would be considerably different. Ranches would be scattered (as they are now) along streams in the higher sections of the basin floor near the mountains. Here and there a few villages or hamlets would perform market functions, just as at present. A ribbon of irrigated land and associated ranchsteads would follow the floodplain of the Green River, as it now does. But the dry central portion of the basin would probably be almost devoid of population, instead of containing the principal settlements of the area. The latter, associated with the major transportation lines of the basin, are so large that they completely overshadow the sparse population associated with the livestock industry. All the larger urban areas in the basin—Rock Springs, Green River, Evanston, Kemmerer, and Granger—are located on the rail lines. Rock Springs, the principal city (population 10,800), has a small market-town function and some employment associated with transportation, but for decades its principal economic activity was coal mining. Now coal production has declined drastically, unemployed miners are numerous, and Rock Springs is severely depressed economically. The city's future is uncertain.

Most of the floor of the basin is uninhabited. One can ride across the range or drive along the few roads for miles in almost any section of the basin without encountering a person, house, barn, or even a fence or windmill. Settlement is confined largely to the stream valleys.

The Green River is the major stream of the basin, and a discontinuous string of ranchsteads is found in the northern section of its valley. The major tributaries of the Green—Fontenelle Creek, Slate Creek, and Hams Fork—enter from the west. They rise in the Mountains of Western Wyoming and flow eastward to the Green. Each has a narrow ribbon of irrigated land along its floodplain, dotted at intervals with ranchsteads. Other tributaries of the Green flow northeastward off the northern slope of the Uinta Mountains; the main ones are Muddy Creek, Blacks Fork, Cottonwood Creek, and Henrys Fork. Irrigated hay lands and ranchsteads are found along each of these and along some of their tributaries. Cattle ranches predominate, but sheep ranches are also present. The floodplains of some of these creeks have the interesting characteristic of being quite wide where the creek leaves the mountains and narrowing downstream, becoming so narrow in places that there is no flat land to be irrigated. This is high, sparsely settled country, more than 7,000 feet in elevation. The ranches still have a pioneer aspect, though it is now seventy years since the beginning of settlement.

Most of the east bank tributaries of the Green rise on the floor of the basin, and thus are intermittent or have an extremely scanty flow through most of the year. Little or no irrigation and settlement are found along them; those in the southern part of the basin support a few ranches, mostly sheep ranches.

Big and Little Sandy creeks in the northeastern corner of the basin rise on the humid southeastern slopes of the Wind River Mountains and flow southwest toward the Green River. The Bureau of Reclamation has created a reservoir on Big Sandy Creek to store water for the small Eden irrigation project. It incorporates 7,000 acres of land worked by 80 farmers. Farming on the Eden project bears little relationship to range land use. The farmers raise dairy cows and irrigated crops. Other livestock are grazed on the range lands immediately adjacent to the project. A little feed is sold by the irrigation farmers to the range ranchers from time to time.

In extreme western Wyoming and adjacent parts of Utah and Idaho, an area lying outside the Bridger Basin (but inside the boundaries of Wyoming Grazing District 4) is of major importance to land use within the basin and to the administration of the grazing district. It is the valley of Bear River. This stream rises near the junction of the Uinta and Wasatch ranges in extreme northern Utah, flows northward along the Utah-Wyoming boundary at the east base of the Wasatch Range for nearly a hundred miles, there turns abruptly westward and strikes directly into the Wasatch. In the stretch east of the Wasatch the floodplain of the Bear is broad, in some places several miles wide, and the waters of the stream have been used to irrigate a wide strip of land which supports a substantial number of cattle and sheep ranches.

In the Bridger Basin and Bear River Valley are approximately 800 ranches. They maintain a total of 350,000 sheep and more than 50,000 cattle, but the distribution is not uniform. Sweetwater County, which covers most of the central and southern sections of the basin, contains the headquarters or owner's residences of ranches that account for about 160,000 sheep, although most of the latter spend only part of the year on lands within the county. Less than 10,000 cattle are owned by Sweetwater County ranchers, of which several hundred are dairy cows on the Eden project.

Nearly all the cultivated land is devoted to hay and pasture, though southwestern Wyoming does raise about 4,000 acres of oats and 5,000 acres of barley each year.

The surface of the Bridger Basin exhibits great topographic diversity; it ranges from flat to exceedingly rough. Large areas have long, smooth, gentle slopes. Other extensive areas are undulating to rolling. True badlands are extensive, particularly in the areas adjacent to the Green River and in the high country along the southern edge of the basin (see Fig. 10). In the southern section each valley is separated from the next by a high flat-topped ridge. Rough canyon lands create a difficult topography in the southeastern portion of the basin.

The floor of the Bridger Basin slopes upward away from the center. The lowest parts are about 6,000 feet in elevation, while the very highest sections reach 8,000 feet. The Green River flows on the surface in the northern section of the basin, but, after passing the lowest part of the basin, it begins to incise itself more and more into the underlying rocks. Thus in the southern section it flows in a deep canyon, and the small tributary creeks that enter it have steep gradients and have produced extensive badlands.

Most of the Bridger Basin is arid. The floor at lower elevations generally has less than 10 inches of rainfall annually; the higher parts have more. The relationships are shown in Table 7. Precipitation is erratic both from year to year and from month to month. Annual precipitation at Green River has varied from 4 to 12 inches; at Evanston from 9 to 20 inches. A high proportion of the precipitation falls as snow. In the Bear River Valley the mean annual snowfall totals about 70 inches. In the high country near the southern border of the basin snowfall averages about 50 inches, and the lowest parts of the basin average around 30 inches. The snow is commonly dry and is accompanied by strong winds which sweep most of the countryside bare and pile the snow in drifts. This drifting is a matter of major importance to the livestock industry because it keeps the ground relatively free from snow and thus makes

TABLE 7

PRECIPITATION DATA—BRIDGER BASIN

Station	Elevation	Average Annual Precipitation
Green River..	6,083	7.2
Eden.........	6,665	6.4
Lyman.......	6,800	11.9
Evanston.....	6,860	14.2
Border.......	6,085	13.0

forage available while leaving the snowdrifts as a source of water for sheep.

Temperatures are quite uniform over the basin. Minimum temperatures on winter nights average from 0° to 10° F.; winter maximum temperatures average a little below freezing. In summer, daily temperatures generally climb into the high seventies, but nights are cold; the average summer minimum daily temperature is not more than 10° above freezing. Winter brings occasional temperatures that are extremely low. Evanston has had temperatures colder than — 25° F. in every month from December to March inclusive. Green River has had readings as low as — 40° F., Eden as low as —48° F. Temperatures that remain far below freezing for several consecutive days are not at all unusual.

The cropping system of the Bridger Basin ranchers is adjusted to the short, cool summers, being confined almost entirely to the production of grasses and hardy grains. A critical event in the yearly temperature cycle is the first frost in fall that is severe enough to halt the growth of irrigated grasses.

The Bridger Basin is not a particularly sunny area. Cloud cover averages a little less than 70 per cent during the winter and spring; only in summer does the basin receive more than half of the possible sunshine. The basin is also very windy. Wind velocities average nearly as high as those found anywhere in the United States.

Various species of sagebrush dominate the vegetation; more than three-fourths of the basin is covered by plant associations in which sagebrush is the dominant plant. In a few places it exists in almost pure stands. Although the most widely distributed grass is Indian rice grass, the wheat grasses are more important as a group. In areas high in alkali the vegetation is dominated by greasewood, salt grass, and other kinds of tolerant vegetation. In short, the vegetation pattern of the Bridger Basin is not greatly different from that of the basins lying to the east which have been described earlier.

The carrying capacity of the range lands of Wyoming Grazing District 4 is low. Figure 17 reveals a number of interesting points concerning the

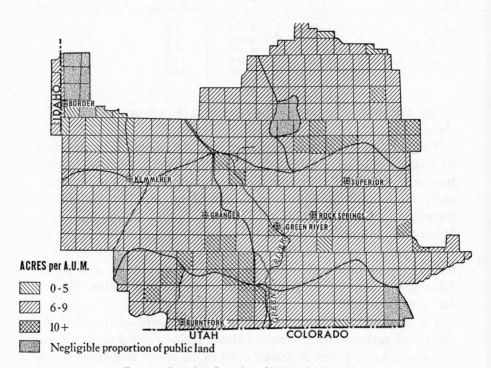

FIG. 17.—Carrying Capacity of Wyoming District 4

management and condition of the district. For one thing it indicates that detailed range surveys have not been made. It also shows that carrying capacity of the range lands is relatively uniform over broad areas of the district. Most of the district falls in the 6 to 9 acres per a.u.m. category. A square mile of such land will support at best about 9 head of cattle on a year-round basis; an entire township will support only 215 to 325. In most parts of the district sheep graze a particular section of range for about four months a year on the average. Lands of the middle category (6 to 9 acres per a.u.m.) thus support 90 to about 130 sheep per square mile during the four winter months. Only one large section of the district has a higher carrying capacity. It is located northwest of Kemmerer in an area sufficiently elevated to receive substantially more rainfall than the district average. Areas of exceptionally low carrying capacity (more than 10 acres required per a.u.m.) are widespread in the eastern and southern sections of the district. Such areas reflect a variety of adverse conditions; some are badlands, others are steep rocky slopes, others are areas of dune sand. Some areas, particularly the lands of low capacity in the northeastern quadrant of the district, are so poor that 16 to 18 acres are required to produce an animal unit month of forage. Such land is very close to the margin of grazing utility and the best one could hope for in grazing it would be to keep the animals from losing weight too rapidly.

Land Tenure Pattern

Railroad lands in checkerboard pattern form an east-west band through the middle of Wyoming District 4. The extraordinarily regular distribution of private, state, and federal lands in the checkerboard is shown in the detailed land tenure map of the Rock Springs Grazing Association Lease (Fig. 18). There is, however, a major difference between the checkerboard lands of District 4 and those previously described in District 3. In the Divide District, most of the land originally granted to the Union Pacific Railroad has been sold to local ranchers; but in District 4, particularly in the eastern two-thirds, the railroad has retained title to more than half the land it was originally granted. On Figure 18 it will be noted that three "islands" of private land, in the vicinity of Rock Springs, Green River, and Granger are the only significant interruptions in the regular pattern of railroad ownership.

Both north and south of the checkerboard the range is almost exclusively public domain; only two sections of state-owned land and a section or two of private land per township interrupt the continuity of the Taylor lands. Tiny areas of private land occur in a few places in river valleys.

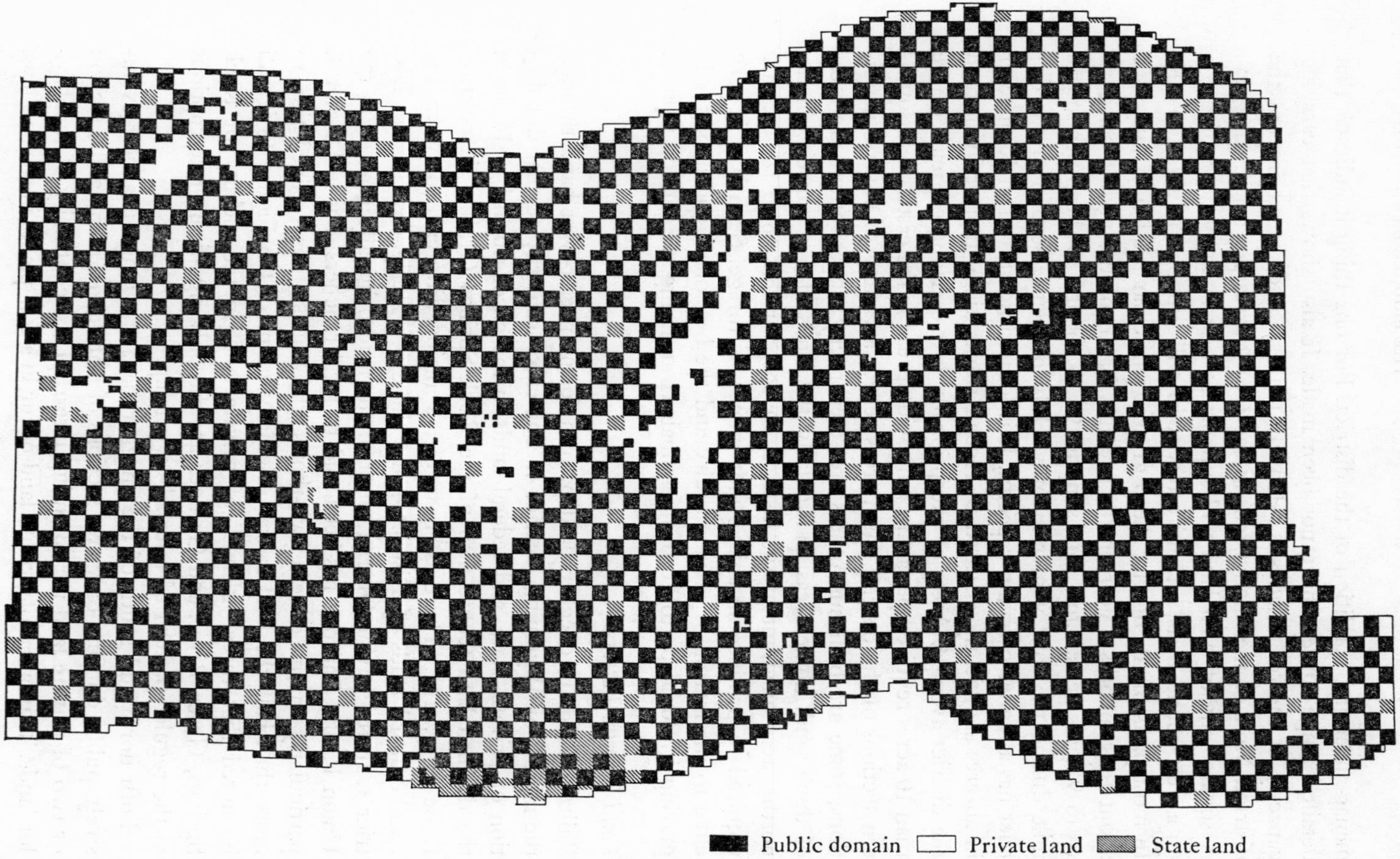

FIG. 18. Central Bridger Basin Detailed Land Tenure

Public domain ☐ Private land ▨ State land

Five such areas occur north of the railway checkerboard: (1) along Bear River and one of its tributaries, Smiths Fork, (2) along Hams Fork and one of its tributaries, (3) along Green River, extending a short distance south into the district, (4) in a compact and fairly extensive area on the Eden project; from the latter a ribbon of private land extends up Big Sandy Creek and a discontinuous ribbon up Little Sandy Creek, and (5) in a narrow and discontinuous strip along Sweetwater Creek in the extreme northeast of the district.

South of the checkerboard lands the noteworthy areas of private land border the streams flowing north and northeast from the Uintas. The largest area is along Blacks Fork. It will be noted that the southwestern corner of the Bridger Basin is not within District 4. The proportion of private land in that part of the basin is so high that it has proved more satisfactory to administer the areas of public grazing land by means of Section-15 leases.

Exploration and exploitation of the Bridger Basin began in the 1820's by trappers in the employ of William Ashley. Most of the streams of the area are named after early trappers. Settlements associated with the Overland Route to the Pacific Coast were established at a very early date—the best-known being Fort Bridger on Blacks Fork established in the early 1840's. The early settlements were all located along the floodplains of the streams that flow north and east out of the Uinta Mountains in the southwest corner of the basin. In 1853 Mormons from Utah began to move into this area and to establish agriculture. Settlement gradually spread to the western and northwestern sections of the basin in the years 1855 to 1885. Cattle preceded sheep in the basin; sheep ranching was often instituted by conversion from cattle ranching. The development of towns and, for that matter, of commercial ranching had to await the arrival of the railroad in 1868.

Organization and Administration of Wyoming Grazing District 4

The district office of Wyoming District 4 (the Green River District) is located in Rock Springs. Ten employees serve the district; eight are technical employees. The district is large, containing 4.6 million acres of public land. It embraces a variety of land types and tenure patterns; and the various combinations of these two factors have elicited an interesting areal diversity of range use practices, range administration problems, and solutions to the problems. They will be the focus of attention in this district.

Range Allocation in the Green River District

When the grazing district advisory board, the district manager, and the future permittees of the district began the process of range adjudication in the Green River District, their first move was to divide the district into eleven units of unequal size, called "ranges." For their location see Figure 19. Physical conditions within some ranges are relatively homogeneous; that is, the landforms, climate, vegetation, and water supply conditions are somewhat similar over the entire unit. But this is not true of all ranges, and those that are not homogeneous are further divided into subunits. Prior to organization of the district the sheep or cattle of most ranchers were confined entirely to land now within a single unit or in two or three units. Hence, the operations of each rancher tend to focus on one or at most two or three ranges within the district, and he has little personal interest in the management of the rest of the district. When range management problems within an individual range were being con-

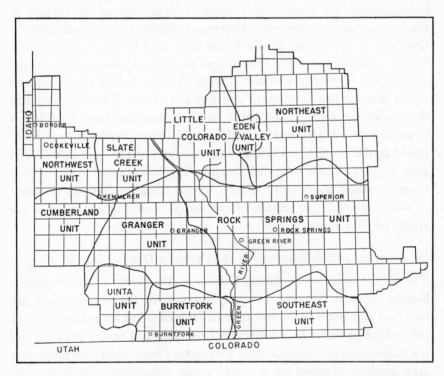

Fig. 19.–Location of Ranges in Wyoming District 4. The lines separating the northern and southern units from the central units follow approximately along the outer margin of the checkerboard lands.

sidered, only the ranchers whose stock utilized that unit needed to be consulted. Each range had special problems of adjudication and management that were peculiar to it.

Each unit was adjudicated separately, and grazing priorities were allotted in the following manner. First, the advisory board determined the maximum number of livestock an applicant had grazed on the open ranges of the district during any two-year period from 1929 through 1934. Second, the board established a figure for the maximum number of stock that could be supported for one hundred days each year on the applicant's private land and on his leased state land, the latter being treated as though it were private land. Such private land and leased state land is "dependent" land in the phraseology of the Taylor Act; it is also referred to as "commensurable" land or "demand" land. The smaller of the two figures (largest number of stock previously grazed or number of head that could be supported for one hundred days on the applicant's private land) became the applicant's class-1 right or demand. It had to be satisfied before any class-2 permits[1] could be issued. In practice, class-1 demands not only pre-empted all the available range forage, but far exceeded the ranges' carrying capacity.

After all class-1 demands had been established, the advisory board estimated the total animal unit months of forage available in the unit. Commonly this figure was considerably lower than the total class-1 demands; so a ratio was established between the total carrying capacity and the total demands, and each rancher was permitted his proportionate or *pro rata* share of the available forage. The reductions necessitated by this procedure were severe. In five of the eleven units in the district, permittees were assigned 50 per cent or less of their class-1 demands. In only two units were no cuts necessary. These figures are highly instructive. The determinations of range carrying capacity were made by the ranchers themselves or their representatives,[2] who, it may be presumed, set the estimates as high as they reasonably could. Since reductions as great as 50 per cent were still necessary, we must conclude either that the range had previously been subjected to serious overgrazing, or the ranchers had secured class-1 demands for stock numbers that were far in excess of the numbers actually being grazed.

The proportional allocation of permits by units encountered two major

[1] As defined in the *Federal Range Code*.

[2] Few range surveys had been made in the district before the capacity estimates were made.

difficulties. One of these arose whenever a man tried to establish priority on grazing in an unfenced area where public and private land were complexly interspersed and in which the applicant owned no land. Where the percentage of private land was high, say 50 per cent, it was almost mathematically certain that he must have established half his priority while his stock was in trespass on the private lands of the unit. The local landowners, who were also trying to establish priorities in the unit, did not, one may be sure, look kindly on these claims. For years such claims constituted a persistent source of difficulty and disagreement. In some sections of the Green River District many of the cattle ranchers who had never obtained any private lands in the central section of the basin had to take sharp cuts in their allowable a.u.m.'s because it was alleged that they had established part of their priority in trespass. A second difficulty sometimes arose when a rancher used two units at different seasons. His private land and his permit in one unit would often be sufficient to support his ranch operation throughout most of the year, but if he had to take a cut in his use of the second unit, it would oblige him to trim all of his operations to the smaller figure unless some adjustment could be made. Sometimes it was possible to make the adjustment by allowing him to shift part of his use from one season to another in the unit where he had the larger permit.

Range Use and Management

In the Bridger Basin, the forage consumed by sheep far exceeds that consumed by cattle. Records of the Green River District show that nearly four times as much range forage is used by sheep as by cattle—126,000 a.u.m.'s for cattle and 427,000 a.u.m.'s for sheep. The total number of cattle permitted is 33,000, the total number of sheep nearly 535,000. But the permittees themselves show no such distribution. Cattle permittees number 218, but there are only 119 sheep permits. This is a common situation in the Middle Rocky Mountain basins. Each district has a large number of cattle permittees, most of whom have very small permits. Sheep operations average much larger. However, the distribution of permits by size in the Green River District is somewhat different from the distribution in the Wind River and Divide districts. Although there are some very large livestock operations in the Green River District, the concentration of the available a.u.m.'s in a few permits is not so marked as in most other districts. The four largest operations, constituting little more than 1 per cent of the permittees, are permitted only about 8 per cent of the total livestock on the district. However, most of the district's forage is utilized by ranching operations of relatively large size. A few dozen small operations use only a tiny part of the total forage.

The general pattern of livestock movement over the district reflects the location of the various ranch headquarters and the seasonal movement of stock from summer to spring-fall to winter ranges. Sheep in general travel much farther than cattle.

Range use, management, and administration problems vary more from unit to unit in the Bridger Basin than in any other district in the Middle Rocky Mountain basins. To present a picture of the internal structuring of a district, and also to delineate the range management problems most effectively, the balance of the chapter will treat the characteristics and problems of the individual ranges of the district.

UINTA RANGE

The southwestern corner of the Green River District, the Uinta Range or Unit (Fig. 19), contains 120,000 acres of land, about two-thirds of which is federal range. The unit lies on the southern rim of the Bridger Basin. On the south it is bordered by the Ashley National Forest, which occupies the eastern end of the Uinta Mountains. The land to the west of the Uinta Unit is largely in private ownership and thus was excluded from the district; the federal land there is administered under Section-15 leases by the Rock Springs office. The Uinta Unit is traversed by several creeks that head in the Uinta Mountains. These creeks have narrow irrigated floodplains that produce hay and pasture. Scattered along the creek bottoms are the ranch headquarters.

Range activities in this unit, dominated by cattle ranching, are not typical of the district. Even in the early days of the district, cattle use was greater than sheep use, and since that time the trend has been steadily toward more cattle. The ranchers in this unit have so-called "term permits"—ten-year leases. Before these ten-year leases were issued, severe cuts—35 to 50 per cent—had to be made in the ranchers' class-1 demands. After the unit was organized it was managed for a time as an entity; that is, cattle and sheep licensed on the unit were allowed to graze anywhere in the unit; but as the number of cattle increased and sheep numbers declined, several allotments were made and some of these were fenced.

All operators in the Uinta Unit are expected to support their stock for six months on their deeded land or leased state land. The seasonal grazing pattern is one of summer cattle use and winter sheep use. The cattle are turned onto the dry range lands of the unit about May 1.

They drift back on the ranches in September and October, and all are off the range by the end of October. Almost all the cattle in the unit are grazed in one or another of approximately 25 fenced allotments. The sheep, most of which are grazed on Ashley National Forest in summer, are wintered entirely on privately owned range lands within the unit or on irrigated pastures or feed lots. A few bands graze the allotments in winter.

A strip of land at the eastern margin of the unit is not fenced. Stockmen from the next unit east also use this strip, and the cattle are allowed to move back and forth across the unit boundary.

The Uinta Unit is fairly simple for the BLM to administer. During the early days of the unit there was considerable competition between sheep and cattle ranchers for the available forage; but this problem has been greatly alleviated by the decline in sheep numbers, the fencing of the allotments, and the large cuts in class-1 demands. One other factor helping to simplify the administration of the unit is the relatively short distance that most of the livestock move. Cattle trailing is at a minimum, and sheep migrate only to the national forest and back.

CUMBERLAND RANGE

The Cumberland Unit lies at intermediate elevation along the western border of the district near its southern end (Fig. 19). It is predominantly spring-fall range, providing an excellent range lambing ground, and is intensively used for this purpose by sheep moving west into the Wasatch Mountains, south into the Uinta Mountains, or north into the Mountains of Western Wyoming. The forage-production capacity of the unit is not very accurately known, but the original permits granted much more use than was available. Since that time there have been substantial cuts in sheep numbers and the season of cattle use has been shortened. These cuts have reduced range use to its estimated carrying capaicity, but the range is still in only fair condition.[3]

Although in the approximate center of the unit an allotment is reserved exclusively for cattle use, the balance of the unit is used by both sheep and cattle. Greater use of the range forage is obtained by making it available to both kinds of animals, as the range produces both shrub browse and grass. Each individual band of sheep, however, is confined to a bounded allotment, determined in size by the number of a.u.m.'s of

[3] Estimate by Bureau of Land Management. All range condition estimates are subject to great uncertainty because of the prolonged and severe drought in the Green River District during the mid-1950's.

grazing to which the permittee is entitled. Most sheep use of the range is confined to the months of May, June, and October. The unit is too low and dry to supply much fresh summer feed for sheep, but a few sheep do remain in the unit all summer.

West of the Cumberland Unit lies the Bear River Valley, where ranchers using the unit have their headquarters. Cattle in the unit come off the irrigated lands of the Bear Valley about May 1 and are allowed to range over the entire district. The bulls are turned onto the range about July 1. The Bear River ranchers have a cattle association, but they furnish only one range rider. One man cannot properly control the cattle on such a large area, so forage use is spotty and the calf crop averages only 55 to 65 per cent.[4]

A considerable number of small cattle operators had class-1 demands in the Cumberland Unit based partly on small, scattered private land holdings in the area. A strong effort was made to group several of the small operators into a single allotment. To do this necessitated extensive exchanges in range use and in land titles. The new arrangement made it possible to use water supplies more efficiently and to reduce the amount of trailing from one piece of private property to another. Water sources in the Cumberland Unit are neither numerous nor well placed, and they cannot be utilized properly if the individual allotments are too small.

Cattle graze the range lands of the Cumberland Unit in summer. Originally the grazing season for cattle began May 1 and ended October 31, but it has since been shortened by 15 days. The cut was motivated partly by the fact that grazing pressure was visibly too heavy, but mainly it was due to the ranchers' awareness that their cattle were usually in better condition on October 15 than they were two weeks later, because the late season supply of forage on this range was so small that even though the cattle grazed it intensively they could not find enough forage to maintain their body weight.

NORTHWEST RANGE

Much of the Northwest Unit stands at high elevations—above 9,000 feet in the highest areas. In the southern end (lowest part) of the unit the vegetation is sagebrush and grass, but in the higher areas aspen and associated shrubs and grasses adapted to the cooler and wetter conditions become prominent. Because the area is high and is adjacent to the Bridger

---

[4] That is, only 55 to 65 per cent of the stock cows have calves in any one year. Ranch profits are closely related to the percentage of the calf crop: the higher the calf crop percentage the more profitable are the year's operations, other things being equal.

National Forest, it is heavily used by wildlife. The Bureau of Land Management estimates that about 2,000 deer spend part of the winter in this area and that several hundred remain all summer. Occasionally elk use the area also. Approximately 2,000 a.u.m.'s are set aside for wildlife grazing.

Bear River flows south to north through the western part of the Northwest Unit on a wide, flat, irrigated floodplain. One of its tributaries, Smiths Fork, flows southward out of the Bridger National Forest, and a minor tributary, Twin Creek, flows in from the west. The northeastern part of the unit is drained by Hams Fork, a tributary of the Green River. The headquarters of the ranches in this unit are located along these floodplains.

Prior to the Taylor Act, the range lands of this unit had long been used for lambing grounds. Some sheep bands were brought into the area from winter ranges farther east in the basin, while others came from irrigated pastures where they had spent the winter. The Northwest Unit was also used for a holding ground. Ranchers would bring their sheep into the area during the spring and hold them there until the national forest opened. The area was used again by sheep for a short period in the fall after the national forest closed.

About 150,000 sheep trail through the unit each year on their way to and from the national forests. One main trail follows the divide east of Hams Fork from Kemmerer to the boundary of the Bridger National Forest. The most heavily traveled driveway runs from Kemmerer to Cokeville. All animals coming from the winter ranges lying to the east use this driveway. At Cokeville the trail splits into various segments leading toward different entrances to the national forests. The trail from Kemmerer to Cokeville is seriously overgrazed; the others are in relatively good condition. Private landholdings of numerous ranchers are scattered about in various parts of the unit, there is constant trailing from one of these properties to another, and many trespass complaints in connection with such trailing. Cattle (8,000) in this district are turned out about May 15 and rounded up about the middle of September.

The Northwest Unit is, for several reasons, possibly the most difficult unit in the district to administer. The land tenure pattern is highly complex; privately owned, irrigated farms and dry range lands are closely interspersed with federal range lands. There are 557,000 acres of land in the unit; 248,000 acres are private land and 309,000 acres federal land. Other complications grow out of the fact that the unit is traversed by the two major livestock driveways leading to the summer ranges of the Bridger and Caribou National Forests in the Mountains of Western Wyoming.

Further administrative difficulties derive from the personalities and attitudes of many ranchers in the district, particularly the owners of large sheep ranches. They tend to be quite independent, rather swashbuckling individualists who intend to use the range as they see fit, and whose attitude toward the Bureau of Land Management is somewhat less than cooperative.[5]

Although class-1 demands for use in this district had to be cut in half before 10-year permits could be issued, the BLM believes that some of the area is still overgrazed, though only partial range surveys have been made and carrying capacity must therefore be estimated. There is much trespass and improper trailing. Complaints to the BLM are numerous, and an excessive amount of administrative time is consumed in dealing with these. The bureau would like to keep a representative in the unit most of the time, but the available personnel are too few to permit this. Consequently, the BLM has relatively little control over the area. When complaints are registered, it takes so long to reach the scene of the infraction that usually the stock have been moved before the area can be inspected, and the best the BLM technician can do is write the transgressing rancher a letter exhorting him to follow the range rules in the future.

SLATE CREEK RANGE

Few range areas in the West have been used and abused so thoroughly or in so many different ways as the Slate Creek Unit lying just east of the Northwest Unit. On the south this unit is bordered by the checkerboard lands along the Union Pacific Railroad, on the east by the Green River, and on the north by the Sublette Grazing District.

Prior to organization of the range under the Taylor Grazing Act, any operators in the basin whose hay supplies became exhausted during the winter would turn their stock onto the range lands of the unit. The unit

[5] Nothing could illustrate better the difficulty of arriving at an accurate estimate of BLM-rancher relationships than the case of the ranchers in the Northwest Unit. The last district manager of Wyoming 4 who was consulted flatly contradicted the statement cited above, stating in a personal letter that the "BLM has very good cooperation with all stockmen in this unit." This statement, in turn, was directly contrary to statements made by several technicians during earlier periods, including previous district managers. In fact, I have numerous direct quotes in my field notebooks making far stronger statements than mine above. The assertion of "good cooperation" is also contradicted by several letters in the files of the BLM's Rock Springs office. One letter to a rancher in the Northwest Range contained the phrase "you have completely violated the agreement that we all made," and another asked, "how can we have any order on the range if permittees do things like that?" Perhaps BLM-rancher relationships have improved. Perhaps someone is mistaken.

lands were also used for winter sheep range by ranchers whose base properties were located outside the unit or who, in some instances, had no base properties at all. Large shearing corrals were located within the unit, and sheep were often held on the range for days while waiting to be sheared. This constant and intensive use reduced the range to sad condition by the time some control of grazing use was initiated by the BLM after the Green River District was organized.

About 175,000 sheep now trail through the unit on their way to and from the summer ranges in the mountains. It is used as spring-fall range for 60,000 sheep and as summer range for 2,200 head of cattle. Two large shipping points for stock are located along the Oregon Short Line within the unit boundaries. They handle cattle and sheep from the Green River District and also many of those marketed from the Sublette Grazing District to the north. Livestock from a wide area are trailed through the Slate Creek Unit to these points of shipment.

The unit is organized in an interesting and unusual way. Cattle are on the range from May 1 to the end of October and are allowed to wander over the entire unit. The sheep are divided into two groups, those who use the unit strictly for trailing, and those who use it for spring-fall range and as a lambing ground. The trailing sheep use the stock driveway, a strip of land to which the sheep must be confined as they move across the unit. The sheep are allowed six days to cross the unit. Under this arrangement they can be grazed across the unit rather than trailed rapidly. The Bureau of Land Management has worked out individual allotments for the ranchers who use the unit for spring-fall range. Rotation grazing schemes will be developed to try to raise the carrying capacity of the range, which currently is quite low.

The trail herds, however, will constitute a difficult obstacle for any program to increase forage production on the allotments. The herders often flagrantly violate the established rules and procedures for use of the range. In many instances this is done with the consent or even upon the advice of their employers. If a herder knows or discovers an area where the forage is particularly good, he will trail rapidly for a day or two to reach the area, stay and graze for two or three days until the area is nearly stripped of forage, and then trail on across the unit. On occasion a sheep band may be kept on the unit for several additional days in trespass. Enforcement of range rules is difficult and often politically disadvantageous, so that these practices go on sporadically eliciting no action more drastic than a letter of reprimand.[6]

[6] The District Manager in 1959 flatly denied the truth of this paragraph. The same comments apply as in footnote 5 of this chapter.

LITTLE COLORADO RANGE

To the east across the Green River from the Slate Creek Unit is an area of severe erosion and of difficult administration—the Little Colorado Unit or Little Colorado Desert. For decades prior to the establishment of the Green River Grazing District, bands of sheep from the mountains to the west and from the Wind River Mountains to the north would race from the summer ranges to this unit, each trying to reach and use the best forage first. Sheep coming from the west would have to make a hundred-mile extra trail to reach the bridge where the Green River could be crossed. Usually the herds reached the unit long before snow began to accumulate, and consequently the sheep needed water. To secure water, they were forced to return regularly to the Green River or Big Sandy Creek. As a result of so much grazing and trailing close to the streams, the vegetation deteriorated rapidly and erosion was sharply accelerated.

Deterioration of the plant cover has been especially serious in the canyons, for two major reasons. In the first place, camps and bed grounds have often been established there, with resultant heavy grazing in the vicinity. Second, the canyons have generally been chosen as the easiest routes out of the area when snow fell and the sheep bands began to trail to the uplands to spend the winter. In addition to use by trail herds from outside the area, the Little Colorado Unit has been subjected to rather heavy grazing pressure in the spring, summer, and fall by sheep and cattle belonging to locally-based ranchers. A few big operators with private holdings of irrigated land along the Green River use the area as a lambing ground because they have no other range suitable for the purpose. Their sheep come off the winter ranges to the south about April 15. A combination of all the foregoing conditions has seriously depleted the forage resources of the Little Colorado Unit. Even under controlled grazing the vegetation has been slow to recuperate.

After the Green River District was organized, one of the first range improvement projects of the Grazing Service was construction of a bridge across the Green River in this unit so that bands of sheep coming from the west would not have to make the long detour south to the bridge and back in order to reach the unit. Another early project was the establishment of truck trails along the principal ridges extending toward the Green River. It was expected that camp sites would be located along the truck trails, thus increasing the amount of grazing on the lightly used ridges and lessening the grazing pressure on the heavily used and damaged canyon lands.

Some sheep graze this range from May 1 until December 15. The combined use by trail herds and by the local herds is too heavy for the available forage, and thus far no satisfactory solution has been discovered. Trail herds now are kept off the unit until November 1, so that ordinarily they are not on the unit long enough to damage the vegetation near water before snow cover enables them to utilize all the range. Some of the trail herds stay in the area until December 15 and others stay until January 15, when they finally drift down to lands of still lower elevation.

NORTHEAST UNIT

The Northeast Range is the largest in the district and furnishes the greatest number of a.u.m.'s of federal grazing. A typical view in the Northeast Range is shown in Plate XV. It also has by far the lowest average carrying capacity of any unit. The best parts of the area are about equal in capacity to the average for the other units, and poorer parts furnish only one a.u.m. of grazing for each 12, 15, or even 20 acres of land. Such land is scarcely worth grazing. It is mostly used as spring-fall range by sheep, though a very small number of cattle use it as summer range. Sheep drift into the unit from summer ranges in the Wind River, Ferris, and Green Mountains to the north, and gradually make their way to the desert ranges in the center of the basin, where they spend the winter. The unit is used as a lambing range in spring.

No grazing cuts were made in this unit when ten-year permits were issued. The entire unit is unallotted; but the operators have divided it informally on a gentlemen's agreement basis; this suggests that there is for range of any character both an upper and lower limit of area size that can be managed effectively as a unit. Apparently the Northeast Unit is too large for utilization as a single area.

Plate XV, however, illustrates another major problem in range land use and administration in all the Middle Rocky Mountain Basins. The small white marker marks a common corner for three types of land tenure—private land, state land, and public domain. It may be judged from the illustration that such a small inconspicuous marker would be difficult to find in this vast expanse of empty range. But the marker illustrated is an exceptionally good one; most property boundaries are much more sketchily marked or are not marked at all. The difficulty of proving wilful trespass under such circumstances can easily be imagined.

SOUTHEAST UNIT

The Southeast Unit is a mixed cattle and sheep range, but sheep predominate. Most of it is well up on the southern rim of the basin. The small perennial streams which flow east into the Green River have tiny irrigated floodplains that support a few scattered ranches. Some cattle graze out from these ranches in summer but are on irrigated pastures and are fed hay during the winter. The heaviest use, however, is by sheep, who use it as spring and late fall range. Sheep do not go on the unit in spring until May 1, and they may delay until a few days later if the season has been unusually cold. In general, they are brought back on the unit as late in the fall as possible and are kept there until December 15, when most of them begin moving to winter ranges in the center of the basin. A few sheep graze on the unit all summer, but most of them move south in summer to Ashley National Forest.

The pro rata grazing cut on the Southeast Unit was only 10 per cent, and the unit is still in a state of adjustment. A number of years ago extensive sections were used by a very large ranch, which since has been liquidated. When the ranch was sold, parts of the operation were purchased by several different ranchers, and the very difficult process of readjustment has been going on ever since. It is clear that grazing use on this unit is too heavy. Strong evidence for this is furnished by the fact that some of the aggressively expanding ranch owners have bought range permits and retired them by taking non-use for more than five consecutive years. The greater portion of the unit is taken over by eight large ranches whose owners have divided up the district pretty much to suit themselves, using differences in elevation, topographic barriers, and negotiated lines to bound their respective operations. Formal agreements sanctioning these procedures have been drafted, approved by the Bureau of Land Management, and filed in the district manager's office. The following is a sample of one of these agreements:

We the undersigned users of the Federal Range request that we be allowed to make our own range divisions for the reason that we think we are able to make a better livestock unit. These agreements will be given full consideration by the Advisory Board of Wyoming Grazing District No. IV. It is understood that these agreements can be changed by government regulations. It is also understood that should any difference arise as to range allotments the Bureau of Land Management Representative shall act as arbitrator, such arbitration subject to the approval of the Advisory Board.

The remainder of the agreement then describes the desired boundary arrangements.

BURNTFORK RANGE

The Burntfork Unit, west of Green River, has some difficult land management problems. Cattle ranches located on the floodplains of short streams flowing east into the Green River utilize the area for summer range, and sheep migrating between the Uinta Mountains and the floor of the basin use the unit in the spring and fall. Lands along the northern and eastern boundaries are used by sheep in winter. Some of the surface is very rough, and there are five large, almost mountainous mesas within the unit. Soils are thin and easily eroded. A large number of small operators use the area. There are sixty-two permits for 43,000 sheep and 6,000 cattle, but they call for a total of only 50,000 a.u.m.'s, although livestock are in the unit throughout the year.

ROCK SPRINGS UNIT

In an east-west band through the center of the district, in the lowest sections of the basin, are the checkerboard lands running in a strip twenty miles wide on each side of the Union Pacific Railroad. The checkerboard lands are divided into just three large units—the Rock Springs Range on the east and the Granger Unit and Carter Lease on the west. The organization, administration, and functioning of these three units furnish some of the most interesting and instructive data on range management to be found anywhere in the West.

The Rock Springs Unit contains two million acres. The lowest parts of the unit are characterized by salt sage, and these areas are somewhat overused. The higher parts of the unit, supporting a black sage vegetation, have not been utilized intensively enough because of lack of water. In effect, the Rock Springs Unit is leased to just one permittee—the Rock Springs Grazing Association. The Granger Unit has two major permittees—the Uinta Development Company and the Western Wyoming Land and Livestock Company. The operations of these units can be understood only in terms of these large grazing associations.

The Rock Springs Grazing Association

Of all the solutions to the problems engendered by the complex western land tenure pattern none is more unusual, interesting, and instructive than the organizational and administrative arrangements developed by the Rock Springs Grazing Association. The organization of the association considerably antedates the Taylor Grazing Act, and it represents an early private attempt to rationalize and organize range use during the anarchical period of free and unrestricted use of the public ranges. The heart of the operation was a lease on all Union Pacific Railroad lands in a strip forty miles wide and seventy miles long stretching east and west of of Rock Springs.

A number of local circumstances probably contributed to a recognition of the necessity for some solution to the land tenure problem and the practicality of the particular form of organization that was developed. As described previously, the Bridger Basin, the central portion of which is winter range, is surrounded on three sides by mountains that furnish big supplies of spring, summer, and fall forage. In late fall the herds from all these highland areas would converge on the winter range lands in the lower sections of the Bridger Basin; moreover, many bands would trail from one edge of the basin to another in both spring and fall, traveling from the mountains to the winter range lands lying farther to the east or southeast. It has been estimated that in the earlier period as many as 150,-000 to 200,000 sheep would trail across the basin during the winter season. A second important consideration was the fact that huge acreages of private checkerboard land could be acquired by a single lease from the Union Pacific Railroad. Extensive sections of the Bridger Basin are underlain with commercial coal; consequently, because they were valuable as mineral lands the Union Pacific had not sold its lands in the Bridger Basin as it had in the range areas further east, and the Bridger lands thus were available for lease directly from the railroad.

The more complex a pattern of land tenure the more difficult it is to control grazing use. If numerous bands of sheep are entitled to be in an area, every band must be closely observed to determine whether it has any right to be in the area at all, and whether it is on land where it has a right to be. If a band is discovered in trespass it is easier for its owner or herder, when the pattern of holdings is complex, to plead inadvertent error or to insist (until the herd has been moved) that the stock are there legally.

Prior to the passage of the Taylor Act, ownership or control of all the private lands in a checkerboard area gave absolute control over the alternate sections of public domain because of the physical impossibility of driving a herd of sheep or cattle from one public domain section to another without trespassing on the adjacent private lands. The association was formed to try to organize and control grazing use by taking advantage of the circumstances just outlined.

The Rock Springs Grazing Association was organized in 1907 by nine livestock men, at least two of whom had major interests other than livestock ranching; one was a banker and another a lawyer. The association was organized as a corporation, and it was the lawyer who had the requisite experience in both the ranching and legal aspects to set matters up properly.

After the company was organized, the original nine ranchers each bought at least one share, voted themselves the board of directors for a period of seven years, and then threw the stock open for subscription. Every director still must own stock in the company. The company was originally to be capitalized for $700,000; there were to be one hundred shares at $7,000 each. A share of stock could be purchased by a down payment of $1,500, and each share would then be assessed $700 per year for 10 years. A total of 87 shares were sold. Since then the company has bought about a dozen of the original shares and retired them.[7]

At the time the association was organized each share of stock was declared to permit its owner to graze 3,500 sheep on the association lease. The number of sheep per share has never been increased, although tens of thousands of acres of grazing lands have been added to the association's grazing area and hundreds of a.u.m.'s of grazing rights on the association's lease have been purchased and extinguished. Clearly the original estimations of the grazing capacity of these areas were far too high. Of more importance, it illustrates the point made previously, that the rated grazing capacity of an area is a highly elastic notion. The Rock Springs lease would undoubtedly continue to support the original number of sheep assigned, although forage production would be held down by the intensive grazing and the amount of feed per animal would be considerably reduced. The members of the association prefer more feed per animal and not so many a.u.m.'s per unit area.

When capital had become available the company began operations by leasing checkerboard land from the Union Pacific. Its location is shown on Figure 19, and it embraces most of the area represented on Figure 18. The association also began to acquire privately owned lands by purchase. Throughout the life of the association, grazing land purchases have been made regularly. For the first thirty years large acreages of grazing land were purchased for 50 cents or 75 cents per acre. In a single purchase over 30,000 acres were acquired at 75 cents per acre. During World War II, the members established the policy of buying any lands available at 50 cents per acre, although some land was purchased at 75 cents per acre.[8] After the war the price of dry grazing land rose steadily until by 1949 the association was paying $5.00 per acre for some desert grazing land. During the period from 1937 to 1951 the association purchased more than 65,000 acres of private land.

In connection with the purchase of private lands the association has

[7] The company paid more than $10,000 per share for those most recently purchased.

[8] Minutes of the association on file in association office, Rock Springs, Wyoming.

also acquired Taylor grazing rights on the Rock Springs lease area and has extinguished them.[9]

The association manages a truly impressive amount of land—a total of 1,960,000 acres. Of this the association owns 510,000 acres; they have bought 87,500 of these acres in recent years. The association leases 527,000 acres of private land, all of which, except about 4,000 acres, are leased from the Union Pacific Railroad. The association's lease from the Union Pacific calls for the payment of a flat fee for the entire acreage leased plus payment of the taxes on the land. Prior to 1948 the rental was $5,000 plus taxes; in 1948 it was raised to $10,000 plus taxes. The association pays a total tax of $15,179 per year, about half of which is for its Union Pacific lands and about half on its own land. The total yearly rental for the Union Pacific lands thus comes to about 3½ cents per acre.

Together with these private and state lands the association also uses 908,000 acres of federal range which it holds under a Taylor grazing lease. The federal land is calculated to furnish 105,000 a.u.m.'s of grazing. This estimate rests on two assumptions made on the basis of inadequate data. It is assumed that 9 per cent of the total area is wasteland, useless for grazing. It is also assumed that the area averages out at seven-acre land; that is, on the average it will require seven acres to furnish an animal unit month of grazing. Of the total grazing units within the lease boundaries 14,000 a.u.m.'s are used by ranchers who are not members of the association.

Among recent additions to the association's holdings are nearly 80 square miles of federal land in District 3, acquired by purchase of Taylor leases. These increased forage supplies were added with no increase in stock numbers grazed by association members.

The foregoing figures afford an excellent opportunity to compare the cost of forage from leased private lands and from public domain lands. It must be assumed that the average grazing value of all Union Pacific checkerboard lands is about the same as for the interspersed public domain lands; which seems an entirely reasonable assumption. On this basis, the grazing fee on Union Pacific land is approximately 3½ cents per acre and federal range grazing fees come to approximately 2 cents per acre.

A similar comparison of the cost of leasing range land with the cost of owning it, shows land ownership in a most unfavorable position. Almost no grazing land can be purchased in the Bridger Basin for $1.00

[9] This indicates clearly that the association places considerable reliance on the stability of Taylor leases, and also that the level of grazing intensity can be profitably lowered, even at considerable expense.

per acre; but a purchase price of only $1.00 per acre, an interest rate of 5 per cent, and taxes of 1½ cents per acre annually, produce a total cost of 6½ cents per acre annually from privately owned grazing lands, compared with 3½ cents for Union Pacific leased lands, and 2 cents for Taylor lands. On a purchase price of $3.00 per acre (much more realistic) we arrive at total costs of 16½ cents per acre annually, or 3 times the lease rate and 8 times the Taylor rate.

Interestingly enough, the Rock Springs Grazing Association operates on year-to-year leases with both the railroad and the BLM. Neither lease is exactly precarious. The association has leased essentially the same lands from the railroad throughout the fifty years since the association was organized, and it has had a Taylor permit since Wyoming District 4 was organized. The directors of the association have various relationships with the railroad; one, for example, is the railroad's local attorney. The railroad finds it more convenient and profitable to have one large lease than numerous small ones. Finally, the lease is of some interest to the railroad traffice department because the association imports its purchased feed by rail and ships its wool and lambs to market by rail. Locally, at least, the association is in an equally strong position with respect to its Taylor grazing lease. The president of the association is also president of the Grazing Advisory Board of Wyoming District 4. Four of the six sheep ranchers' representatives on the local advisory board are also shareholders in the association.

The Rock Springs Grazing Association is not a profit-making enterprise, in the usual sense of that term. Its members never receive a monetary dividend, and every year they are subject to a substantial assessment. The association is simply a device for providing a stable supply of winter forage for the members' sheep. Any profits resulting from the association's activities are realized through the sales of the individual members' sheep, lambs, and wool. The annual assessment is divided into two parts, of which about 80 per cent is used for current expenses. By far the three largest regular expenses are taxes on the association's own land and on the land leased from the Union Pacific, rent on the Union Pacific lease, and grazing fees on the Taylor lands. Together these items make up nearly 90 per cent of the total operational expenses. The remainder goes for salaries and expenses of the officers, salary for a range rider, office rent, and other minor items. The second part of the annual assessment is for "investment"; that is, for purchasing more land. Usually the investment part of the annual assessment is much the smaller, but occasionally special large assessments are made either to buy shares of the association's stock and retire them or to make unusually large land purchases.

The corporation also has a few other minor sources of income. It rents a little of its land for non-grazing purposes and receives a small income from granting rights of way. A minor amount of permitted sheep trailing across its land produces a little cash, and a few hundred dollars a year is obtained from trespass charges.

The association has approximately fifty stockholders. The largest shareholder owns eight shares, or slightly more than 10 per cent of the stock. A livestock company owns five shares, and another rancher owns four and a half shares. A financial institution owns a share which it obtained by foreclosing a mortgage. Some stockholders own only a half or quarter share. The grazing privileges attached to a share of stock can be assigned to non-stockholders, and the sheep grazing under these assigned leases are a major problem in the physical management of grazing on the association's land.

The Rock Springs Grazing Association as a corporate entity attempts to regulate and administer use of the association's land holdings, although the actual harvesting of the forage is done by herds under the control of the individual stockholders. It is of great interest that the association has encountered the same kinds of grazing administration problems faced by the Bureau of Land Management in the administration of grazing on the federal lands.

Ever since its formation the association has been faced with the problem of excessive grazing pressure on its lands. The association members have attacked the problem with vigor and success. They have steadily increased their acreage of deeded land. They have also bought up more than a dozen association shares and retired them, thereby reducing total grazing claims on their unit by more than 40,000 head of sheep annually. In addition the association "absorbs shares of grazing rights," as it is expressed in the association minutes. Any stockholder can turn in his share for non-use during any year. The association will pay him $500 for the non-use and exempt him from the annual assessment. The association also pays $250 for a surrendered half-share and $125 for a quarter-share. In 1946 a motion was introduced at the annual meeting to discontinue the practice of paying for surrendered shares, but the motion was defeated. The amount of non-use taken is usually substantial, varying from 5 or 6 full shares to as many as 16 or 18. These two items alone—share retirement and annual non-use—probably have reduced total a.u.m.'s of pressure by at least a fourth. The decrease is reflected in the terms of the Taylor permit. The earliest permit was for 245,000 sheep and 500 horses. The current lease permits only 203,000 sheep: this despite the substantial increase in land resources noted previously.

The control of unherded cattle on an unfenced sheep range is always a problem. Over much of the Rock Springs Range cattle are not a serious problem. Much of the range is unsuited for cattle either because of the type of forage or lack of water. At various places along the margins and near the Green River, however, cattle use is important. The association has bought up numerous cattle permits and extinguished the rights by taking more than five years of consecutive non-use, but there are still 14,000 a.u.m.'s of cattle use in the Rock Springs Unit. This is the equivalent of nearly 3,000 head for five months during the summer, the period of maximum cattle use. There is some cattle use in spring and fall, however. The cattle belong to a total of twenty-eight ranchers; the largest operator has 450 head on the range during the summer.

The members of the Rock Springs Association operate the entire Rock Springs lease as a unit. The lease is not subdivided or allotted; the herds of all members are allowed on any part of the lease. The association has never solved the problem of how to use the range with maximum effectiveness. The Rock Springs Unit has the general form of a great shallow saucer; the highest lands are on the margin, and the lowest lands are along the railroad in the center of the lease. Very commonly in the rush to reach the new forage the higher lands near the rim were not adequately utilized during the early winter, and when all the bands moved down to the lower elevations the lands in the center of the basin would be overused. A number of years ago the following letter went out from the board of directors to the members of the association.

> You now have a permit from the Federal Government and the Rock Springs Grazing Association to *GRAZE* your sheep on the checkerboard lands of the Rock Springs Grazing Association lease. . . .
>
> This does not mean *TRAILING* your sheep. Please note that the word "trailing" is written in capital letters. I want you to get the difference in meaning between these two words in your mind. You are allowed to graze your sheep, but you are not allowed to trail your sheep.
>
> Hold your sheep up against the northern boundary as long as possible and reserve the low-lying lands for later use. It is not necessary to pull your camp and move your sheep every day or is it necessary to move your sheep five miles or more per day. Whenever you do you are *trailing* your sheep which is against our rules, and it means you are entitled to pay a fine of 1½ cents per head per day.
>
> The majority of our members are willing to play fair in trying to get the most benefit from our winter pasture and the trailing of sheep must stop.
>
> Our range rider has instructions to report any misconduct.

A number of advantages would arise from assigning allotments in the area, the two most important being better distribution of use of the forage and considerably less necessity for trailing. Allotments have not been assigned for several reasons. First is the sheep ranchers' almost congenital dislike of any barriers on the range. One portion or another of the range is unusable for part of almost every winter either because of no snow, and thus no water source on the range, or an excess of snow which makes it impossible for the sheep to reach the feed. Lastly it would be difficult to make range allotments that would satisfy all members of the association: ranges with equal accessibility, forage resources, water supplies, and protection against storms in winter. Also, many members would be reluctant to accept allotments made up largely of leased private lands for fear that cancellation of the lease would leave them without claims to a source of winter feed. Despite the difficulties involved in allotting the Rock Springs lease, several members of the association feel that it should be done.

To some extent the larger operators on the lease have informally apportioned certain parts of the allotment among themselves, but such agreements have no force other than informal practice and may be upset at any time, particularly when new bands of sheep are introduced. It is also possible to use various little devices to retain some control of the grazing pattern. One long-term association member grazes his bands in an area of canyon lands in the south-central portion of the lease. Whenever another band of sheep is seen approaching the mouth of a canyon the herder scatters his band near the entrance to the canyon. It is then impossible for the approaching herder to enter the canyon without hopelessly mixing the two herds, so his band is turned in another direction. Sometimes a band moving across the lease will encounter one band after another in this fashion. This constant "bumping" is apt to result in excessive trailing, especially by newly introduced bands.

The bands of rams of any association member are allowed on the lease at any time. The association also has an agreement with the railroad to permit any amount of stock trailing free of charge to or from any railroad loading point. The association employs a range rider who inspects the range and reports to the board of directors. He is directed particularly to check on trespass and excessive trailing. The association charges a trespass fee of $50 per band per day. In most years only a few days of trespass occur.

Each association member manages his own band or bands on the lease. The lease is winter range, and nearly all the sheep are fed some concentrated feeds while they are on the lease. A common practice is to feed soybeans during mild weather and corn for heat during excessively cold weather. Browse, particularly salt sage, is important on the Rock Springs lease, but grass is scarce. Salt sage is high in protein but low in heat-producing carbohydrates; hence the use of corn during cold weather. Opening date on the Rock Springs lease is December 10. The herds leave the lease in time to reach the lambing grounds.

The experience of the Rock Springs Grazing Association seems to indicate that steps leading to a simplification of the pattern of land control (control here being distinguished from ownership) is a step toward rationalization of grazing land use. Certainly within a grazing district it makes for much more simple administration under the provisions of the Taylor Grazing Act. The more than 200,000 sheep grazed on the Rock Springs lease might under separate ownerships necessitate issuing several score permits for a few dozen allotments in an area of complex land control. On the one large lease trespass is easy to discover and easy to establish because of the enormously simplified boundaries. In the case of the Rock Springs lease the association itself assumes part of the burden of inspecting and controlling grazing practices on the unit. Tight control by a large well-managed organization has also led to a willingness to reduce grazing pressure.

If, however, land control unification in an area of complex land tenure is a long step forward in rationalizing grazing land use, it is not the only step. Experience on the Rock Springs lease indicates that unification of range use management is of equal importance. The Rock Springs Association has never been able effectively to solve the trailing problem nor to bring about an even distribution of grazing pressure on all parts of the lease. Moreover, so long as each member avoids trailing his bands and honors the opening and closing dates on the lease, the association is powerless to control his grazing practices within the rudimentary and highly permissive association rules.

The sheep bands of the association are under the direct care of hired herders. Some members give very specific guidance and direction to their herders concerning the grazing pattern and practices to be followed; other members leave such decisions to the herders. Most affairs of the association are handled by the board of directors with policy guidance from time to time by the entire membership. An outsider wonders why it would not be entirely feasible for the membership to set forth the general policy on the physical management of the range grazing patterns and practices on the unit and then permit the board of directors to plan, direct, and enforce the movements of all stock on the lease during the grazing period.[10] Such an arrangement might be the solution to the problems of adjusting the range grazing patterns and practices. The only objection would appear to be that the individual members would lose an apparently not very useful or desirable right of independent action.

Experience on the Rock Springs lease seems to indicate that it is too large an area to be operated as a unit. Here again an upper limit of effective unit management size appears to have been exceeded, and thus the association is faced with the same physical management problems that the BLM encounters in many of its units and large allotments.

The relationships between the Rock Springs Grazing Association, Wyoming Grazing District 4, and the Bureau of Land Management are a fascinating example of politics, government management of natural resources, legal administration, and the functioning of a resource management act.

To protect the federal lands lying within the Rock Springs lease from damage through overgrazing and to obtain better utilization of the forage within the lease, the district manager of Wyoming District 4 might decide that it was necessary and desirable to subdivide the lease into allotments; even persons biased against the idea will concede that it would have some merit in this case. Suppose he were to approach the association with the idea, and the association board of directors decided against it. Could the district manager then go to the grazing district advisory board for independent judgment and support? Perhaps. But four members of the board including the board president would be the same persons he had talked with at the association meeting. If an independent survey by range examiners sent out from the area office in Denver were to conclude that vegetation on the Rock Springs lease had been severely damaged by livestock use and numbers should be greatly reduced, the local office could expect sharp opposition from the advisory board unless the lessee (the association) were previously to concur in the range examiners' findings.

In allocating expenditures of range improvement fees the grazing association members represent four-ninths of the board members, and some of the most influential members. A number of years ago a sportsmen's club recommended putting fifty head of elk on the Rock Springs Grazing Association lease. The association approved, provided that the State Game Commission would transport the elk to the lease, and with the understanding that the herd would not be allowed to increase beyond 200 head.

[10] The district manager in 1959 thought that the association members could manage range use much better individually than centralized management.

If the association had opposed the recommendation, however, it is almost inconceivable that the Grazing Advisory Board would have decided that the public interest demanded that elk be placed on the lease in opposition to the association's wishes.

A determined district manager who decided to disregard the recommendations of his advisory board (as he has the power to do) and impose certain additional regulations on the association would arouse formidable opposition. Several members of the Grazing Association are personally acquainted with the officials of the area and national offices of the Bureau of Land Management, and were these association members to make direct representation of their position to these officials, the association's views would be carefully considered and would carry weight. The greatest strength of the association ranchers lies in their political power. Wyoming's senators are completely responsive to and sympathetic with the objectives and interests of the livestock growers in Wyoming. Members of the Rock Springs Grazing Association are influential men in Wyoming politics. The senators from Wyoming would be willing and anxious to exert their powerful influence with the Department of Interior in behalf of the wishes of the association membership. Such senatorial influence is generally highly effective because both the Interior Department and the Bureau of Land Management are thoroughly aware of the possible effects of senatorial hostility. In short, only under the most extreme circumstances would the Bureau of Land Management oppose its views to those of the association.

In conclusion we may note one typically twentieth-century aspect of the association's affairs. The members of the association themselves are aware that the Rock Springs Grazing Association is widely known, that many of its members are influential men, and that the organization is large, powerful, and occupies a preferred position. The members are also aware that such a prominent organization attracts adverse criticism. They therefore try to be especially careful about "public relations," and in discussing the matter they use that terminology. It may be that the association's efforts to engender favorable "public relations" cause it to be more reasonable and public spirited than its political and economic position would necessitate.

Granger and Carter Leases

In the checkerboard lands west of the Rock Springs lease two other major leases are operated, managed, and administered in a very similar manner. As a matter of fact they antedate the Rock Springs lease. An

Evanston attorney organized them two or three years prior to the formation of the Rock Springs Grazing Association.

The eastern part of the unit is the Granger lease, held by the Uinta Development Company. The lands of the lease extend from north to south completely across the checkerboard area. The Uinta Development Company is owned by approximately twenty shareholders, but there is an extremely wide range in the size of their holdings. The largest shareholder, a corporation, holds more than a thousand times as many shares as the smallest shareholders. The company owns or leases 266,000 acres of checkerboard private land and 235,000 acres of Taylor checkerboard land that are used largely for winter sheep range, and the number of sheep each shareholder can place on the lease is directly proportional to his shareholdings. Unlike the practice with respect to the Rock Springs lease, each shareholder on the Granger lease is billed individually by the BLM for his stock use on the lease. Thirteen other permittees graze cattle in summer on the lease lands. Most of this cattle grazing is on federal lands adjacent to the permittees' private land, and the public lands furnish less than half the total forage used.

The western part of the same unit consists of checkerboard lands having the same natural characteristics as the lands of the Rock Springs and Granger leases. It is also operated as an association—the Western Wyoming Land and Livestock Association. The lands of the lease, however, overlap the Cumberland Unit for a short distance in the northwest corner of the lease. The Carter lease and the Western Wyoming Company are operated in the same fashion as the Uinta Development Company; several ranchers own shares in each company. Many of the larger ranchers of the Evanston area and from the Bear River Valley own shares in these two leases. A few large permittees live entirely outside the area, in Ogden, Salt Lake City, and California.

Summary

The central portion of the Bridger Basin is an area predominantly of winter range of low carrying capacity. The borders are cooler and wetter, and are predominately spring-fall ranges. The Green River District is the only one of the Middle Rocky Mountain basins where sheep are of far greater importance than cattle; but cattle operations are numerous though small.

The management of range grazing on the edges of the district exhibits similar problems and solutions to those encountered in other basins, although range survey and inspection are perhaps made somewhat more difficult because of the great size of the district and the paucity of roads.

In the central part of the basin the extraordinarily difficult tenure problems of the checkerboard land pattern induced the information of three grazing associations to organize range land use and control. Such organizations were possible because the Union Pacific Railroad had retained title to much of its original checkerboard holdings. The grazing associations were successful prior to the passage of the Taylor Act, and they have greatly aided and simplified administration and management of the Green River District since its organization. The largest association in the administration of its own huge lease encounters many problems similar to those met by the BLM in its administration.

These grazing associations are progressive and efficient, they have satisfactory relations with the BLM, and seem to represent a workable solution to problems of range management in an area of complex land tenure.

Chapter Nine

THE UPPER GREEN RIVER BASIN

In the two previous chapters contrasts in grazing land administration and use were described arising out of differences in the land tenure pattern and the history of contrasting private schemes for solving the problem of range allocation prior to the passage of the Taylor Act. In the Bridger Basin it was seen that the privately organized grazing associations provide joint co-operative use and administration of the range, have been a success, and are currently operating vigorously and satisfactorily.

Most of the range lands of the Upper Green River Basin, which is largely covered by Wyoming District 5 (the Sublette District), are utilized co-operatively and jointly by private grazing associations also. The history of the Sublette District associations has been different from those previously described, and they are operating in an area with different natural qualities and a different land tenure pattern. The Sublette District associations pose a most interesting set of problems pertaining to Taylor district administration, because they do not seem to be as vigorous and satisfactory as those in the Bridger Basin, although conditions in the Upper Green River Basin seem equally favorable.

General Geography

The basin occupying the re-entrant between the Wind River Mountains and the convergent Mountains of Western Wyoming is here designated the Upper Green River Basin (see Fig. 10). Physically it is the northern part of the Bridger Basin, because there are no significant breaks in the topography or geologic structure to distinguish the northern section from the rest of the Bridger Basin; but land use and grazing organization are so sharply differentiated that the northern section, the Upper Green River Basin, constitutes a distinctive land use region. This areal unity of land use characteristics in the Upper Green River Basin has been recognized by the Bureau of Land Management by organizing a separate grazing district —Wyoming Grazing District 5.

The Upper Green River Basin is one of the more isolated sections of the United States. The basin opens to the south, and its external connections are entirely in that direction. On the northeast, north, and west nothing but trails and a single highway leading to Jackson Hole exists. The nearest railroad is the Union Pacific, lying nearly fifty miles south of the southern border of the district. Prior to the development of the motor truck and modern highways, this isolation was extreme, and vestiges of it still remain. For example, an old theater in Pinedale, in the northern part of the basin, advertises that it is farther from a railroad than any other theater in the United States. The U.S. Forest Service charges lower grazing fees on the bordering Bridger National Forest than on many others because the Forest Service formula for calculating grazing fees takes into account the additional costs encountered on more isolated forests. Today, distance from the railroad is much less important than formerly, but the isolation of the Upper Green River Basin is reflected significantly in the long distances that the district's livestock must travel to any large consuming center.

The population of the Sublette District is tiny; only 2,800 persons occupy the entire area. About two hundred ranches are scattered along the floodplain of the Green River and its tributaries on the central floor of the basin. Another group is located where the numerous creeks issue from the bordering mountains. Most ranches are lonely and isolated. The population concentrations in the basin are mere hamlets; Pinedale, the largest, contains only 770 persons (see Plate XVI). It is located on Pine Creek, a tributary of New Fork River (a minor tributary of the Green), at the base of the Wind River Mountains in the northeastern section of the basin. Pinedale serves the ranching population of the upper part of the basin, caters to summer tourists, and serves as the local headquarters for agencies of the federal government. The second largest center, Big Piney (population 200), is exclusively a minor local market center for the widely scattered ranching population of the western section of the basin.

The economy of the basin is supported largely by the range livestock industry. Cattle-raising completely dominates the ranching economy. In terms of standard animal units the basin supports 8,600 sheep units and 61,000 cattle. Moreover, the number of cattle is increasing while the number of sheep is steadily declining. The ranches in the basin grow only 1,300 acres of all small grains, but harvest 4,300 acres of alfalfa, and 77,000 acres of wild hay from irrigated land. Thus, more than 98 per cent of all crop land produces hay.

A minor tourist trade and a few small logging operations are not very important. Oil and gas production has become of local importance in the southwestern part of the district.

The Upper Green River Basin is a high intermontane basin, surrounded on all sides but the south by substantial mountain ranges. Most of the basin has relatively smooth and gentle slopes. In a few places bold cliff faces or dissected badlands interrupt the surface. Narrow strips of moderately rough terrain also occur along most of the larger streams. In general, however, the basin floor is remarkably broad and smooth.

The principal stream of the basin, the Green River, rises in the heart of the Wind River Range and flows south through the middle of the basin. Almost in the center of the basin the Green is joined by the New Fork River, which drains much of the southwest slope of the Wind River Mountains. From the west the Green receives a series of short tributaries flowing down the east side of the Wyoming Range. All the streams in the district except those in the southeast quadrant of the basin are perennial streams rising in the humid mountain areas. Although the basin floor is high, the streams are not deeply incised. Most of them flow almost at the general surface level, and even the master stream of the area, the Green, flows in a shallow valley. The southeastern corner of the basin has no perennially flowing streams; the numerous washes that originate on the basin floor contain water for only a few days a year.

The Sublette Basin is cool in summer and bitterly cold in winter, unusually cold for the latitude and altitude. In spring, summer, and fall, Big Piney is often the coldest station in the nation outside of high mountain areas. Frost has occurred in every month, though normally there is a frost-free period of approximately two months. Winter temperatures are severe. Average daily minimum temperatures for the three winter months are below 0° F. The absolute minima for all stations in the basin are colder than −40° F., and periods of a few days with temperatures continuously below zero are a commonplace in winter. Summer days are cool to warm (maxima in the high 70's), but summer nights are chilly. Average minimum temperature at Pinedale in July is only eight degrees above the freezing mark. Fall comes early, and winter lingers. Not until May does the average minimum temperature exceed the freezing mark.

The floor of the basin is arid, the lower parts having an annual precipitation that varies from scarcely more than four inches to eight or nine inches in the wetter areas. Precipitation increases with altitude. On the basin rim (Pinedale) annual precipitation is roughly twice as great as in the lowest areas. Much of the annual precipitation falls as snow. The basin has moderate wind movement; the meager data indicate that wind velocities are considerably lower than in the Bridger Basin directly to the south.

The Upper Green River Basin has a comparatively short history. The earliest settlements were ranches located in the southern part of the district in the 1870's, and settlement proceeded north along the Green River, as successive arrivals located along the next northernmost west bank tributary. The period of most active settlement was the 1890's. Pinedale was not founded until after 1900. Originally Sublette County was divided among Lincoln County to the southwest, Sweetwater County to the southeast, and Fremont County to the east and northeast; but in 1921 the state legislature created a new county approximately co-extensive with the basin.

Organization of the Cattle Associations

Other than settlement itself, the only historical development of real significance with respect to current land use was the development of the cattle associations. The southeast corner of Wyoming Grazing District 5 is almost entirely public land, and it lies on a direct route from the Wind River Mountains to the winter sheep ranges of the Bridger Basin. It is also the best early spring and late fall range in the Upper Green River Basin. Consequently, there was intense competition between the cattle ranchers of the Upper Green River Basin and the sheepmen from the Bridger Basin for this particular area. The Upper Green River cattlemen tried to keep the sheep as far east and south as possible; the Bridger Basin sheep ranchers tried to swing as far north and west and to proceed as slowly as possible in their annual trek back and forth to the Wind River Mountain summer ranges.

In order to increase their effectiveness in this sharp extralegal competition, the cattlemen of the Sublette District organized themselves into six principal livestock associations. These associations have maintained themselves ever since, and the Sublette Grazing District is largely organized around these six associations. They have had a profound effect on grazing administration within the basin.

The associations are organizations for managing the members' livestock on the range. The ranch headquarters of the members of each association are grouped in one section of the district, and their cattle are grazed in the same section. The associations are co-operative organizations, and each member is assessed a part of the annual expenses in proportion to the number of cattle which he grazes.

The annual meetings of the associations are held in late winter, usually in March, to plan the coming summer's operations. The members select a foreman for the range operations, decide on a rate of pay for the riders to be hired by the association, and approve purchases of salt to be scattered on the range. They notify the Forest Service and the Bureau of

Land Management of the meeting, and these two organizations then can take up any business with all members of the association simultaneously or they can deal with the association as an entity. For example, if extreme drought has made it necessary to reduce the number of stock on the association's range lands, the government agency and the cattle association will agree on the total number of a.u.m.'s to be used on the range and leave it to the association to work out among its members the exact way in which the cuts will be made. The individual permittees then take non-use for part of their permit.

Wyoming law requires that one bull must be turned out on the range for each twenty-five cows. In the past the livestock associations bought the bulls, but too much dissatisfaction was expressed by the members. Consequently, each rancher now buys his own bulls. Each spring a committee from the association visits each member ranch and inspects the bulls. All substandard bulls are marked and not permitted on the range. This does not seem a very sensible arrangement, but it is what the members want. Each member of each association pays his grazing lease fees to the Bureau of Land Management or the Forest Service directly; the associations do not lease as organizations in the manner that the Rock Springs Grazing Association does.

Land Tenure Pattern

The land tenure pattern of the Sublette District is much more complex than it appears on the generalized map of land tenure (Fig. 20), but the map makes the major outlines clear. Land on the floodplains and terraces of the perennial streams is private land, and because of the rectangular survey pattern these plots of private property tend to extend for short distances into the bordering dry lands. Little land in the interstream areas of the basin has been alienated by the federal government. Large areas are exclusively federal lands interrupted only by two sections of state land in each township. The most complex land tenure pattern is found in the spring-fall range near the base of the mountains. The early ranchers brought numerous small parcels of land into private ownership for a variety of reasons: some land is irrigable from small streams issuing from the mountains; some land is excellent spring-fall range; and some land has a spring or other water source. The bordering mountains are largely within the boundaries of the Bridger National Forest.

In the southeastern section is a large uninterrupted area of public land, and in the western half of the district are several sizable, compact, exclusively public land areas. However, the map also reveals an extraordi-

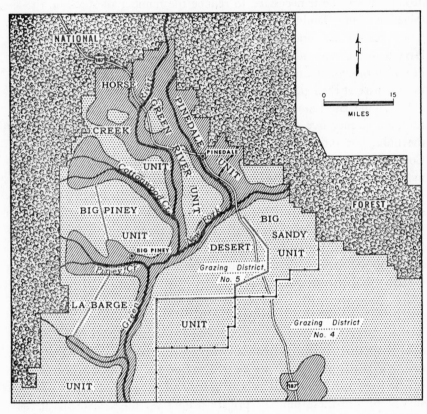

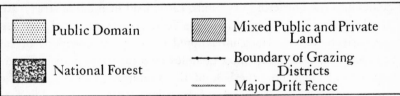

Fig. 20.—Land Tenure in the Upper Green River Basin

narily large area of contact between public lands and private lands. The long stringers of private land interpenetrate and in many cases completely surround the federal lands except in the southeastern corner of the district. Nearly all private lands have direct contact with the public lands, and only the center sections of the most compact public land areas are relatively inaccessible from private lands.

These are conditions especially ill-suited to effective control of grazing on the public lands. Anywhere along the hundreds of miles of private-public land border, cattle or sheep can be turned out into the adjacent ranges, and effective supervision by Bureau of Land Management officials is clearly impossible. The travel distances involved are far too great, and the rougher land adjacent to the river valleys makes observation difficult. But, most important, if livestock are discovered in trespass, the owner can claim that they have just strayed through an open gate or through a hole in the fence. The significance of this trespass is increased when we realize that the attendant overgrazing is on the rougher valley border lands most susceptible to accelerated erosion.

Grazing Practices

Spring arrives late in the Upper Green River Basin. In the southern (lowest) sections of the district cattle and sheep are turned onto the range April 1 at the earliest, but in many years it is ten days or two weeks later. In higher parts of the basin livestock are not turned out on the range until May 1.

Because of the severity of the spring weather most cows are bred to calve in May; thus, the calves are born on the range.[1] Consequently, the Sublette Grazing District is largely a yearling sale country because by October, when the range grazing season has ended, the calves born the preceding spring are still very small to sell. Instead they are held over the winter and sold the following fall.

No livestock go on to the national forest grazing lands until June 15, and some sheep bands do not go on to the high forests until July 15. The stock also goes on deeded lands bordering the forests at about the middle of June.

The animals come down out of the forests from September 15 to October 1. They are taken directly back to the irrigated hay and meadow lands adjacent to the ranch headquarters in the various river and creek valleys in the basin. During the summer a crop of hay is cut from these

---

[1] There is much range lambing also.

irrigated meadows. After the cattle return from the forests in the fall, they graze the irrigated meadows until the snow becomes so deep that they cannot reach the forage. Thereafter the herd is fed the cured hay. Some ranchers put the hay up in stacks surrounded by a fence. The cattle are given access to the feed simply by removing the fence. Winters in the Upper Green River Basin are so severe that livestock cannot survive in the open without some protection, so the ranchers permit numerous large clumps of willows to grow along the outer edges of the floodplain meadows (Plate XVII); then, when blizzards swirl over the basin or extreme cold settles into the river valleys, the cattle can retreat into these willow clumps and the breaks adjacent to the valley edge and there survive even the severest weather. Under such circumstances the ranchers commonly bring the feed to the stock, or have haystacks located in the willows from which the protecting fence is removed during such stringent weather conditions.

Organization of the District

The Sublette Grazing District, the smallest district in the Middle Rockies, embraces 1,106,000 acres of public land. A total of 157 ranchers hold permits on the district to graze 51,000 head of cattle, 103,000 sheep, and 2,000 horses. Approximately 8,000 deer, elk, and antelope are on the district lands part of the year. The public lands of the basin are assumed to furnish 158,000 a.u.m.'s of grazing, although the rated carrying capacity of the public domain lands is 190,000 a.u.m.'s. More than 90 per cent of the a.u.m.'s are used by cattle; sheep use only a little more than wildlife. The Pinedale office also administers about 2,900 acres of Section-15 lands in Jackson Hole in the extreme western part of the state south of Yellowstone Park. Not only is the Sublette District the smallest of the Middle Rocky Mountain districts, it is also believed to be the simplest to administer.[2] The district office, in Pinedale, has the smallest staff in the Middle Rocky Mountain region; about half as many technicians are employed as in the other districts in Wyoming. In addition to the district manager, there are only one range manager, an administrative assistant, a clerk, a forester, and a soil and moisture man who is employed only in summer because the winters are too severe for effective outdoor work. This small district retains a full-time forester because the higher areas in the district include about 50,000 acres of wooded land, of which about 35,000 acres are commercial timber.

The fiscal figures for the district are in keeping with its comparative

[2] According to various administrative-level officials of the BLM.

simplicity and small size. In 1957, total lease receipts for the district were just under $25,000. Section-15 lease receipts were almost negligible, but timber lease charges brought in about $1,000 of the total. Income was less than half that of any other district and only a fourth of what was received in Districts 2 and 4. The ratio of expenditures to income was probably not as high in Pinedale as in the other districts. In 1957 the district expenses probably amounted to nearly $50,000.[3]

The district has a few large ranches which lease or own a lion's share of the range forage. The largest ranch utilizes about 10 per cent of all the forage in the district, and the ten largest ranchers use a fourth of the total forage. Very small cattle ranchers are less numerous in the Sublette District than in other districts, perhaps because of the long feeding period in winter and the relative scarcity of off-farm employment. The greatest number of operators in the district handle from two hundred to five hundred head.

For purposes of grazing organization and administration the district is divided into seven major units. These units are separated by the major water courses of the district which are represented by the heaviest black lines on the land tenure map (Fig. 20). Each unit is partially subdivided into allotments that are used in a particular way at a specified season by one or more ranchers. Joint use of the range lands is and has been more prevalent here than in any other Wyoming district.

DESERT UNIT AND GREEN RIVER UNIT

The largest unit, the one occupying the southeastern section of the district, is called the Desert Unit. As its name implies, it is a dry, desert shrub area with no natural permanent water sources. Consequently, from the beginning of settlement the land was used mainly for sheep grazing, except along the western margin near the rivers. The rivers furnished a supply of water for cattle that grazed on the adjacent ranges. Thus, there was intensive use of the range lands in a fringe a few miles wide along the western margin of the unit near the Green River, which caused rapid deterioration of the range vegetation and the onset of erosion. Of all the lands in the district these are in the least favorable physical condition. They represent an extension of the lands of the Little Colorado Desert Unit of the Green River District just across the district boundary to the south, with

[3] Fiscal data from a special compilation made for me by the BLM. Since some costs are compiled by type of operation for the entire Wyoming area rather than by district, it is necessary to pro rate such costs for each district; hence district expenditure figures are only approximate.

the similar grazing problems described previously. Twelve ranchers from the vicinity of Cokeville (i.e., from another district) run their sheep on the Desert Unit during the fall and early winter.

The map of land tenure (Fig. 20) shows a fence running east-west across the southern part of the Desert Unit. This fence marks the boundary between range use by cattle from Sublette County on the north and by sheep from the Bridger Basin on the south.[4] There seems no good reason why the lands south of the fence should not be included in Grazing District 3 to the south, because all use of this land is by permittees from that district.

North of the fence the Desert Unit is a mixed sheep and cattle area. Cattle, from the willow meadows along the streams, and sheep are turned on to the range simultaneously sometime between April 1 and April 25; the exact date depends on how cold the spring is. The importance of flexibility in administration of grazing land use is emphasized by this practice. It also highlights one of the advantages of having complete joint use of an allotment. If each rancher on the allotment grazed his herds there individually, all ranchers would feel obliged to turn out on April 1 in order to prevent the other permittees from harvesting a disproportionate share of the forage by turning their stock on the range on the earliest legal date. If everyone turns out simultaneously after the weather has improved and the grasses and shrubs have made a good vigorous spring growth, each rancher gets his share of the forage and at the same time the range vegetation is sensibly managed.

One of the six cattle associations, the Green River Cattle Association, uses the large allotment lying east and south of the junction of Green River and New Fork River. In earlier times it was difficult or impossible to hold cattle out on this allotment because of lack of water. Since the organization of the Sublette District, however, the Bureau of Land Management has put in numerous water development projects, using funds from the grazing fees allocated for range improvement. Several large reservoirs are scattered over the unit, but they are not a completely reliable source of stock water because some years are so dry that the reservoirs do not fill. Consequently, the BLM, to obtain effective use of the unit's forage resources, has drilled a half-dozen wells in the southeastern section of the unit where water is most scarce.

The cattle are allowed to distribute themselves over the Desert Unit;

[4] This fence and the north-south fence separating the Desert Unit from the Sandy Unit to the east have a fourteen-inch bottom gap to permit antelope to crawl under. Such a procedure helps to ameliorate sportsman opposition to range fences.

they utilize the lower lands early in the season and then drift to the higher mesas and rims as summer advances. They are owned by ranchers who are members of the Green River Cattle Association. Most matters relating to stock handling on these two units are taken up at the cattle association meetings.

The cattle stay on the Desert Unit until about June 15 and then proceed to the single bridge crossing over the New Fork River. At the bridge they are intercepted and counted and the calves branded. The cattle are released on the north side of the river on the Green River Unit—the long narrow unit lying between New Fork and Green River. Many cattle, however, do not drift north to the New Fork River, but linger on the high rims and mesas or in better-watered draws of the Desert Unit. Riders must search the unit carefully, round up these cattle, and get them north of New Fork River on the Green River Unit.

The few bands of sheep that use the Desert Unit in the spring use it as a lambing ground on their trail to the forest about July 1.

The Green River Cattle Association uses the Green River Unit as a driveway to the national forest. It is approximately thirty-two miles from the bridge to the Bridger National Forest boundary near the north end of the Green River Unit, and the cattle take only a few days to trail this distance. When they arrive at the forest boundary, riders employed by the association pick them up as unsorted groups (that is, with no attention to brands) and scatter them in the various draws and valleys of the forest in the numbers stipulated for each area by the Forest Service. Association riders keep the cattle properly distributed on the forest throughout the summer.

At the end of September the riders bring the cattle down from the forest and trail them to an underpass beneath the fenced highway running west from Pinedale. There the cattle are sorted by brands and returned to the private lands of the various ranchers where they spend the autumn and winter. The base period for Taylor range rights (that is, the period when ranchers must support their stock on their private property) is five months, but most ranchers keep their cattle on their private lands for six or seven months. The following spring the cycle begins again.

This procedure of turning the cattle out on the Desert Unit and allowing them to graze and slowly migrate to the boundaries of the forest essentially unherded is locally called the "Green River drift." It constitutes an interesting range practice, especially because the BLM range managers hold such divergent views about it. Those who take a somewhat more ecological and managerial point of view of range management than do many of their colleagues regard it as a highly inefficient and wasteful practice. They stress the large amount of range forage wasted because the unherded stock do not spread out enough to use it, the range damaged by overgrazing where the cattle bunch up, particularly near the bridge across the New Fork River, at the highway underpass, and near the entrance to the forest. They also stress the considerable loss in weight if the cattle are permitted to drift back to their home ranches in the fall. Conversely, other BLM technicians emphasize the very low costs involved in the Green River drift and argue that these low costs result in a much greater return on investment than would be the case with greater fencing or herding costs even if the range forage were somewhat more effectively harvested.

All the privately owned, irrigated, willow meadows along the streams are fenced, but, the open range has few fences. The more important ones for control of livestock are indicated on Figure 20. In the Green River Unit, the allotment lying just across New Fork River from Pinedale (the Mt. Airy Allotment) is completely fenced from the rest of the unit to prevent its use by cattle drifting north through the unit. This allotment is used by ranchers who own the immediately adjacent private lands along the New Fork River. They turn their cattle out about April 15 and keep them on the range until it becomes too dry, whereupon the stock return directly to the willow meadows—an example of the simplest range land–irrigated land integration.

BIG SANDY UNIT

Range organization in the easternmost unit in the district—Big Sandy Unit —is extraordinarily complex. Running northwestward through the district to New Fork River is a small tributary, Muddy Creek. Along this creek are scattered pieces of private irrigated land and the headquarters of several ranches. Scattered bits of private land are also located on the high pastures near the forest boundary along the eastern margin of the unit. Associated with this complex land tenure pattern is an intricate grazing pattern.

Three sheep operators use the unit as spring-fall range in association with the forest to the east and north, the Desert Unit to the southwest, and the Little Colorado Unit of Grazing District 4. Three other sheep ranchers from District 4 use the southern part of the unit as a lambing ground on their way to the forest toward the north and east.

The principal use of the district is by cattle owned by the ranchers located within the unit. The southern part of the unit is used as one big allotment by the Square Top Cattle Association made up of fifteen cattle ranchers. Their stock are turned out and herded in common. The cattle go out from the irrigated lands within the unit about April 15, remain on the unit until about the fifteenth or twentieth of June, and then are trailed to the forest lands to the northeast.

The northern part of the unit is less well organized and regulated. Cattle are turned out at the same time in the spring—April 15. Some stay on the lands of the unit all summer; others go to the forest. Some are confined to allotments; others graze over the entire northern part of the unit.

PINEDALE UNIT

Only 48,000 acres of public domain are included in the Pinedale Unit, which lies along the valleys of New Fork River and Pine Creek and in the rugged foothills of the Wind River Range. In the higher parts of the unit are approximately two million board feet of timber. The federal range is assumed to furnish only 6,500 a.u.m.'s of grazing annually. Approximately two-thirds of the annual production of forage is consumed by cattle, a fourth by horses, and the balance by deer, elk, and antelope. The proportion of horse use in this unit is high, and is associated in part with the tourist industry of the area. Horses are needed for pack trips and for the dude ranches.

The Pinedale Unit is composed largely of private land intermixed with numerous scattered tiny federal holdings in fenced allotments. The ranchers within the unit turn cattle on to the range lands of the unit in spring. Some go to the forest; some stay in the unit all summer, in the higher lands along the forest margin. The area of predominantly public domain in the eastern part of the unit is high and humid. In this area several successful applications for land under the Desert Land Act have been patented in recent years; subsequently the land has been used as high-grade private pasture. The Pinedale office expects further Desert Land entries in this area in the future, and since there are lakes and mountain streams in this same area, applications for acreages for recreational purposes under the Small Tracts Act may also be expected.

LA BARGE UNIT

The La Barge Unit occupies the southern part of the district west of the Green River. The principal lessees of the unit are members of the La Barge Cattle Association, who use most of the unit in common. The cattle are turned out approximately on May 1, but the opening date is adjusted to variations in weather and the onset of grass growth. The cattle wander over the entire unit. The association retains a rider or two who place salt on the range, break up any bunches of stock, and keep the bulls widely distributed. The land tenure map (Fig. 20) shows a major drift fence in the northern part of the La Barge Unit[5] that is anchored to the fencing along the irrigated lands adjacent to the two creeks shown. Soon after the cattle are turned out in May, they begin to drift slowly toward the higher lands to the west, but they cannot pass the drift fence. They would bunch up against it if not prevented by the riders. About the middle of June the drift fence is opened and the cattle are allowed to move into the higher lands in the western part of the unit. About July 1 or a little later the ranchers with forest permits take their cattle onto the forest to the west; but some cattle remain on the La Barge Unit all summer.

The La Barge Unit does not have quite the simplicity of organization just described. A few ranchers have private allotments immediately adjacent to their irrigated land holdings, which they use for periods of various lengths. Four sheep operators use the northern part of the unit from about April 15 until early July, when they go on the forest, and then graze it again for a short period in the fall before crossing the Green River to the Desert Unit. A few thousand sheep stay in the unit all summer.

BIG PINEY UNIT

The Big Piney Unit has almost the same physical characteristics and the same type of range organizations and administration as the La Barge Unit. It is used entirely by members of the Big Piney Cattle Association, whose cattle are turned out approximately on May 1, and are held to the lower lands by a major drift fence (see Fig. 20) until the higher lands are ready. Some cattle go to the forest and the rest graze the higher lands of the unit during the summer. Small private allotments are scattered along the edge of the irrigated lands.

HORSE CREEK UNIT

Federal holdings are small and widely scattered in the Horse Creek Unit except in the southern part. The area of predominantly public lands in the southern part of the unit is divided into seven allotments. The cattle are turned out onto these allotments and begin to work their way slowly westward or northward toward the forest lands. Cattle from the large ranches in this unit may be scattered over hundreds of square miles

[5] The location of the fence on the map is partly diagrammatic, because the land tenure pattern to which the fence is adjusted is generalized.

throughout the summer, but in fall, when they drift down to the lower lands, they are rounded up, sorted, and returned to their home ranches by the Rye Grass Roundup Association, which functions in this unit.

Land Sales and Exchanges

Exchange and sale of federal land has been somewhat more active in the Sublette District than in the others in the Middle Rock Mountain basins. There are a large number of small scattered plots of federal land in the district. During the early days of Taylor Act administration exchanges were made with the state of Wyoming, and (as in the Divide District) state lands in the dry basin floors were exchanged for spring-fall ranges of greater carrying capacity in the higher and more humid lands.

The district has carried through three or four isolated tract sales each year, but these have not been easy to engineer. It will be recalled from chapter iv that Section 14 of the Taylor Act stipulates that such isolated tracts are put up for bid, but cannot be sold for less than the appraised value. Owners of adjacent lands have a preference over the highest bidder provided that within thirty days they meet the highest bid or bid three times the appraised price. If they do neither the land is sold to the highest bidder. In the Sublette District in many cases there may be more than one adjacent owner, and all will meet the maximum bid. Since the Bureau of Land Management does not like to break up forty-acre tracts, these multiple bids have made isolated tract disposal difficult. On the other hand, if an isolated federal tract is entirely surrounded by lands of a single rancher neither he nor anyone else is very anxious to buy it, because it is more or less useless to anyone else for grazing and the adjacent landlord sees little reason to buy what he already has for his exclusive use. Hence, despite the fact that the Sublette District office takes a favorable view of isolated tract sales, the program has moved slowly.

A District in Transition

Study of the operations of the Sublette District is highly instructive. During early visits to the district, I came to regard it as an example of a successful solution to the difficult range management problems ordinarily engendered by a large number of relatively small ranch units operating in an area with a complex land tenure pattern. In the Upper Green River Basin the joint use of large units by the well-established and traditional cattle associations appeared to be an effective and satisfactory scheme of range administration and management.

Numerous factors seemed to favor the arrangements. The practice of range use co-operation was well established and antedated federal management of the public domain. Trespass is easy to establish and check. The methods used are most interesting. As all cattle in the district are on the irrigated meadow lands during the winter, BLM technicians visit the various ranches late in the winter to count the cattle. In the Upper Green River Basin almost no cattle are either bought or sold in spring. If a rancher has more stock than entitled by his permit on his association's unit, he must either explain where they are after the range grazing season begins or still have them on his own irrigated meadows. Since numbers are so easy to check, the only trespass problems occur in conjunction with the opening or closing dates for the range grazing season, and in recent years these have been the only trespass violations.[6]

Because of the very long periphery of public and private lands in the Upper Green River Basin (see Fig. 20), it would be difficult or impossible for Bureau of Land Management officials unaided to prevent cattle or sheep being turned onto the ranges adjacent to the various ranches in violation of the opening and closing dates. However, since the units are used in common, every member of each association has a direct stake in preventing anyone's turning onto the range early or staying late, and consequently each member of every association will report all cases of trespass which he may observe, thereby greatly increasing the effectiveness of range use inspection.

Other geographical factors seem to favor using the units in common. Most of the units are bounded by fences along national forests or private, irrigated lands. Since cattle migrate with the seasons, a few drift fences and a relatively few riders can maintain good control and distribution of the stock. Various bottlenecks on the range (either natural or artificial) make it easy to catch, brand, and count the stock. Above all, the area has a long tradition of co-operative use and management of the range.

Certain difficulties are apparent, however. Joint use of the range makes it difficult for an individual rancher to improve the quality of his herd. He may buy superior bulls, but he must then turn them out on the range

[6] Here in the Upper Green River Basin also the district office is reluctant to assess trespass fees. A recent intrabureau report of the Pinedale office notes that, "no trespass actions were instigated although seven operators were warned of stock being on the range after expiration of the season of use. These operators immediately removed their stock." Bureau of Land Management officials say that this was the correct action to take because their objective was to remove the stock from the range and still retain the co-operation of the ranchers. They may be right. However, it would seem that failure to assess trespass fees or punitive damages is an incitement to trespass, because forage may be obtained without paying for it if the trepass is not discovered, and there is no penalty if it is.

with his entire cow herd together with all the cows and bulls of the other ranchers during the breeding season.[7] Obviously the quality of calves produced will be determined by the poorest bulls on the range as well as by the best. The continuing dissatisfaction with the bull programs of the various associations reflects this difficulty.

Many ranchers do not like to have their yearling heifers bred, but cannot avoid it if this stock is turned out on the jointly used range units. Thus a rancher is forced to keep his yearling heifers on his irrigated meadow lands throughout the summer, but if he had a small fenced private range allotment, he could turn them out there.

Finally all range improvements on jointly operated ranges must be geared to the speed at which the least progressive ranchers are willing to proceed. This, of course, profoundly irritates those ranchers who would like to move more swiftly.

Despite the numerous local advantages for using large range units in common, there seems to be as strong a trend toward individual allotments in the Upper Green River Basin as in any other. The shift to individual allotments has advanced faster since it became the policy of the Pinedale office of the BLM to encourage the change, but ranchers in the past have on their own volition applied for individual allotments, and it is my impression (though based on rather scant personal evidence) that Sublette District ranchers react with alacrity to suggestions that they change to individual allotments.

Experience in the Upper Green River Basin suggests that despite the numerous advantages of joint use of ranges and the disadvantages of individual allotments some strong factors impel ranchers in the direction of individual allotments. Among them are: (1) the desire for independence of action in range management and improvement, (2) the value attached to greater flexibility and close control of stock that can be attained with an individual allotment, and finally (3) the satisfaction of having one's own individual allotment which can be used as heavily or as lightly as one wishes and wherein all range improvements will accrue more directly to the lessee.

[7] A few ranchers keep their cows on their private lands until after the breeding period.

Chapter Ten

THE BIG HORN BASIN

The Big Horn Basin, the northernmost of the Middle Rocky Mountain basins, has a number of characteristics that differentiate it significantly from the other basins in its grazing use. Summer and winter high and low temperatures are higher than in other basins. Although the differences are not great, the higher temperatures have a noteworthy effect on both present and potential agricultural land use, because the longer growing season and greater summer heat permit a greater variety of crops to be produced than is the case in any of the other basins. This greater range of possibilities for using the irrigated land results in different arrangements for range and irrigated land integration than are found in the other basins. The Big Horn Basin is the most arid of the Middle Rocky Mountain basins. This aridity affects the grazing patterns, and also makes large sections of the basin vulnerable to erosion, because the vegetation cover is too sparse to furnish adequate cover for the soil, particularly if the vegetation is depleted by intensive exploitation. Lastly, range rights under the Taylor Grazing Act within the grazing district that covers the Big Horn Basin are made by a system of "range line agreements," a method of range use allocation not used extensively elsewhere in the Middle Rocky region.

General Geography

Fur trappers traveled through the Big Horn Basin before the middle of the nineteenth century, but it was not until the 1880's that white settlement by cattlemen coming up from the south brought about the first extensive use of the basin lands. Settlement moved from south to north. Except for the very earliest period the Big Horn Basin cattlemen had two possible rail routes to the eastern markets. They could trail the cattle north to the Northern Pacific rail line in the Yellowstone Valley, just north of the basin, or they could trail more than a hundred miles south to the Union Pacific line. Most ranchers used the easier Northern Pacific route. Sheep invaded the basin at an early date and had become the dominant form of ranching by the turn of the century.

Irrigation began almost as early as stock ranching. The Mormons, who came to the Big Horn Basin in considerable numbers in the 1890's, initiated a few irrigation enterprises, but the real expansion of irrigation did not take place until the early years of the twentieth century. Several private ditch companies of moderate size were organized along the Bighorn River, and one of the earliest Bureau of Reclamation projects was the construction of Buffalo Bill Dam on the Shoshone River in 1905 and later. From 1900 to 1912 the Burlington Railroad extended a line south through the basin from Billings, Montana, and eventually connected it with a line through Nebraska to the East. The line still furnishes rail service to the basin.

The economy of the basin has the same economic supports that have been described for several of the other basins—range livestock ranching, oil and gas production, and tourists—but in the Big Horn Basin irrigation agriculture producing crops other than grass is also important to the economy.

Population distribution is shown on Figure 11. The population of the Big Horn Basin has been growing rather rapidly; from 1940 to 1950 it increased by about 20 per cent and has been growing steadily since. Population is concentrated on the irrigated land, and the largest areas of irrigated land support the most population. The basin does not have one large dominant city. The two largest centers are Worland, in the south central part of the basin, with slightly more than 4,000 inhabitants and Cody, on the Shoshone River in the northwestern part of the basin, with fewer than 4,000 inhabitants. Four other towns—Powell, Thermopolis, Lovell, and Greybull—support more than 2,000 persons and serve as local marketing and processing centers.

The Big Horn Basin is flanked on both east and west by prime recreational country. Both the Absarokas on the west and the Big Horn Mountains to the east have excellent hunting, fishing, hiking, riding, pack trails, and other attractions. Fishermen, hunters, and tourists patronize the stores, shops, hotels, and dude ranches in the basin or at the edge of the adjacent mountains. One of the three main motor routes into Yellowstone Park passes through the northern section of the basin, and Cody is the eastern motor gateway and one of the rail gateways to the park. Thermopolis, with large hot springs, does a small business as a mineral spa.

The petroleum industry of the Big Horn Basin is large and of major importance. The Big Horn Basin is the largest oil-producing area of Wyoming. The livelihood patterns of Figure 12 indicate the pipelines that carry oil from the basin north to Billings and southeast to Casper. However, at least five oil refineries, located in the principal basin cities, bring additional income and employment to the basin.

Agriculture is the most important industry in the Big Horn Basin, and range livestock ranching is the most important form of agriculture, but it does not have here the predominance it has in the other Middle Rocky Mountain basins. There are slightly more than 2,200 ranches in the basin, but the total number has been declining slowly despite increases in the amount of land under irrigation, because the average size of ranches is increasing in the Big Horn Basin as in all the others.

More than 275,000 acres are under irrigation in the Big Horn Basin. Hay crops make up less than half the total irrigated acreage; nearly a fourth of the irrigated area is devoted to grain-production, the next most important crop. Silage corn for livestock feeding also is an important crop. Two cash crops—beans and sugar beets—are major income producers, although they utilize relatively little acreage.

Despite the importance of field crops in the basin, however, livestock are the principal source of income. In 1956 the basin supported about 240,000 head of cattle, of which about 8,000 were milk cows. The basin ranches also served as the headquarters for more than a quarter-million sheep, but in terms of animal units cattle were nearly five times as abundant. Sheep numbers have been steadily decreasing here, and cattle numbers have been increasing, in the same manner as in other Middle Rocky Mountain basins. The basin also supports about 9,000 hogs and 7,000 horses.

Crop and range livestock agriculture are integrated in the Big Horn Basin. Although many lambs and steers are shipped out of the basin directly from the range lands, many others are fed to higher condition or grade on the products of the basin's irrigated lands. Lambs coming off the ranges at the end of the summer are fed on irrigated alfalfa pasture and sugar beet tops for a month or two and are then placed in feeds lots for 90 to 120 days and fed more concentrated feeds such as alfalfa and molasses, sugar beet pulp, corn imported from the plains states, and locally produced oats, barley, and wheat. Yearling steers are also fed on the basin feed lots and pastures.

Although there are many integrated ranching operations in the Big Horn Basin, there are also many specialists. Some ranchers raise only field crops and some raise field crops and buy range cattle to feed. Other ranchers are mainly range cattle producers but raise some irrigated crops and do some feeding. Still others raise only enough irrigated hay to carry their stock through the winter and sell their range animals in whatever market they can obtain the best return.

The Big Horn Basin is a true topographic basin—a shallow saucer-like depression surrounded by a mountain rim except for a narrow opening to the north. The entire basin measured up to the crest of the bordering mountains embraces about 13,700 square miles. An eighth of the basin extends north into Montana; the remainder is in Wyoming, but the entire area is in the Missouri River drainage basin.

Around the edges of the basin floor the rocks have been crumpled into small folds which have been eroded into hill lands or badlands. The intricate dissection and complete barrenness of these badlands are shown in the background of Plate XVIII. Badlands are particularly extensive in the southern section of the basin. Other structural movement has produced some small mountain groups within the central basin section. In general, however, the central section of the basin is made up of flat alluvial plains or terraces.

The master stream of the Big Horn Basin is the Bighorn River, which is simply the lower reach of the Wind River. The Bighorn River accumulates flow because it receives several tributaries from both east and west that originate in the mountains and hence are perennial streams. The two largest are the Shoshone and Greybull rivers. The Bighorn and its principal tributaries are used extensively for irrigation within the basin.

The driest parts of the Big Horn Basin have the lowest precipitation and the greatest aridity found anywhere within the Middle Rocky Mountain region. Parts of the northeastern section of the basin receive less than five inches of rain annually. Precipitation on the basin floor increases westward and southward, but the greatest average annual total received anywhere on the basin floor is only twelve inches.

Three aspects of the climate are of major significance for agricultural land use: (1) the dryness of the basin floor and the humidity of the mountains, (2) the length of the growing season—120 to 140 days at lower elevations—and the high temperatures of summer, and (3) the comparative rarity of protracted and severe storms and cold waves in winter.

The floor of the basin is covered with a sparse xerophytic vegetation except along the stream courses. Because of the extreme aridity and the extensive areas of badlands within the basin, wide areas are almost devoid of vegetation or have only the most sparse growth.

Because of their relatively high agricultural value, the alluvial soils of the Big Horn Basin have been more intensively studied than those in any other area in the Middle Rocky Mountains basins. The principal areas of alluvial soils are the floodplains and terraces along the major streams; the irrigated lands are on these soils. They vary greatly in physical character and in management characteristics. The best are excellent soils, but others suffer either from excessive drainage or inadequate drainage. The residual soils of the basin floor occupy the interstream areas. Many of them are derived from shales and are shallow, poorly drained, alkaline, and easily eroded.

Land Tenure Pattern

The land tenure pattern in the Big Horn Basin is complex, and the pattern of land jurisdiction is even more tangled, but it is possible to make some generalizations concerning them. The floodplains and low terraces along all the principal streams are in private ownership—altogether about a fourth of the lands in the basin (shown in white on Fig. 21). Along the margins of the larger areas of private land are other lands called "reclamation withdrawals" that could not be irrigated by private enterprise but are held for possible later irrigation by projects of the Bureau of Reclamation. Approximately 350,000 acres of such reclamation withdrawals are scattered over the Big Horn Basin, about half of which are administered for grazing use by the BLM.[1]

The BLM, through three district offices, administers about 3.5 million acres of vacant, unreserved federal land in the basin. The Bridger Grazing District of Montana covers that section of the basin floor that extends north into Montana.[2] Wyoming Grazing District 2, with headquarters in Lander, overlaps slightly into the southern fringe of the Big Horn Basin.[3] District 1, the Tensleep District, administers the rest of the Taylor lands in the basin—the areas indicated by the heavy slanting lines on Figure 21. The largest and least interrupted blocks of Taylor land are located in the interstream areas in the central part of the basin.

Relatively little of the public domain is in uninterrupted blocks of federal land. The state of Wyoming owns sections 16 and 36 in most townships, and numerous scattered blocks and ribbons of private land also interrupt the federal holdings. The state of Wyoming owns slightly more than 400,000 acres in the basin. Immediately adjacent to the Shoshone National Forest in the southwestern part of the basin is a relatively small compact area of state land that resulted from exchanges in lieu of state lands within national forests, national parks, and reclamation withdrawal areas.

[1] Calculations made by the Billings Regional Office, BLM, 1950.

[2] Not shown on Figure 21, which covers only the Wyoming section of the basin.

[3] The stippled area shown on the southern edge of Figure 21 is the area included in District 2.

Figure 21 indicates the complex land tenure and administrative situation along the margins of the basin. The higher spring-fall ranges bordering the Big Horn National Forest in the southeast corner of the district contained such a high proportion of private land that they were excluded from District 1. Along the western margin of the basin floor much of the land is high, better pasture. Consequently, all through this area the proportion of private land is so high that it also was excluded from the Tensleep District. The vacant public domain lands in both of these marginal sections are administered under Section-15 leases. Other sections of highly variegated land tenure patterns are found in the eastern part of the district, and in the north central section (see Fig. 21).

Two other federal agencies administer land within the basin—the Forest Service and the Indian Service. About a fourth of the drainage area of

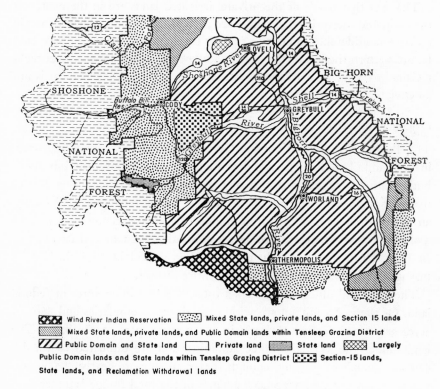

Wind River Indian Reservation   Mixed State lands, private lands, and Section 15 lands

Mixed State lands, private lands, and Public Domain lands within Tensleep Grazing District

Public Domain and State land   Private land   State land   Largely Public Domain lands and State lands within Tensleep Grazing District   Section-15 lands, State lands, and Reclamation Withdrawal lands

Fɪɢ. 21.—Land Tenure in the Big Horn Basin

the Big Horn Basin—that is from the drainage divide on the west to the drainage divide on the east—is national forest administered by the Forest Service. Forest lands are entirely within the mountains. In the southwestern part of the basin, lands of the Wind River Indian Reservation extend for several miles north of the Owl Creek Mountains into the Big Horn Basin.

The land tenure pattern of the Big Horn Basin poses numerous difficult problems of range administration. As in the Upper Green River Basin, the numerous long, narrow, stringers of private land produce an extremely long public-private land border. However, trespass problems are much more difficult than in the Upper Green River because there are no livestock associations whose members are interested in reporting trespass. Furthermore, the land tenure pattern on the dry range lands themselves is far more intricate than that found in the Sublette District.

The fact that many of the private, irrigated lands are in the center of the basin and the spring-fall ranges are in the higher lands near the margin makes a considerable amount of trailing inevitable. With the present land tenure pattern the job of the district advisory board and the district technicians in trying to work out a satisfactory range grazing pattern is not an enviable one.

Organization of the Tensleep District

The Tensleep District, Wyoming Grazing District 1, has its headquarters in Worland. The district has a dozen employees, although the job distribution is not identical with that of the other district offices. The district manager is aided by three range managers. Three range conservationists, an agricultural engineer, and an engineering aid carry on the soil and moisture work. There are also an administrative assistant and two clerks. In 1953 the district had only eight employees, and in 1945 the district manager and a clerk administered the entire district.

The Worland office administers a total of 3.15 million acres of federal land. Of these, 2.8 million are within the district boundaries and 350,000 acres are under Section-15 leases in the western part of the basin. The lands under the Worland office administration are estimated to furnish 470,000 a.u.m.'s of grazing, enough forage to support nearly 40,000 animal units per year. About 54,000 a.u.m.'s of the total forage is under Section-15 leases. For various lengths of time the federal lands of the district are grazed by 50,000 cattle, 211,000 sheep, 1,000 horses, and about 13,000 deer and elk.[4] The latter are on the district lands only for short periods in winter.

The Tensleep District has issued 458 permits to 423 individuals or groups. About a fourth of the permits are ten-year, or term, permits. On the Section-15 lands 205 leases are held by 193 operators. Since the Section-15 lands make up only a little more than a tenth of the total lands administered by the Worland office, it is obvious that the Section-15 leases are far smaller than those within the district.[5]

Wyoming District 1 has an extremely wide dispersion of permit sizes. Six operators use about a fourth of all the forage in the entire Tensleep District, and the smallest-scale, 40 per cent of the district permittees graze only 4 per cent of the stock on the district. About half the forage in the district is used by medium-sized operators: by cattlemen running a few hundred head or sheepmen having two or three thousand sheep. In the Big Horn Basin as in the other Middle Rocky Mountain basins, a major part of the administrative costs and of the district's work load is attributable to a large number of small operators all of whom furnish only a tiny fraction of the district's receipts.

In the Tensleep District, as in the others, grazing lease receipts probably do not cover more than half the total administrative and construction costs incurred within the district. In 1957, total receipts were $63,000; total expenditures within the district probably were about $120,000.[6] Two cost items currently account for about three-fourths of all district expenses—technicians' salaries and soil and moisture work.

The temporal and areal grazing pattern in the Big Horn Basin is intricate. In general, of course, there is seasonal migration from the basin floor to the mountains and foothills and back, just as in the other Wyoming basins; but the pattern is not neat and orderly. Some grazing and migration patterns are very simple; others are confused and complex.

A relatively compact and simple operation is that utilizing the two big

[4] Estimates of wild life numbers and a.u.m.'s of wildlife use are little better than guesses.

[5] The current number of Section-15 leases is another reflection of the improved administrative conditions resulting from increased staff size. A considerable number of Section-15 holdings and leases have been consolidated in recent years, and the number of leases thereby greatly reduced.

[6] Figures taken from a special compilation made by the BLM. Since some costs are compiled by type of operation for the entire Wyoming area rather than by district, it is necessary to pro rate such costs for each district; hence expenditure figures are only approximate.

allotments marked "A" on Figure 22. These allotments are assigned to a large corporate mixed-ranching organization called the LU Sheep Company. They graze approximately 1,000 cattle, 12,000 sheep, and 100 horses. The size of their operations varies little from year to year. It is some indication of the complexity of the grazing arrangements within the basin that even this large ranch does not have truly individual allotments; parts of both of their allotments are used in common with other ranchers who use the allotments mostly for trailing. Much land in both allotments is the property of the LU Sheep Company, and more than half the forage produced in both allotments comes from the company's own land. In recent years the company has been using 23,184 a.u.m.'s of federal forage for which they pay approximately $3,000. The company is an old one; it applied for one of the original permits when the district was organized. In recent years the company has been taking from 8,000 to 10,000 a.u.m.'s of non-use every year—another example of the practice of carrying non-use solely for its capitalized value. All persons concerned are aware that the additional 10,000 a.u.m.'s of forage are not being produced on these lands.

The company normally plans to carry its stock on the range throughout the year. Both cattle and sheep are grazed on the eastern allotment (marked "A" on Fig. 22) throughout the winter. About 8,000 sheep are on the public ranges of this allotment, but the company puts 3,500 on other lands of its own. In spring the cattle and sheep begin to drift west and south, the sheep to lambing grounds on the high area in the southwest part of the western allotment marked "A" on Figure 22. About the middle of July, 5,200 sheep go onto the Shoshone National Forest, where they stay until the middle of September; the balance of the stock stays on the western allotment. When the sheep come off the forest, the lambs are separated and placed in special holding pastures and the ewes are placed in other special pastures. Both pastures are in the southwestern part of the western allotment, which is subdivided into large individual pastures. For a long period in the fall, however, about a third of the sheep and cattle are grazed on private lands of the ranch. Most of the deeded lands of the ranch are in the extreme northern end of their western allotment.

The BLM technicians now regard the LU operations as a relatively simple administrative problem, because of the large allotments and the simple trailing pattern, but such has not always been the case. Formerly the company was regularly involved in trespass problems, being accused of trespassing on their neighbors' allotments or complaining that their neighbors were trespassing. In recent years, however, the company, its neighbors, and the BLM have expended more than $13,000 on fencing the allotments. The ranchers contributed well over half the cost of the fence and agreed to maintain it. The fencing has served greatly to reduce trespass problems, but has not completely eliminated them.

The areas marked "B" on Figure 22 represent an entirely different and much less satisfactory situation. These lands are all used more or less in common by a group of 18 operators. The big area marked "B_z" in the northwest corner of the area is used entirely in common, and other areas, shown on the map as subdivided, are used as individual allotments part of the year and in common part of the year. The entire allotment supports cattle throughout the year, and sheep in fall, winter, and spring. Most of the operators have their headquarters along a creek bottom which runs east-west approximately through the center of the area, but one operator is located west of the border of the Tensleep District, another is located forty-five miles to the north in the valley of the Shoshone River, and others are scattered in various other parts of the basin.

Both the ranchers and the BLM technicians regard the current arrangements as highly unsatisfactory. There is about a third more grazing use of the allotments than there is forage to support it. Moreover, the area was haphazardly organized when it was originally set up during the organization of the district. For example, the area marked "B_x" on Figure 22 was intended to be used individually by one operator at one season and in common with others at other times, but who the "others" were was never specified. Consequently, no one has ever known who has rights in the area and who does not. Finally, the date on which each rancher brings his sheep onto the allotment in the fall depends entirely on what forage he has available elsewhere. Some ranchers come on as early as October, others not until December. The earliest arrivals find the best forage, the last to arrive must take what is left. Moreover, excessive trailing within the allotment is caused by herders looking for the best forage.

So unsatisfactory is the situation that the BLM recently undertook to reorganize the area into individual allotments. They tried first to divide the big area marked "B_z" into allotments, but soon discovered that use in that allotment was so inextricably tied to use in all the other allotments marked "B," that they finally found it necessary to throw all the areas marked "B" into one unit. They then established the total amount of use currently permitted in the entire "B" area and each rancher's proportional share of that use. Each rancher was asked to sign an agreement that the share allocated to him was satisfactory. The present plan is to divide the entire area marked "B" into eighteen new areas, proportional to each rancher's share of the total, and each assigned to an individual rancher. Most of the allotments will be fenced. The one remaining formidable hurdle to reorganization is to draw allotment boundaries that will be satisfactory to everyone. This may be impossible because the ranchers who formerly came onto the big "B_z" allotment earliest have opposed the reorganization and may be able to block it by refusing to agree to any reasonable private allotment pattern. If the allotments are finally drawn in satisfactory fashion, each rancher will then take a one-fourth cut in permitted use.

An example of a tiny individual allotment is that marked "C" on Figure 22. It is fenced and entirely surrounded by the lands of the "B_z" allot-

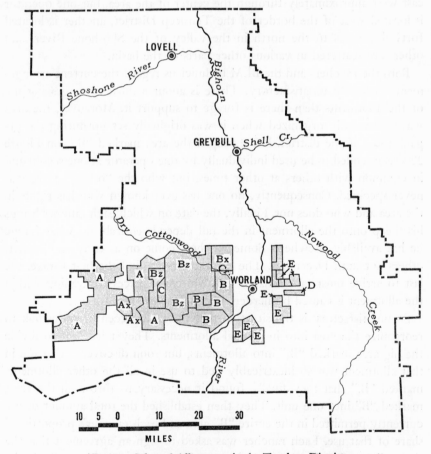

Fig. 22.—Selected Allotments in the Tensleep District

ment. The "C" allotment is used exclusively by a single rancher who grazes 1,200 sheep on the adjacent "B$_z$" allotment from November 1 to March 31, and on his private "C" allotment or on his irrigated lands at the southern end of his allotment. He puts 65 head of cattle on the "B$_z$" allotment from May 1 to September 30, moves them to the "C" allotment until November 15, returns them to the "B$_z$" allotment for six weeks, and then moves them back to his "C" allotment for the rest of the grazing year. If the "B$_z$" allotment is successfully broken into individual allotments, his present allotment will simply be extended further east.

The areas marked "E" on Figure 22 constitute a most interesting situation. There is a total of twelve separate allotments in the "E" areas. All the "E" areas are utilized for summer grazing by the cattle of a group of irrigation farmers located along the Bighorn River just west of the "E" allotments. The allotments are for sheep use in the winter; each sheep band is supposed to be confined to its own allotment, but cattle may wander over all the "E" allotments.

In fact, the permitted cattle use the "E" allotments only very slightly. When the permits were issued during the original organization of the range, these irrigation farmer lessees were turning dairy cows out on the "E" areas. Dairy cows would not stray far and would return to the ranch each night. In subsequent years, the ranchers have replaced nearly all the dairy stock with range cattle. When the range cattle are turned out in spring they follow up the creeks toward the southeast and shortly pass entirely out of the "E" allotments, using the southern "E" allotments only briefly and the northern "E" allotments almost not at all. Under the new range plan the cattle of this group are to be confined by fences to the southernmost allotments but whether the plan can be carried through is problematical.

These examples are sufficient to indicate the character and problems of the types of allotments found in the Tensleep District. The district contains more than 90 individual allotments, to which the lessee is confined during the period he is on the range, but there are 136 allotments that are used individually for part of the year and in common for part of the year. Finally, there are 24 group allotments used by 2 to 19 operators. This extreme condition of interlocking range rights and use makes final adjudication of the Tensleep District particularly difficult, because it is almost impossible to work for partial or individual solutions. If the BLM technicians consider the case of an individual rancher's range rights with a view to giving him an individual allotment and a term permit, they almost invariably find that certain of his rights interlock with those of other range users with whom negotiations must be made, and the affairs of these in turn interlock with those of others, until finally it becomes necessary to try to adjudicate a whole block of rights simultaneously as seen previously in the "B" allotments on Figure 22. The intricacy and difficulty of such negotiations can well be imagined, and any significant group opposed to the proposed arrangements can almost certainly prevent any agreement by making excessive and unfair demands before the final settlement.

Another difficulty in the way of final adjudication of the Tensleep District lies in the fact that though determinations of commensurability were made in this district, they were not a factor in the assignment of licenses because an applicant who could establish prior use of the range almost invariably had sufficient private land to meet the base property requirements of five months. The reason why commensurability determinations were unimportant is revealing. Within the Big Horn Basin were many range ranchers who had relatively small amounts of irrigated land and private range land, but who grazed large numbers of stock on the open ranges. Conversely, there were large numbers of irrigation farmers with the capacity to support stock for long periods of time in the winter season who had never made very extensive use of the range. The range ranchers were anxious to establish some formula that would be effective in keeping the irrigation ranchers off the range. Commensurability was not such a formula; its applicability could be expected to affect adversely only the range ranchers, not the irrigation ranchers. The irrigation ranchers were in a weak position on the matter of previous range use, and since previous use is one of the two major criteria for allocation of range rights, it effectively eliminated most irrigation farmers. Just why the irrigation ranchers had not used the range prior to the establishment of the Taylor Act is not clear, but their failure to do so proved reason to keep them off. The views of the range livestock ranchers are well summarized in the minutes of one of the early meetings of the Tensleep Grazing District Advisory Board in explaining their reasons for rejecting the application of one group of irrigation farmers: "their [the irrigation farmers'] set-up is such that the members of the Advisory Board expressed the belief that if they were given rights to the public domain, other farmers with similar set-ups would come in with good commensurability and drive the legitimate stockman off the range."

The Tensleep District was organized by range line agreements. It will be recalled that here and there a unit or a part of a unit was organized by range line agreement in other districts in the Middle Rocky Mountain basins, but such arrangements were the exception. The Cumberland Unit in the Bridger Basin was so organized, for example. The entire Tensleep District is organized by range line agreements.

In organizing a unit or a district two general approaches to the problem are possible. The permittees can be assigned grazing areas in common, or at different seasons, but the differences in the total number of a.u.m.'s of forage to which they are entitled can be compensated by adjusting for each rancher the number of animals he can graze or by adjusting the length of his permitted period of grazing. A second approach is the range line agreement. A rancher with a large permit is assigned a large allotment for exclusive use, a rancher with a small permit is given a small allotment. The ultimate effects of range line agreements on the allocation and administration of the range are not much different from those resulting from other methods; only the method of arriving at the result is different. The bargaining that preceded the final allocation consisted, in effect, of tentatively moving allotment boundaries back and forth to balance claims, rather than discussing variations in the length of the grazing season for each applicant or variations in the number of stock that each would be permitted on the range.

As a whole the Big Horn Basin is more vulnerable to erosion than any other of the Middle Rocky Mountain basins. The extremely sparse vegetation and the widespread areas of badlands (as illustrated in Plate XVIII) will stand very little abuse. Consequently, heavy grazing pressure has resulted in widespread induced erosion. Plate XIX shows a particularly spectacular example of gully erosion, but large areas that are undergoing somewhat less obvious attack are of greater importance. The Big Horn Basin is an area especially in need of research on the relationships between grazing pressure, vegetation density, and erosion rates, because the basin contains widespread areas of badlands in which geological erosion was taking place before the arrival of the first steer. A series of researches by the Wyoming Agricultural Experiment Station are going forward on the relations of vegetation, grazing pressure, and erosion in the Big Horn Mountains, but similar studies are needed in the basin lands also. Until such data are available range administration can be little better than a guessing game.

In many ways the Big Horn Basin is the most difficult of all the basins about which to draw conclusions. To the observer, it appears that the ranchers administer the range about to suit themselves, at least so far as stocking rates are concerned. It is also my distinct impression that the district technicians think the range not just overgrazed, but so seriously overgrazed that, in view of the minor adjustments in stocking they are able to make, the situation is practically hopeless. This impression is not simply the reflection of one manager's point of view, for visits were made to the district under three different managers. However, the BLM is now making noteworthy progress (again as the result of the recent staff increases in the district offices) in effecting some reorganization of range use and intensity. Final adjudication of the permits of more than 100 operators is underway, and this adjudication will result in cuts on many of the allotments from 25 per cent to as much as 75 per cent in extreme cases. This reduction in many cases involves only what the BLM calls "paper cuts;" that is, the final extinguishing of permits for numbers of livestock on which the operators have been taking non-use steadily for many years. Even the "paper cuts" represent progress, however, because they prevent future increase of grazing intensity, unless there should be another major upheaval in BLM administration. Recently some organized opposition has developed in the southern part of the basin, similar to that in the Lander area discussed in chapter vii. Even if the reductions are successfully effected it will be difficult to ascertain their results on range condition because of the inadequate soil and moisture data that have been commented upon previously.

Special Range Problems

A number of problems relatively minor in the other basins assume greater importance in the Big Horn Basin. Halogeten is more widely dispersed and a greater potential threat to the livestock industry in the Big Horn Basin than in any of the other Wyoming basins. Since it tends to invade areas where the vegetation has been disturbed or severely overgrazed, its wide dispersion seems to support the conclusion that grazing pressure is much heavier relative to range carrying capacity in the Big Horn Basin than elsewhere in the region. It has also spread along highways, truck trails, and railways. Thus far it has not caused significant livestock losses within the basin, but modest sums must be spent each year to eradicate concentrations of the weed and to prevent its further spread.

Physical range improvements are among the most effective activities of the district BLM offices. An example of such work is furnished by another poison weed problem in the Tensleep District. Larkspur is a plant extremely poisonous to livestock during the period in spring when it is green, succulent, and growing. As summer advances, larkspur rapidly loses its toxicity. In a particular area along the eastern margin of Wyoming

District 1, there was a serious infestation of larkspur. Cattle turned out on the range in spring would promptly migrate to the higher lands adjacent to the national forest, and occasionally some died from grazing on the young larkspur. To prevent this, it was necessary to construct fences within the allotment, to keep the cattle from entering the higher lands until later in the summer. The fence was financed by equal amounts of money contributed by the BLM from the range improvement funds and by the rancher.

Another somewhat unusual type of range improvement carried on by the BLM in the Big Horn Basin is ant control. Moderately large areas suffer from extremely heavy infestations of ants; they almost denude the area of vegetation. The control work is under the direction of a technician from the area office in Denver, but is carried out largely by local district personnel.

The staff of the Tensleep District is actively interested in the promotion of isolated tract sales, but the rate of sales is not high; ordinarily about ten or fifteen tracts a year. They have also been attempting to promote Section-8 transfers; that is, exchanges of lands to create larger solid areas of public and private lands. Less than a half-dozen such exchanges are made each year, indicating that here, as in the Upper Green River, they are extremely difficult to consummate.

Sheep trailing has caused difficulty in the Big Horn Basin. Numerous ranchers who own several scattered areas of private land must spend a good deal of time trailing along the stock driveways and on other ranchers' allotments. The practice is not looked on very favorably, but legitimate requests to trail are difficult to refuse. Both the trailing problem and the great pressure for cheap federal forage are well illustrated by an application that came into the Tensleep District office a few years ago. The applicant was short of range forage and bought a piece of private range in the southeastern corner of the basin. He then put in a request to spend 10 days trailing from the northern part of the basin to his newly acquired lands in the southeast, to stay on the private land 14 days, and then to spend 10 days trailing back to his lands at the northern end of the basin. His proposal, in short, was to spend three weeks trailing largely on federal land in order to use two weeks of forage on his own land. This request was so outrageous that the trailing permit was refused, and the applicant was told he would have to truck his sheep to his newly acquired property. But, had the request been somewhat more reasonable the permit might have been granted.

The administration of reclamation withdrawal lands is a greater problem in the Big Horn Basin than elsewhere. It was noted previously that the proportion of reclamation withdrawal lands in the Big Horn Basin is greater than in the other Middle Rocky Mountain basins. Some of these lands have been turned over to the BLM to be administered for grazing purposes until such time as the Bureau of Reclamation needs to use them for reservoir sites or for irrigation farming. Others have been retained under reclamation administration. There is little co-ordination between these two bureaus of the Interior Department, and occasionally the same lands are leased for grazing purposes by both agencies to different persons, or a piece of such land is discovered that has not been leased by either agency (and tiny amounts of revenue thus lost), although surely the land was used by someone for grazing purposes.

Summary

The Big Horn Basin has certain characteristics that distinguish it markedly from the other basins in the Middle Rockies. It has a much larger area devoted to irrigated agriculture and the warmer climate permits a much greater variety of crops to be grown. Integration of range land use with irrigated land use is somewhat closer than in the other basins, largely because the irrigated land base is more extensive. Because of greater aridity and less favorable soils the range vegetation cover of the Big Horn Basin is the most sparse of any of the Middle Rocky Mountain basins, and this makes many of the Big Horn Basin range lands more susceptible to erosion than lands elsewhere in the region.

The same problems of range administration encountered in the other basins occur also in the Big Horn Basin. Overgrazing has been widespread, has sadly depleted the range in many areas, and induced serious erosion problems. Thus far it has proved extremely difficult to bring about reductions in the intensity of range use, but some progress has been made recently. A large quantity of superfluous range rights are still retained by Big Horn Basin permittees by continually taking non-use. The complex land tenure pattern makes range administration and management difficult and ineffective, but the BLM has had almost no success in simplifying it.

Little research is in progress on the condition and trends of range vegetation and soil and moisture conditions, although all the evidence indicates that the range lands of the Big Horn Basin are in relatively serious condition. The lands of the basin also exhibit a number of special local physical problems of management.

The BLM's management activities, the federal land management problems, the patterns of land tenure, patterns of range land use, fiscal aspects of range land management, and some special physical problems of range management have been described and analyzed for each of the basins and grazing districts of the Middle Rocky Mountain area. Although all these aspects of the occupance of these basins are of considerable interest in themselves, they have not been studied, analyzed, and described in such detail for their inherent interest. The data are of greater interest for the light they may throw on Taylor land management policy. Certain conclusions seem justified by the evidence. Those conclusions and some corollary recommendations constitute the balance of this volume.

Chapter Eleven

FINDINGS AND RECOMMENDATIONS

In order to clarify this concluding discussion it may be most effective to set forth the principal findings and recommendations at the outset and subsequently elaborate and discuss them in detail.

Finding.—Relatively little is known quantitatively about the relationships between density of vegetation, grazing pressure, soil conditions, and water and soil movements in the Middle Rocky Mountain basins. Such information is vital for a rational program of grazing land management.

Recommendation.—The federal government should institute a range research program of a size adequate to furnish reliable data on the grazing, vegetation, soil, and moisture relationships for its range management program.

Finding.—The BLM does not exert sufficient control over range grazing use to insure conservation of the federal lands. This lack of control is traceable to the political weakness of the BLM and the partially selective character of their personnel recruitment program.

Recommendations.—Stricter control of range use can be brought about by politically strengthening the BLM, by broadening the staff recruitment base, and by more range inspection.

Finding.—The greatest single non-political source of difficulty in Taylor management is the complex land tenure pattern.

Recommendation.—Establish a positive program of land tenure simplification.

Finding.—The current program of land consolidation is a disappointment.

Recommendation.—A new set of directives are needed, a new program of land consolidation should be set in motion, with personnel assigned exclusively to carry out the program.

Finding.—Forage from the Taylor lands is priced far below its true value, and this leads to a number of undesirable results.

Recommendation.—Raise federal range fees to something near their true values.

Finding.—Western range livestock ranchers are slowly building proprietary rights to the Taylor lands through use, and the assignment of individual allotments will accelerate the trend.

Recommendation.—Dispose of such lands by sale rather than by administrative decision.

Finding.—Land and water use and land management problems differ markedly from place to place in the West, as a result of differences in physical land conditions, land tenure patterns, types of range organization, and previous history of use.

Recommendation.—The solutions to land policy problems should vary from place to place as do the problems themselves. Classify each piece of land in terms of the policy questions involved.

It is hoped that the findings and recommendations will be considered in two separate categories. The findings are believed to be relatively objective and based on evidence that has been presented in the previous chapters. Displeasure with the recommendations should not cause the reader to fail to consider the implications of the findings.

Current Views of the BLM'S Grazing Control Functions

The preamble of the Taylor Grazing Act announces that the purpose of the act is "to promote the highest use of the public lands pending its final disposal. . . ." Two schools of thought have contended about this statement. One school holds that the statement means exactly what it says; that the Taylor Act was intended purely as a stopgap measure to authorize and direct the use of the western unreserved and undivided public domain until plans and actions could be carried through for its disposal.[1] The other school of thought maintains that the original intent of Congress is now beside the point. According to this view, the Taylor Act has become a directive for managing the public domain for the indefinite future. Its proponents hold that the public domain is now reserved and not available for disposition, except under special circumstances where a strict construction of the various applicable land laws—the Desert Land Act, Homestead Act, Small Tracts Act, and the like—clearly applies. By them, the public domain "has come to be thought of in terms of resources possessing public values, to be held in perpetuity in the public interest."[2]

These opposing viewpoints are represented at all levels of activity within the Bureau of Land Management. Administrators of the BLM are classed by their fellows as either "disposers" or "managers." The predilection of disposers is to aid and assist in the transfer of property to private ownership, meanwhile allowing the ranchers to manage grazing

[1] See p. 53.

[2] Peffer, *op. cit.* p. 314.

on the Taylor lands to suit themselves. Managers, on the other hand, tend to put all possible obstacles in the way of public land disposal and to concentrate their energies on the management of the public lands.

If experience in the Middle Rocky Mountain basins is typical, it is my conclusion that the program of the BLM is neither one that anticipates federal management in perpetuity nor a mere stopgap program pending disposal. If it were the latter, presumably in the quarter-century since the passage the Taylor Act some concrete plan for disposal would have developed. But no such plan yet exists, and there is no evidence to indicate that any agency of the federal government is making any move to develop one. A program for managing land that endures for nearly twenty-five years without plans being made to terminate or significantly change it can scarcely be regarded as a stopgap measure.

But it is equally difficult to regard the BLM's actions under the Taylor Act as a program for public domain management in perpetuity. Nearly all the history of the act in the Middle Rocky Mountain basins gives the impression of day-to-day administration. An effective management program has not developed. The term "effective program" should be read precisely. The subdivisions of the Interior Department that have managed the public domain since 1934 have developed numerous effective procedures for handling administrative and management problems on the Taylor lands. Moreover, except during their most difficult times, the BLM or its predecessors have always had a long-range management program. The BLM has one currently; most districts in the Middle Rocky Mountain basins have twenty-year programs of soil and moisture control and range improvement. But such comprehensive long-range programs have invariably been ineffective. Employees of the BLM, even if they assert that the present program will be a success, are willing to admit freely that the programs of the past have always foundered, either because of program changes or inadequate staff to carry them out. The implications of this conclusion need to be thoroughly explored.

If the Taylor Act was a stopgap measure "pending final disposal," the responsible officials would have developed and launched some policy and program for disposal. This has not been done, though numerous laws now in force provide means for transferring various physical kinds of public domain land to private ownership. Only small quantities of land have been finally transferred from federal to private ownership. There have been no net transfers to the state of Wyoming, nor to the Forest Service or other federal agencies. No active plan for land disposal currently exists. If disposal were regarded as an important function of the BLM, presumably there would be an active program in effect to make the necessary transfers of ownership. Under an effective disposal program lands would be classified on the basis of their suitability for homesteading, for sale under the provisions of the Taylor Act, for disposal under the terms of the Small Tracts Act, and so on. Homesteaders and purchasers would be actively sought. But in actual fact, the BLM's disposal program is almost entirely passive. If someone comes into a bureau office with a request to homestead or purchase a tract of public land in order to use it for agriculture, recreation, commerce, or some other function recognized by the various land-disposal laws, his application may be slowed or it may be expedited, depending in part on whether he encounters a disposer or a manager. But the bureau does not actively seek such applications. It rarely initiates a transfer to private ownership except in a few instances under the terms of Section 14 of the Taylor Grazing Act which provides for sale of isolated tracts. In the Middle Rocky Mountain basins ordinarily there are less than a half-dozen transfers per grazing district annually.

It may well be objected that it is in no way the duty of the BLM actively to dispose of the public domain. Certainly the language of the Taylor Act makes no such directive; it simply outlines the broad specifications for federal management "pending" disposal. If for purposes of discussion the alternative view is accepted, that it is the intent of Congress for most of the remaining public domain to stay in federal ownership and be managed by the BLM for the indefinite future, then the bureau's program must be examined in those terms, that is, in terms of a long-range management program. What would be the elements of such a program and how well does the BLM program measure up?

A satisfactory long-range program would be one which managed the land so that it served useful functions while maintaining the productivity of the land and above all not impairing its condition. The Taylor Act specifically directs the Secretary of Interior "to stop injury to the public grazing lands by preventing overgrazing and soil deterioration, to provide for their orderly use, improvement, and development. . . ."

Orderliness is a matter of degree, and use of the federal range is now more orderly than it was prior to passage of the Taylor Act. Perhaps the two greatest factors making for orderly use have been the elimination of the tramp sheep operator and the establishment of regulatory procedures for newcomers desiring to graze the federal range. Whether federal range use is as orderly as it could or should be is another question.

It is difficult to appraise the net effect of federal control over grazing use of the federal lands. There can be little doubt but that total grazing use has decreased. Most of the reduction has probably resulted from removing some previous users from the range; perhaps a little from regulation of the range activities of current lessees. One Taylor lease holder—an intelligent and informed Wyoming attorney inclined toward cynicism—made the following observations: "The Taylor Act does exactly what we wanted it to do. It uses the police power of the federal government to get the tramp operators and the irrigation farmers off the range. It protects our leases. It benefits the range, because it lets each operator manage his range in the way he knows it should be managed." His contention was that lessees graze their allotments as they see fit and do not worry about the terms of their Taylor leases. The reason they do not come into serious conflict with the BLM, he asserted, lies in a general consensus among experienced range men, both ranchers and BLM officials, that there is really only one sensible and feasible way to utilize a range. The core of his argument was that the Taylor Act has had a stabilizing and favorable effect on the range and the western livestock industry by according protection to the ranchers' "range rights," thus enabling each rancher to manage his part of the range as it should be managed. On the other hand, one director of the Bureau of Land Management maintained that the Taylor Act merely induced "licensed abuse."[3]

Both of these views are serious exaggerations. In the Middle Rocky Mountain basins there is no question but that the BLM allows ranchers to make large deviations from the terms of their permits, and that additional departures occur of which the bureau is not aware. Some variation from year to year or season to season is, of course, not only unavoidable but absolutely necessary and desirable. The range livestock industry harvests naturally produced forage and it must, therefore, adapt to nature's vagaries. An especially cold spring may necessitate an abnormally late start for the range grazing season, while a late fall may permit the stock to stay longer than usual. Abundant precipitation may make possible unusually heavy stocking of the range; persistent drought may decrease range forage almost to the vanishing point. Moreover, variations in range practice often have a favorable effect on range condition. A rancher who stocks his range lightly because he has marketed a large part of his herd at unusually high prices may actually improve range condition. Temporary overstocking may have little adverse effect on the vegetation cover.

But all unsanctioned range practices are not so benign. Ranges are some-

[3] Clarence L. Forsling as reported in S. T. Dana, *American Forest Policy* (New York: McGraw-Hill, 1956), p. 287. Forsling was deprecating severe appropriations cuts which he asserted had ruined range administration.

times severely overstocked for long periods. Sheep are trailed excessively. Range grasses are damaged because cattle have been turned out too early. Poor stock distribution may severely damage a range.

Whether range use is in conformance with the permits issued by the BLM or even whether it is orderly are in themselves of small moment. What is important is the effect of range use rules and practices on the range livestock industry and on the range itself. In the Middle Rocky Mountain basins federal regulation of grazing land has had a beneficial and stabilizing effect. Before the Taylor Grazing Act, ranchers had to struggle, scramble, and compete (sometimes ruinously) for forage. Such practices are no longer necessary. Even in those circumstances, described in earlier chapters, of continued competition for forage, the competition takes place within quite narrowly prescribed limits. Perhaps the greatest administrative success in the implementation of the Taylor Act has been the curtailment of such competition.

What of the success of federal administration and management in stopping "injury to the public lands by preventing overgrazing and soil deterioration?" On the basis of observations and discussions of the Middle Rocky Mountain basins, I am convinced that there is no definitive answer. Literally, no one knows! Objective data are insufficient to permit even a useful judgment to be made. Specific questions that need to be answered are: (1) Is the rate of runoff and soil erosion increasing or decreasing? (2) What effect would changes in vegetative cover have on water and sediment movement rates? (3) What are the trends in density and composition of the vegetation? (4) What are the relationships between grazing practices and vegetation trends?

To supply answers to these questions a major research effort is needed. It should include extensive studies of runoff and characteristics of sediment movement in sample areas widely scattered over the federal range lands. This could not be a short-term program. In many areas appreciable amounts of runoff occur only once a year or once in two or three years. Extensive researches on vegetation trends should accompany the soil and moisture studies. Areas should be subjected to grazing use of various intensities and seasonal distributions to determine the effect on vegetative composition and density. To achieve valid results, the vegetation studies would need to be sustained for a long period in order to eliminate the short run influences of weather, as well as to evaluate the relationships among vegetation, grazing pressures, and weather. Such studies would not represent any innovation in range research; vegetation research programs of exactly this sort are being carried out by several agricultural experiment stations in the intermountain region. But the studies should be more numerous, more intensive, carried on for longer periods, and co-ordinated with soil and moisture studies of the same areas. What are the reasons underlying each of the four recommendations? The recommendation that the number of studies be increased grows out of the almost infinite variety of natural conditions in the grazing areas of the West. Areas with differing slopes, soils, vegetation, and moisture conditions may be expected to react quite differently to a particular grazing practice or combination of practices.

The recommendation that the studies be more intensive implies that there should be a much greater number of variations in grazing practice on different plots. Research now being carried on is too narrow in scope. A common form of grazing pressure study is to handle three plots in identical ways except that one is grazed "heavily," another "lightly," and a third with "medium" pressure. But this type of study ignores important practical questions. Suppose we had three others where all conditions were the same except that the cattle were turned onto the range a month earlier; what would result? Suppose the cattle were turned on the range for a month, then off for a month, then on again? What of sheep-cattle combinations? What if cattle were removed from one plot after a specified period of drought, but were not removed from another? These are all questions of the utmost practical importance in range management, but currently few scientific answers are available.

It is equally important that the experiments run long enough so that the results will reflect the reaction of vegetation to the vicissitudes of weather normally occurring during the course of a decade or two. Short-term results may prove to be quite at variance from those obtained from a longer study.

The fourth recommendation—that the vegetation studies be co-ordinated with the soil and moisture studies—grows out of the decided lack of such co-ordination in many studies attempted thus far. It is commonly assumed that changes in range vegetation will have important effects on the water regime of an area, and consequently will affect sediment movements. But vegetation is just one factor influencing the water regime. Too many researches into grazing-vegetation relationships and into water and sediment conditions have not co-ordinated these two. It may be that in many cases great changes in vegetation will have relatively little effect on the water-soil relationships. In other cases such changes may be of crucial importance. But at present it is not possible to speak with much assurance on these matters. Objective information is urgently needed.

At least three additional types of range research are needed: basic research in the ecology of range vegetation; research in the economic aspects of grazing resources and grazing practices; and research on range reseeding. Basic theoretical research into the ecology of range vegetation would almost certainly prove necessary in order to make a sensible interpretation of the results from the studies of vegetation-grazing pressure relationships described above. Moreover, it might point to new avenues of inquiry, as well as to cheaper, faster, and more effective ways of conducting the applied researches already envisioned.

Of immediate interest to the western range livestock industry would be studies dealing with the economic aspects of grazing practices and range vegetation. Such studies would not need to be so extensive as those referred to previously; some data exist already and many of the analytical tools have already been developed by agricultural economists.

Research in range reseeding may eventually turn out to be of the greatest importance. The relatively few experiments conducted thus far have received such widespread publicity that few persons are aware of how meager in sum total such efforts have been. Far more extensive studies are needed. Not only should there be reseeding experiments with many more types of grass, but the experiments should go forward on a variety of sites, with the reseeded plots subjected to different kinds and levels of grazing pressure, and the studies continuing sufficiently long to expose the plots to a wide variety of precipitation conditions.[4] Some reseeded ranges flourish for a few years, but then the introduced grasses die out rapidly, leaving the range in poorer condition than previously. The grasses in other reseeded ranges are not able, even initially, to compete successfully with native plants. This is partly related to grazing pressure, but little is known of such relationships. The economics of range reseeding is of critical importance and should also be studied in conjunction with the ecological aspects of reseeding.

It may be objected that the foregoing recommendation for a major research effort in the fields of range ecology and economics constitutes a typical academic response—survey a problem and then recommend additional research. However, some other major portions of the federal range management program need not wait for the results of the recommended ecological and economic research in order to go forward; but federal

[4] For a discussion of the preliminary work necessary before range reseeding experiments can go forward see John L. Schwendiman, "Testing New Range Forage Plants," *Grasslands,* American Association for the Advancement of Science *Publication* No. 53 (1959).

range grazing management cannot be administered on a rational and scientific basis unless it is guided by the results of such research. According to the wording of the Taylor Act itself, the justification for federal management is the stabilization of the livestock industry and the prevention of undesirable soil and water movement on the land. Until we have scientific data on the matters described above, range management must remain an art or a series of political maneuvers.

It may be further objected that our knowledge of range ecology, range economics, and soil and moisture relationships is more extensive than has been intimated. Certainly great advances have been made in the past twenty years. One of the ranking BLM administrators in the Middle Rocky Mountain basins writes: "We must disagree with your statement that too little is known about the practice of range reseeding and that additional research is necessary. There has been a considerable amount of research on reseeding which we feel is applicable to Wyoming grazing districts. . . ." Of course, it is possible for experienced BLM technicians to make some judgments (and doubtless accurate ones) concerning certain aspects of the various range management problems. A range on which vegetation is flourishing and where plant litter is widespread and undisturbed by water movement can be recognized and interpreted by any competent range manager; but he will not have adequate data to enable him to predict with any certainty how the area would respond to various kinds of range reseeding measures. At the opposite extreme, a competent range manager can tell almost at a glance that vegetation on an area has been severely abused and depleted and that there has been excessive runoff, sediment movement, and erosion. But he cannot forecast with much accuracy how the vegetation would respond to a 25 per cent, 50 per cent, or 90 per cent cut in grazing intensity, and he would have even less idea of how increases in vegetation density would affect future hydrologic conditions. My interpretations of range experience in the Middle Rocky Mountain basins are in agreement with those of E. A. Coleman: "There is need for research of a more quantitative nature. For example, grazing intensity must be expressed in quantitative terms that can be related to the erosion and runoff susceptibility of various kinds of soil in various places."[5]

Until some quantification of these range relationships is possible, range management and administration must be guided largely by precedent, guess, and political pressures. When a rancher opposes a reduction in his

[5] E. A. Colman, *Vegetation and Watershed Management* (New York: Ronald Press, 1953), p. 310.

range use on the grounds that the range is in as good condition as could be expected and that there is little or no erosion on his allotment, a BLM technician may know that the statements are wrong qualitatively but he would find it almost impossible to produce any objective quantitative data to substantiate either his estimates of current range condition or his predictions concerning the effects of grazing reductions on vegetation or runoff conditions.

Such extensive range research on grazing lands of low productivity would certainly be costly in comparison to the value of the land on which it was carried out. However, the results would be more or less applicable to all the tens of millions of acres of federal grazing lands in the West, and would continue to be useful and applicable so long as range grazing and erosion control were aspects of land use in the West.

It would seem imperative that the federal government undertake this research promptly so that scientific management can be put into practice on all federal land at the earliest possible moment. The federal government continues to urge the nation's farmers, ranchers, and forest owners to manage their properties rationally, scientifically, and conservatively, but on its own vast public domain, land use is guided, in considerable part, by little more than a resolution of political forces.

Improving Range Management

In the preceding section it was carefully pointed out that it is entirely feasible to make useful qualitative judgments concerning range conditions and range grazing practices, even though knowledge is insufficient to make more precise determinations. In fairness to the BLM it must be said that the bureau, though lacking adequate data to manage the range scientifically, knows how to manage it considerably better than it now is being managed. In this section the principal causes for the present relatively unsatisfactory range grazing pattern will be reviewed and some suggestions made for its improvement.

Unquestionably the Bureau of Land Management's political weakness on both the congressional and the departmental level is the most important single reason why the bureau and its predecessors have never instituted the grazing pattern the bureau's technicians would like to see. On the congressional level the bureau has almost no supporters, except in a limited number of cases where its interests exactly coincide with those of the western range livestock industry or the western tourist industry (particularly the segment catering to hunters). It has been repeatedly pointed out both in this study and elsewhere that the western range livestock industry is extraordinarily effective in enlisting wholehearted and strenuous congressional support of its position in any disagreements with the BLM. No western pressure group feels very strongly that its interests are identical with those of the BLM. Public domain lands in the Middle Rocky Mountain basins are generally of minor importance as watershed lands and are relatively unimportant in the tourist trade. Consequently the BLM has found it difficult if not impossible to build support for its program which might counterbalance the opposing political power of the stockmen. Eastern congressmen have exhibited sustained interest only in the budgetary aspects of the BLM and consequently it has never been possible to enlist much in the way of eastern congressional support.

The grazing affairs and fees of the BLM are only one part of the total activities of that bureau and are an even less important portion of the total functions of the Department of Interior. The latter has a tremendous stake in the West, and it will not jeopardize its huge reclamation and other programs in order to defend staunchly the interests of one relatively minor division of a single bureau. Consequently, the Grazing Service and the BLM have never been able to resist successfully the political pressures that could be developed against them by the western range livestock ranchers.[6]

From the standpoint of range administration, the political weakness of the old Grazing Service and the BLM has had two unfortunate effects. In the first place, it has obliged these agencies to operate with wholly insufficient personnel. As noted previously, the budget of the BLM has roughly tripled since 1952. Whether the current staff of the grazing division of the BLM is adequate in size is a question that cannot be answered unequivocally. It depends almost entirely on what managerial duties are to be undertaken and upon the intensity of management. In the Middle Rocky Mountain basins the various technicians believe that the present staffs are adequate; the feeling is that it will take a long time to get range use organized and stabilized, but that the present staffs could do it. All such estimates are based on particular assumptions concerning the size of the task.

A second major weakness of the BLM resulting from its political vulnerability lies in the necessity for it to follow an extremely soft line in its dealings with the ranchers whose operations on the federal lands it is supposed to be regulating. In the chapters on Taylor Act administration in the various basins of the Middle Rockies, it was emphasized repeatedly

[6] I have already recounted briefly the unfortunate political history of the Grazing Service and the BLM to about 1950 (see pp. 76–80 and note).

that changes in grazing intensity, grazing pattern, period of use, or stock distribution which BLM personnel recommend are postponed, held in abeyance, or profoundly modified if the affected ranchers oppose them strongly enough. At least two factors contribute to this situation. One is the lack of scientific data to buttress the BLM's position; but the major factor is the bureau's political weakness. It is unnecessary to reiterate the information on this point presented in earlier chapters, but perhaps two additional pieces of evidence, somewhat indirect and suggestive, will be revealing. In discussing this matter with a high-ranking official of the BLM, I cited to him one case after another in which it seemed to me that political pressure or the threat of political reprisal had caused the BLM to refrain from taking some action that the technicians were convinced should be taken. Finally, he said, in effect: we both know that in the past political pressure against the bureau has been devastatingly effective; in the light of that experience we are, of course, extremely sensitive to political pressure. You would be too. This was a point which I was entirely willing to concede. Again, in commenting on an early draft of part of this volume the Wyoming State Supervisor of the BLM wrote: "It is not true that we have little power to effect grazing reductions and, in fact, in recent months we have successfully *negotiated* a number of quite heavy reductions."[7] (Italics mine.) The word "negotiated" seems revealing here, because it expresses, in my view, the managerial situation. On occasion the BLM technicians can persuade ranchers to reduce range use or make other grazing changes; but if persuasion proves impossible, such changes are not likely to be made. Rarely is a change put through over strong rancher opposition. Whether this is a desirable state of affairs is not for the moment the issue.

The relationships between the BLM and western ranchers are also biased in a way favorable to the ranchers by (1) the amendment to the Taylor Act which required all ranking officials of the BLM from 1936 to 1946 to be bona fide residents of one of the western states for at least one year prior to their appointments to such positions, (2) by the recommendation in the Taylor Act that the Civil Service Commission give consideration to the "practical range experience in public-land States of the persons found eligible for appointment." Most of these appointees are still staff members of the BLM. A degree in range management is a requirement for many technical positions in the BLM, the result being that nearly all the technicians are hired from agricultural colleges of the west-

[7] Letter from Ed Pierson to the author dated June 17, 1958.

ern states. Some BLM staff members are former ranchers, while others are ranchers' sons. Nearly all are westerners. Consequently, there is among most BLM personnel a strong feeling of identification and solidarity with the ranching interests, and a latent feeling of being westerners as opposed to easterners. So basic and pervasive is this identification with the range livestock ranching industry that many members of the bureau in all probability are wholly unaware of it most of the time. Since much of their time is spent in "negotiating" with ranchers about one problem or another, they probably feel consciously antagonistic toward the latter more often than otherwise; but such differences are analogous to quarrels within a family. Fundamentally the point of view of both parties is the same.

Local BLM officials are quite probably strongly affected by adverse social pressures on themselves and their families. Most BLM offices are located in small western towns whose culture and livelihood are largely oriented to the range livestock industry. Public opinion is entirely that of the ranching interests. Consequently, a district manager who strongly antagonizes the local livestock interest will soon find himself and his family largely isolated from the social life of the community. Few managers or staff members experience this social disapproval, because they rarely antagonize the rancher community.

Repeatedly in discussions of range regulation, management, and administration, BLM technicians revealed their virtually complete identification with the ranchers whose use of the federal ranges they were ostensibly regulating. Many illustrations could be given, but only one need be cited. To a senior official of the BLM I suggested that the bureau's present practice of assigning exclusive individual allotments to ranchers might, if the allotments were allowed to stand undisturbed for long periods, confer a strong proprietary right in these allotments. This I tended to regard as a highly unfavorable development. "Oh, yes, I feel sure it would," he responded cheerfully, apparently discerning nothing undesirable about a rancher's obtaining proprietary rights in a piece of federal land through a purely administrative decision.

In the foregoing discussion it was probably not difficult to detect a definite bias of the writer's in favor of stronger and more positive control and management of the range by the BLM, a bias against any diminution of the federal government's complete control of its property, and a bias against the acquisition by ranchers of any legal rights or claims in the public domain that they did not previously enjoy; biases which are here explicitly acknowledged.

Insofar as closer control of the Taylor lands by the BLM is desirable, how can it be brought about? One obvious move would be for the BLM to modify its policy of hiring westerners almost exclusively. If a few graduates of eastern departments of botany, forestry schools, conservation departments, or agricultural engineering departments were added to the staffs of the grazing divisions at the beginning technical levels, they would be able to learn range management long before they reached positions of influence and responsibility, and would have an opportunity in the meantime to introduce a different point of view and thus to modify the somewhat monolithic philosophy which now holds undisputed sway in the bureau.

Another change that would undoubtedly strengthen the BLM's program and stiffen its attitude on range management and organization would be an increase in the bureau's political power and strength. But under present conditions there seems little likelihood that this will come to pass. The range livestock interests are so powerful politically in the western states (if unopposed by other western interests) as to make it virtually certain that western congressmen will be highly responsive to their requests. The only other possible political support must come from the East.

For more than a quarter-century, proposals have been made that the Bureau of Land Management and the lands it administers be transferred to the Department of Agriculture and combined with the Forest Service into a new agency called the Forest and Range Service. The most redoubtable of these proposals was made by the Hoover Commission in 1949.[8]

The commission majority recommended that the BLM be merged with the Forest Service and transferred to the Department of Agriculture. A minority also recommended merger, but wanted to locate the new agency in the Interior Department. Another minority also recommended merger, but advocated placing the merged agency in a new Department of Natural Resources. The principal arguments that have been advanced for consolidation are as follows: (1) Many national forest grazing lands lie in close proximity to Taylor lands and are used for the same purposes. (2) Many ranchers graze their livestock on national forest land at certain times of the year and on Taylor grazing land at other times; it is alleged that increased efficiency would result if the lands were leased from a single agency. (3) It is asserted that the current arrangement involves wasteful duplication of staff, services, office space, and administrative parapher-

[8] *Commission on Organization of the Executive Branch of the Government, Department of Interior,* a report to the Congress, March, 1949.

nalia, and wastes a rancher's time by making him deal with two agencies, obtain two or more permits, pay two different fees, and learn and follow two sets of regulations.

The proponents of locating the new combined agency within the Department of Agriculture maintain that grazing is an agricultural enterprise, and that the Department of Agriculture already possesses the necessary research facilities and staffs to investigate problems connected with the grazing industry. Persons advocating that the combined agency be placed elsewhere have asserted that range management is not agriculture in the ordinary sense and that the handling of the Taylor lands involves a host of problems which lie outside the traditional purview of the Agriculture Department.

All proposals to merge the Forest Service and the BLM (or its predecessors) have met with violent and implacable opposition from the various western livestock associations; opposition engendered largely by the assumption that the proposed consolidated agency would be dominated by the Forest Service. It is assumed that if the two organizations were merged under the leadership of the Forest Service, control of grazing on the public domain would tighten and the intensity of management would increase. This conclusion is substantiated by a comparison of current range management by the two agencies. In general the Forest Service, as custodian of the national forest lands, assumes that it is its duty to foster the use of these lands for a wide variety of purposes by various groups of people. Forage production is just one function of the national forests, in many cases not a particularly important one. Even on lands where forage production is of primary importance, the Forest Service will not necessarily prefer that the forage be grazed by domestic stock rather than by wildlife. Consequently, control of grazing on national forest allotments has always been tighter and more restrictive than control on the Taylor lands. The Forest Service is not insensible to the welfare of the western range livestock industry, but when a choice must be made between reducing grazing pressure or possibly damaging the forest land under its jurisdiction, the Forest Service will favor the function that it regards as primary, namely, care of the forest lands. The service may not reduce grazing pressures as rapidly or as drastically as it would like, but it never loses sight of its goals and, over the decades, has succeeded in steadily lessening the pressure on most of its lands and increasing its control over grazing practices and patterns. Moreover, the Forest Service has been outstandingly successful in fending off political pressure generated by the western range livestock industry against grazing reductions. It has been able to mobilize counterpressures from water users (urban, industrial, and irrigation) interested in maintaining the watershed qualities of the national forest lands, from wildlife interests, from tourist and recreation interests, and from eastern conservation interests. Of course, the Forest Service is by no means wholly insensitive to political pressure. When attacks by livestock interests are particularly active and strong, the service may slow an unpopular program or even halt it temporarily. But on the whole it modifies its course remarkably little under such pressure. The ineffectiveness of the western range livestock industry in exerting any substantial influence on Forest Service policies is exposed most revealingly by the violence of rancher opposition to any projected control of public domain lands by the service. The ranching interests anticipate that Forest Service management would produce grazing pressure reductions, greater federal control over grazing practices, and a sharp diminution of rancher influence on management of the public grazing lands. It is probable that they are right in their expectations. The political power relationships between the ranchers and the Forest Service would not be changed by the proposed merger of the Forest Service with the BLM. Consequently, if the end in view is to increase governmental control over grazing activities on the Taylor lands, a powerful argument can be made that this would be facilitated by transfer of such lands to the Forest Service.

As compared with that of the Forest Service, Bureau of Land Management administration is much looser, more flexible, and more permissive. All actions pertaining to range management are taken after prolonged negotiations and discussions with the individual ranchers concerned. The closest collaboration is maintained with grazing district advisory boards. In fact, the effectiveness of BLM administration in a district is dependent almost as much on the character of the district board as on the talents of the BLM personnel. Moreover, the BLM cannot be insensible to the effects of its actions on the range livestock ranchers; the Taylor Act not only provides for protection of the public domain, but also directs that the livestock industry dependent on public grazing land be stabilized. It was pointed out earlier that the original scheme of administration envisaged the closest co-operation between the officials and the ranchers of each grazing district. In addition, the close personal ties of many BLM officials and technicians with the livestock industry, and the fact that almost all of them are westerners, have inevitably assured sympathetic consideration of the ranchers' viewpoint on nearly all matters.

It is not here recommended, however, that the BLM be merged with the Forest Service. There are several reasons for this view. First, merger of itself would do nothing to solve the major land management problems faced by the BLM. The land tenure pattern would be no less complex. The lack of range survey data would not be less stringent. Range research would still be a pressing problem.

Of greater importance, however, is the fact that most of the public domain lands have physical and economic characteristics greatly different from national forest lands. The latter even if they are grasslands are very likely to have high watershed values, high damage potential if allowed to erode, and many of them have major recreational values. The BLM lands are primarily useful for grazing. Moreover, they are more intimately associated with the western range livestock industry than are the national forest lands. The Bureau of Land Management works closely with the livestock ranchers and makes the condition of the ranges and the welfare of the range livestock industry the two most important considerations of the management program. This emphasis seems appropriate in the management of the Taylor lands. The Forest Service as presently constituted gives only minor attention to the problems of the range livestock industry, as should be the case with the kind of lands the Forest Service currently administers. Thus, the proposal to merge the two organizations is not here opposed, because the new agency would be less vulnerable politically than is the BLM at present; but neither is it recommended, because the bureau's approach to the range administration problem is more appropriate for lands that are primarily useful for grazing.

Saunderson has suggested that lands whose principal characteristic is their silt production might be turned over to the Soil Conservation Service of the Department of Agriculture.[9] Various other proposals for reorganization of federal land management have been made. Clawson and Held suggested a federal corporation to manage all federal rural lands.[10] Their proposal obviates one problem not ordinarily considered in reorganization proposals; that is, what to do with the BLM's functions of land survey and mineral leasing if control of surface use is transferred to another bureau or merged into a new agency. Under Clawson and Held's federal corporation these functions would all remain together in a single agency. Presumably such a corporation would somewhat strengthen the political hand of local administrators, but otherwise it would do little to solve problems on the local level. An agency of such size might be expected to take relatively little interest in the problems of the individual range livestock rancher.

[9] Mont H. Saunderson, *Western Land and Water Use* (Norman: University of Oklahoma Press, 1950).

[10] Clawson and Held, *op. cit.*, pp. 347–60.

It is rather unprofitable, however, to ponder the relative merits of various forms of bureaucratic organization without first specifying the duties to be carried out and the objectives to be fulfilled. In the case of a going concern such as the BLM it is possible to approach the matter in at least two ways. It may be assumed, on the one hand, that the program of the BLM will remain what it has been in the past; or, on the other hand, a new program may be postulated. In the following sections the federal government's experience in Taylor Act administration in the Middle Rocky Mountain basins will be summarized and then some conclusions drawn and some recommendations made concerning the future program of the BLM; first, under the assumption that the managerial situation will remain about as it is now, and second, under certain postulated changed circumstances.

Simplifying the Land Tenure Pattern

Assume that the present general situation with respect to the public domain lands will continue indefinitely; that is, that the Taylor Act will continue to be administered by the BLM and that all the other relevant land laws pertaining to management and use will remain in force (particularly those pertaining to alienation of public lands). What, then, are the principal problems to be solved? And what solutions present themselves?

Among the purely local[11] factors affecting the organization and management of the Taylor lands, none creates greater difficulties than the complex pattern of land tenure prevailing in so many areas of the Intermountain West. A complex land tenure pattern is not an insuperable obstacle to orderly and efficient range practices,[12] nor will a relatively simple pattern insure that the grazing pattern will be orderly; but, in general, difficulties of range organization increase with increasing complexity of land tenure arrangements. A complex tenure pattern makes it difficult to develop water sources satisfactorily, to detect and prevent trespass, and to establish satisfactory allotments. Fencing costs are likely to be increased. In case of disagreement with ranchers, it is practically impossible for the government to refuse, or even threaten to refuse, the use of its range. In case of disagreements that cannot be resolved, the federal lands are apt to bear the brunt of range abuse during the period of disagreement.

Consolidation of ownership has proved not just difficult, but nearly impossible. Section 8 of the Taylor Act makes it possible to simplify the

[11] Political power relationships that affect range management are not primarily "local" in nature.

[12] As demonstrated by experience in the Bridger Basin and Upper Green River Basin.

land tenure pattern by the exchange of federal land for private or state land. The rarity of such exchanges in each of the Middle Rocky Mountain basins has been noted previously. The total acreage of completed exchanges represents only a minute fraction of the interspersed lands. At the past rate it would require decades to consolidate any substantial part of the intermingled tracts.[13] The fact the few exchanges have been made leads to the conclusion that neither of the two groups concerned (the BLM or the ranchers) is particularly interested in land exchanges and consolidation of properties.

Section 14 of the Taylor Act provides that isolated pieces of federal land up to 760 acres in size may, under certain circumstances, be sold to adjacent landholders or others. Such sales have not been brisk in the Middle Rocky Mountain basins. The BLM has been so seriously understaffed for long periods that its personnel could scarcely keep abreast of routine management problems, and had no time to initiate and carry through sales of isolated tracts. But, ranchers have generally exhibited little or no interest in purchasing isolated tracts. Ordinarily they could be induced to buy the land only if it threatened to fall into other private hands.

Three factors seem to account in large part for the almost complete stagnation of the BLM's program to consolidate ownerships. (1) No one within the BLM is responsible for the program of land exchanges and sales except the district manager, who has so many other responsibilities that Section-8 and Section-14 actions generally are crowed out of a busy schedule. (2) Both the sale and the exchange procedures founder on a reef of inflexibility. (3) Neither the ranchers nor the BLM are especially interested in simplifying the land tenure pattern. It seems fair to assume that under existing procedures the pace of exchange will not be speeded, even though simplification of the land tenure pattern appears to be a highly desirable line of action. The ensuing section offers a plan designed to overcome these difficulties.

A Plan for Land Ownership Consolidation

As a first step in the proposed program for land tenure consolidation, it is advocated that one BLM employee be appointed in each state whose sole responsibility it would be to administer the program. He would work closely with the local district offices, but would have the necessary free-

13 Exchanges of federal land for state land were brisk for a time, but only because the federal land involved was more valuable on an acre-for-acre basis than the state land. When the federal government began eventually to insist that all traded lands be equal in value, exchanges with the states virtually stopped.

dom of action to work effectively on a state-wide basis. Congress would appropriate or authorize to be taken from grazing receipts a relatively small sum of money (perhaps a few million dollars) to be used as a revolving fund for land consolidation throughout the entire Intermountain West. This fund would be used primarily for buying and selling range land, but it could also be used to supply flexibility to the exchange provisions of Section 8 of the Taylor Act.

Suppose, by way of illustration, that the land consolidation officer of the BLM were to enter into negotiations for the exchange of two sections of federal land for two sections of private land, it being agreed that the federal sections were worth 50 cents per acre more than the privately owned sections. Under current Section-8 procedures the exchange could not go forward unless unequal amounts of land were exchanged, since the BLM employee would not accept responsibility for the financial loss to the federal government that would result. But under the plan here proposed the consolidation officer would be able to accept the exchange, since the owner of the private land would pay an additional $640 to compensate the government for the difference in value. Conversely, if the federal land to be exchanged were worth 50 cents per acre less than the private land, the land consolidation officer could pay out of the revolving fund the required amount to make up the deficiency in value of the government's acres.

Over a period of years the number of acres bought by the federal government could be kept approximately in balance with the acreage sold, and the quantity of money spent for purchases could be balanced approximately by the returns from sales.

Large segments of public opinion in the United States would be opposed to any program calling for a large net dispersal of public domain lands. Opposition would be particularly strong to any "giveaway" program. On the other hand, bitter opposition would be aroused in the West if large-scale extensions of federal ownership were proposed. The plan here advocated would largely circumvent these difficulties, since the net amount of federally owned land would remain approximately the same and no sizable monetary loss to the government would result. But federal, state, and private holdings would be consolidated. If the final acreages and the final monetary fund were about the same as at the beginning of the program, the presumption would be that the land purchases, sales, and exchanges had about balanced out, although a regular exchange of better quality federal land for poorer quality private and state land could be concealed in such a bookkeeping system.

In order to avoid this latter possibility, the BLM could be asked to report each year to the Senate Committee on Interior and Insular Affairs and to the House Committee on Public Lands. These committees would require data on the number of acres bought, sold, and traded (with a map showing their location) and would ask for a statement concerning receipts and disbursements of money. The committees might retain an independent agency to review the financial results, or might attempt the review themselves.

Clearly the land consolidation officers would need to act rapidly and efficiently in order to keep unit consolidation costs low. If an officer whose salary and expenses were $20,000 per year succeeded in exchanging 200,000 acres of land per year, the resulting exchange costs of 10 cents per acre might appear reasonable to the Congress and a good investment. However, if he exchanged only 2,000 acres per year, the cost per acre would be $10, and it certainly would appear more economical to Congress simply to give away some federal land and purchase other acreages at the market price (if it were considered desirable to maintain an unchanged total acreage of federal land).

As long as the adjacent landowner is given the option of buying isolated tracts at no more than three times the appraised price or the highest bid, ranchers will exhibit little interest in purchasing or exchanging for isolated tracts, because they would rather rent the land at its current low lease rate than own it; especially since they know that they have priority to purchase the land at a limited price. However, if such preference could be at the option of the BLM, ranchers might be more receptive to land exchange proposals for fear that if they did not purchase the land it might be sold to someone else.

No one can say whether the plan would succeed. Certainly it could not be more ineffectual than the present program, and it seems to incorporate features that would overcome the principal difficulties now being encountered in land exchanges. It would certainly fail unless it were carefully made clear at the outset that it was neither a plan for net disposal nor for net acquisition of land by the federal government.

Intensified Range Inspection

The federal government as a lessor of grazing land should unquestionably intensify the inspection of its range—inspection, that is, both of range use and range condition. On the large leases—the Rock Springs lease and Carter lease—in the Bridger Basin, the grazing associations find it advantageous to employ their own range riders during the period of grazing on the leased land. Nearly all of the larger ranches and many medium-sized ranches employ range riders or herders on their relatively limited acreages. The Forest Service has a carefully planned program of range inspection. In all cases the inspection has a dual purpose: to observe range grazing practices, and to inspect the condition of the range vegetation and soils. Often such inspection makes it possible to correct maldistribution of stock before serious damage is done, or to discover promptly range damage due to faulty herding, poor distribution, overstocking, or excessive trailing, and then to bring a quick halt to these undesirable practices.

Some formal range inspection is now being carried on the by BLM district offices in the Middle Rocky Mountain basins; that is, tours are made solely to inspect the range. Much additional range inspection is accomplished during numerous trips for other purposes. Nevertheless, in sum, current range inspection is clearly inadequate. Even if inspection were intensified, the BLM might not feel in a position to take swift and decisive action to correct all the undesirable situations discovered. But probably if unfavorable conditions and practices were accurately known and were called to the ranchers' attention, the effects on range practices would be salutary.

Two changes in BLM practice would sharply increase the effectiveness of range inspection. If each office had one man assigned to range inspection at all times, the general quality of range supervision would rise sharply, since the informal inspection now made by various BLM personnel in the course of other duties would continue and augment the full-time activities of the designated range inspector. The technician assigned to range inspection of the entire district could make special spot checks where there was reason to suppose an unsatisfactory situation was developing. In open range lands where conditions are relatively homogeneous over broad areas (such as those found in the Middle Rocky Mountain basins), an inspection which covered four square miles per day would be an intensive and thorough one; far more intensive than most range inspections made currently. At this rate a full-time range inspector could survey carefully more than half a million acres per year and thus inspect an entire district in a period of four or five years. The recommendation that one man be assigned to range inspection at all times does not imply that the same man would necessarily perform this duty throughout the entire year.

Occasionally it is desirable to inspect quickly a substantial portion of a grazing district. To accomplish this objective the most satisfactory method is by aerial survey. One helicopter or plane per state would be sufficient. In the Middle Rocky Mountain basins an ordinary light plane based at Lander in the Shoshone–Wind River Basin could reach all the other basins by approximately an hour's flight. It could be used for a day or two to carry out extensive inspections in one district and then be transferred to another. In case of an emergency in a particular district, such as a severe range fire, the plane could remain in the affected area until the emergency was over. At the very least it seems worthwhile to experiment with a plane for such use in a single state. Similarly, the practice of regularly assigning a man to full-time range inspection could be tried in one or two districts as a test before extending the practice to all districts.

Any program for more efficient and complete range inspection will be most useful if prompt and decisive remedial action is taken to correct unsatisfactory conditions revealed by the inspection. It would have a desirable effect on the ranchers' range practices if they knew that a careful and accurate inspection of the grazing situation might be made at any time. It has been pointed out previously that most range inspections are made *ex post facto;* that is, excessive trailing is known only from hearsay, excessive numbers of livestock grazed by a rancher are observable only from their effects on the vegetation or the soil, or from other ranchers' reports, trespass is investigated most commonly by following trails and areas recently grazed. If these undesirable practices were observed or photographed, it would be difficult for the rancher concerned to dispute the allegations and would lend more force to BLM complaints of range practices not in accord with the permittee's lease or the Federal Range Code.

Range Fees

The problem of range grazing fees is a difficult one. Under the current fee scale, public domain forage is such a bargain that pressure is strong to acquire and retain the right to harvest it. However, almost no permits are available except by purchase; all the forage on the public domain has already been leased. In preceding sections it was shown that the difference between the grazing fees and the full value of the forage has been capitalized into the value of the permits. That these values are real and substantial is shown clearly by the fact that Taylor permits are accepted at a bank as security for loans. These valuable Taylor grazing permits were distributed to the original permittees not on any monetary basis, but solely on the twin bases of priority of use and possession of commensurable land. The low fees thus constituted a gift or subsidy to the original recipients. Many of the leases have changed hands since the original permits were issued. To the new lessee the underpriced forage represents no bargain; he pays the market price by virtue of the interest on the money borrowed to secure the grazing rights or the interest foregone on the cash which he has invested in the purchase of the permit. It is more accurate to think of the original underpricing of Taylor leases as a gift to the original permittees rather than a subsidy, because low fees confer no advantage on the purchaser of a permit—only on the original recipient who obtained it free.

The fact that the original permits were gifts that could be sold makes the problem of modifying the fees so difficult. If the fees were raised to the level of their true value, the government's original gift would be retracted, but in all cases where the permit had been sold the gift would be reclaimed not from the original recipient but from a third party who had bought the lease in good faith and had paid its full value.

Nevertheless, it is difficult not to conclude that the sensible course is to raise the grazing fees to their full value. Numerous advantages would result, and the only loss would be the capitalized value of the original gifts.

If low grazing fees conferred some permanent advantage on the range livestock rancher, that would constitute a strong argument for continuing them. But they do not. Any purchaser of a lease pays full value for the forage. He simply pays a large part of the cost in the purchase price of the lease itself. In fact, it might be argued that the rancher is worse off because of the low fees. Under current practice most of his costs are fixed investments in leases. Even if he takes non-use he must still pay the interest on his investment. If grazing fees were high they would be the only leasing cost, and by taking non-use a rancher could curtail his costs far more sharply during periods of stress than he is now able to do.

Numerous other advantages would result from higher fees. The most important would be a reduction of grazing pressure on the range. To some extent every rancher has a choice between obtaining maximum weight gain per cow, maximum forage consumption per acre, or some intermediate combination of these two extremes. When grazing license prices are high (representing high fixed costs) and grazing fees are seriously underpriced, there is a strong tendency to place a maximum number of stock on the range. If fees were higher, there would be a tendency to put fewer cattle on the range, to increase their average weight gain, and thus to pay lower total fees. This would have a beneficial effect on range conditions in many range areas, and above all, it would stop the needless and uneconomic abuse of many ranges resulting from the desire of many poor ranchers with inadequate feed resources to make maximum use of the "cheap" forage of the public lands.

Many ranchers take almost continuous non-use for a significant part of their permitted livestock numbers, but fiercely resist all suggestions that these excessive numbers (which they know to be excessive) be cut, because of their desire to retain the potential sales value of the larger permits. But as grazing fees approached their true value, the pressure to retain excessive range permits would weaken.

There seems to be no way to eliminate the inequity that would result from substantially raising the grazing fees. The mistake was to set the initial fees to low, and it is now too late in many cases to withdraw the gift from the original recipient. But to perpetuate the mistake would be foolish. It seems reasonable therefore to propose that the BLM begin to make substantial increases in its grazing fees, but with no rancher having his grazing fees raised from the current rates until he had used his permits for a period of ten years at the old low rates either prior or subsequent to the change of policy. That is, any rancher who had held a permit for any part of ten years would be assessed a new higher fee immediately upon the ten-year maturity of the lease. The reasoning, of course, is that any lease purchaser who had been receiving the extremely cheap federal forage for a period of ten years would have been largely compensated financially for the purchase price of the lease.

Substantial fee increases would certainly be opposed by the livestock industry; but in the long run the bona fide range livestock rancher would benefit rather than lose from substantial increases in grazing fees. Higher fees would eliminate some inefficient, uneconomic, submarginal, or speculative operators. It would tend to lessen the demand for range rights from irrigation farmers who might well decide that under the new rates their cattle would be better off on the home ranch than grazing the range.[14] Higher fees would greatly improve the competitive position of the more efficient range livestock ranchers.

The current underpricing of federal range permits is so substantial that any proposal to bring fees into line with lease values in a reasonable length of time will inevitably seem unrealistic and even startling to many people. A fairly conservative procedure would be to raise fees five cents per year for three years. They might remain at the new level for two or three years to allow other lease and land prices to become adjusted, and to allow the ranchers partially to fit their practices and plans to the new situation.

[14] It must be noted, however, that sharp increases in the price of federal forage might temporarily have a depressing effect on sales and rentals of private range land. Such land now brings a high price or rent because ranchers depending mostly on federal forage can afford to pay a premium price for private grazing to round out, balance, and supplement their relatively inelastic supply of government range.

The fee situation could then be restudied in the light of experience with the increased fees.

It has often been proposed that federal grazing permits be offered for bid. Permits would be issued for periods of five or ten years (as term permits currently are issued), but the lease would go to the highest bidder. The theory is that the federal grazing would then go to the person who had the maximum use for it or who could use it most efficiently (as evidenced by the fact that he could afford to pay the highest price for it). In theory, this idea has much in its favor, but in practice it would be an undesirable method of assigning grazing leases in the Intermountain West. It assumes a relatively free and competitive market—a condition which does not exist for users of the western public domain. As shown in previous chapters, the arrangement of property boundaries, terrain features, water developments, and other local circumstances often make it more convenient, profitable, and efficient for a particular rancher to use a piece of range than it is for any other rancher to use it. In addition, some ranchers are in a position to make it difficult or impossible for any other rancher to use certain federal properties. Consequently, a system of auction for federal range permits would usually give an advantage to the big rancher On federal lands whose use he could effectively interdict he would bid very low, while at the same time making very high bids for ranges where competition was keen. The small rancher would find himself in an unenviable position. In general the lands he could use most effectively would be those most accessible (i.e., not easily interdicted by another rancher), and bidding for such lands would be spirited. Certainly on the average the small rancher would have to pay substantially more for range forage than his larger competitor. Moreover, in many cases a combination of large ranchers might be devastatingly effective in preventing competition through an agreement among themselves to debar small operators from certain sections of the public range.

Reorganizing the Range Use Pattern

With respect to the organization of range use two firm conclusions are offered, but no recommendations. The first conclusion is that joint use of the range in large blocks is, in most areas, the most effective and sensible way to utilize it. Numerous lines of evidence indicate that this is so. It is indicated by the numerous advantages that large ranches have over small ones.[15] A ranch with exclusive use of a large block of range land

---

[15] They also have relative disadvantages, but since the latter mostly do not pertain to range use, they will not be considered here.

can achieve notable economies by subdividing it into a few large pastures, to be used for rotation grazing or for deferred grazing made necessary by range reseeding or other special circumstance. A relatively small number of water developments, if strategically placed, will give good stock distribution within each large pasture. Furthermore, herding costs per animal on a ranch supporting a large number of cattle will often be low enough to justify the employment of one or more riders to control the herd and thus give better cattle distribution, more effective and even utilization of the range lands (with a consequent improvement in range condition), and faster cattle-weight gains.

Economies of scale can be secured in almost all aspects of range use. If range land is available in large blocks, cattle can be segregated into bands of yearlings, cows and calves, "scrubs," and so on. Better distribution of bulls will be possible. Some economies of scale also apply to sheep ranching, but few sheep ranchers need to be persuaded of the desirability of large allotments and free movement on the range.

In making use of dry range land, small ranching operations have numerous disadvantages and few advantages. Small individual allotments require an excessive amount of fencing. Rotation grazing is not possible unless internal fencing is added, which pushes fencing costs even higher. All cattle allotments, however small, must have a water source within the fenced boundaries or have trailing privileges to a water source. If the small allotment is divided into a number of separate pastures, a source of water must be created within each one—another sharp increase in costs. It is wholly uneconomic to control a small bunch of cattle by herding. Problems of accessibility are commonly increased by small allotments. Frequently it becomes necessary to build access roads or for cattle to be trailed or drifted across properties controlled by other ranchers.

Of the advantages offered by small allotments, the most important by far is independence of action. Each permittee may take any action that he wishes on his allotment without consulting his neighbor. If cattle are unherded, small fenced allotments may give better control than would be the case in large allotments.

Wildlife interests are strongly opposed, indirectly, to small allotments. Such allotments are meaningless unless they are fenced, and thus the creation of numerous small allotments results in a proliferation of fences. It is the fences that rouse opposition. It is believed that they are inimical to the well-being of big game, since they restrict movement and thus make it more difficult for game animals to reach food, escape predators, and survive storm conditions. The whole subject is highly controversial.

The relative merits of small-scale and large-scale operations are most clearly indicated in the actions and aspirations of western range livestock ranchers. It is rare for a large rancher to decrease the size of his operations in order to increase ranch efficiency, whereas most small ranchers are continually striving to enlarge their operations to benefit from the advantages and economies of large-scale ranching.

All the foregoing notwithstanding, however, many ranchers, regardless of how small or large their allotments would be, want individual allotments, and the BLM concurs in this objective.[16] In all of the Middle Rocky Mountain basins there is a strong drive for individual allotments, even on the part of very small cattle ranchers who could expect to receive only tiny allotments.

Because of the numerous manifest advantages of large allotments and large-scale range operations, I should like to be persuaded that the cattle ranchers' preference for individual allotments results from ineffective range organization in the past and unimaginative planning for the future organization, management, and allotment of the range. There is some evidence to support this view, but it does not offer a convincing explanation for the ranchers' attitude. Numerous good reasons for rancher dissatisfaction with large allotments held in common can be adduced. One grave difficulty has been that numerous small cattle ranchers have carried on their operations entirely independently while using a piece of range jointly. Thus they have assured themselves most of the disadvantages of small-scale operation and joint range use without achieving any of the advantages of using the range in extensive blocks. Those ranchers who have formed associations or corporations for common use of the range have achieved all the economies and conveniences of large-scale operation and escape most of the disadvantages of small-scale operation and tiny allotments. The range can be fenced for maximum efficiency of cattle distribution; water is developed more cheaply and efficiently; riders are hired economically; supplies are purchased in bulk; bulls of higher quality are purchased by skilled buyers. The small rancher busy with irrigation farming or off-farm employment can leave his livestock out on the range for months at a time without giving them his personal attention.

Nevertheless, there is evidence that in the Bridger Basin and the Upper Green River Basin organizations of the kind just described are under con-

---

[16] The BLM supports its position by pointing out that ranchers with individual allotments often engage in competition with each other to see who can maintain his range in the best condition.

siderable adverse pressure. The Rock Springs Grazing Association in the Bridger Basin, even though it is an association of sheep grazers, has members who favor splitting the Rock Springs lease into individual allotments. The members of the cattle associations in the Upper Green River are pressing strongly for individual allotments, despite the seeming advantages of their current arrangements. Moreover, nowhere in the Middle Rocky Mountain basins are other associations for joint range use being formed or even considered.

With such strong sentiment favoring them, it is unrealistic for an observer to oppose the delineation of additional individual allotments. But so numerous are the disadvantages of such allotments and so numerous the seeming advantages resulting from large-scale range operations that one cannot support enthusiastically the current trend of thought.

A Long-Range Management Program for the Public Domain

The web of relationships among the land tenure pattern, natural range conditions, and the range livestock industry within the Taylor grazing lands in the Middle Rocky Mountain basins has been described and analyzed in detail in chapters vi to x. In gathering and presenting this material, I have been particularly concerned with its implications for future federal policy. In the previous section an administrative and managerial program for the Taylor lands was proposed and analyzed on the assumption that the status quo will continue permanently. In this concluding section a somewhat broader approach to the problem is attempted and attention is focused on the question of the best possible policy for these lands.

Public opinion in the United States might be construed as indicating a belief that the forces of geography and history have happily conspired to bring about the perfect land tenure pattern in the public domain areas of the West. Evidence to support such an interpretation could be found in the facts that: any move to sell a substantial quantity of federal land or to add to federal holdings by substantial purchases invariably is greeted by a resounding outcry of opposition; and neither western citizens nor the relevant federal agencies show any noticeable interest at present in buying, selling, or trading land. It could, thus, be construed that all important groups concerned are satisfied with the current land pattern. But such a conclusion would seriously misrepresent the true situation.

The land tenure pattern in the Taylor grazing districts and in other parts of the public domain lands is a miserably complicated, nearly unmanageable hodgepodge. It is a haphazard arrangement of properties that has arisen from the interaction of a heterogeneous group of people under a variety of laws made at different times under different circumstances for different purposes. Lands have been acquired under these laws in a pattern adjusted to various physical circumstances, and the acquisition procedures have been further complicated by chance or historical accident. The managerial difficulties of the "checkerboard" lands, in particular, seem almost inspired. Under no circumstances would any rational person have planned a land tenure pattern remotely resembling the one that now exists.

The current remnants of the public domain are the result of a long historical process of picking over. The earliest settlers took the easily irrigable lands, the riparian lands, and lands containing springs. They took mineral lands. Next they began to acquire the best pasture lands, commonly the spring-fall ranges. Watershed lands and timber lands were placed in the national forests, while other federal lands were taken to form the national parks. Power sites were set aside. Lands irrigable under large irrigation projects were withdrawn. What remains is a haphazard array of properties that no one has wanted to acquire or has taken the trouble to acquire. These lands are in a peculiar twilight state of being withdrawn but not reserved. The older laws under which federal land can be transferred to private ownership are still in force and can be used to acquire any tract of unreserved public land, provided the latter has been classified as suitable for withdrawal under the terms of the relevant law. To the older laws for public domain disposal has now been added the Small Tracts Act.

It is easy to forecast the future if current policies are continued. The process of picking over the remaining public domain lands will continue. Ranchers, when they have the money and the inclination, will buy isolated tracts, particularly if they are above average in value. Some lands will be disposed of under the Homestead Act. The Desert Land Act will certainly be used to patent extensive areas of the very best remaining federal range land. And over the course of years the Small Tracts Act will be the means of disposing of millions of areas of land that are desirable for numerous special purposes. When this process has run its course, the public domain will consist solely of land that is virtually useless for any economic purpose. That the process will continue unless something is done to check it is practically inevitable. The land is presently available for not much more than the trouble of going through the legal actions to acquire it. Classification requirements may direct and shape the process, but at times disposal may be looked on more favorably than is now the case. Once a tract of land has been classified as suitable for disposal, it will sooner or later pass into private hands.

There may be nothing wrong with a policy of disposal by citizen selection modified and partially directed by federal classification procedures. There is nothing undesirable about having land in private ownership; most Americans would maintain that it is highly desirable. Perhaps the land most wanted by the citizenry should go into private hands. But the matter may better be approached by asking whether there are valid reasons for the federal government to retain title to the vacant public domain lands now administered under the terms of the Taylor Grazing Act. And the answer here proposed is that the federal government should hold title to lands only in order to achieve specified objectives. Land not primarily useful for legitimate government purposes should be sold.

On the basis of the foregoing considerations, a fourfold management program is recommended for the remaining public domain lands, as follows: (1) the objectives of federal land management to be set forth; (2) lands, both public and private, to be classified according to their utility for achieving federal objectives; (3) land to be bought, sold, and traded pursuant to the classification in order that all lands needed for federal purposes may be brought under federal ownership, and that all lands not serving federal objectives may be made available for private purposes; (4) federal lands then to be managed under a multipurpose arrangement, but with primary purposes taking priority over all others.

OBJECTIVES OF FEDERAL LAND MANAGEMENT TO BE SET FORTH

The question of who is to define the objectives of federal ownership of western land was purposely left unanswered in the first recommendation. The objectives of federal land ownership are to some extent implicit in federal action and policy in the west and in many cases are explicitly stated in statutes.[17] Ideally, perhaps, Congress could set forth a policy statement indicating the legitimate federal objectives in the West and how much land should be devoted to the various purposes. Failing this unlikely development, the Department of Interior could make its own determination of the national policy and shape its program accordingly. Congress could keep the department's programs under surveillance and give directives as deemed necessary.

LAND CLASSIFICATION

In the introductory chapter the critical importance of water and thereby of watersheds to the West was described and analyzed. The federal gov-

17 Clawson and Held, *op. cit.,* argue that management of the public domain for the past quarter-century has been carried out under a policy tacitly agreed to by the ranching interests, the Department of Interior, and Congress.

ernment has undertaken to protect all of the more important watershed lands of the West by putting them into national forests. Federal policy thus seems to assume responsibility for the proper management and administration of lands having important watershed values. In the Middle Rocky Mountain basins (and elsewhere in the West) small areas of Taylor lands have high value as watersheds; such lands should be classified as having greatest utility for this purpose. Generally they are located at relatively high elevations and they are contiguous to or near national forests; consequently it would seem reasonable that they be administered with similar lands in the national forests by the Forest Service. If lands are primarily valuable as watersheds they should be administered with the watershed function paramount. It seems a logical and reasonable extension of the management program for the government to purchase lands in private hands classified as being primarily useful as watersheds. Such a recommendation at first glance seems politically impracticable; but purchase of private land to protect watersheds under a program to rationalize the federal government's land holdings might not encounter insuperable political opposition if the program also involved extensive sale of government lands not classified as primarily useful for any recognized and authorized federal objective.[18]

In the earlier discussions of the Middle Rocky Mountain basins, attention was directed to lands of low grazing capacity and small or negligible water production that, at irregular intervals, slough off thousands of tons of sediment into a major perennial stream. Such lands should be in federal ownership. The principal justification for such ownership lies in the fact that the Bureau of Reclamation has constructed large and expensive dams on most of the major streams of the intermountain region; dams built with a large federal subsidy. The useful life of the reservoirs impounded behind these expensive dams depends upon the rate at which they fill with silt. It is, therefore, directly in the national interest for the federal government to own the areas that are major silt producers in order to control silt movement as effectively as possible and thereby extend the life of mainstream reservoirs. Private owners can scarcely be expected to take more than an indirect interest in problems growing out of silt production from their lands, nor can they be expected either to forego income or to incur any expense in the interests of controlling sedimentation further downstream.

Consequently, all federal lands in the intermountain region so highly erosible that they are major sources of silt should be so classified by the

[18] However, lands with high watershed values are normally excellent spring-fall range and their owners would be reluctant to part with them.

BLM, and on them all grazing of domestic livestock halted; because such land has a vegetation cover that is easily damaged, and the low value of the forage either to ranchers or to the government does not justify even a moderate risk of damaging the vegetation with attendant ill effects on water and silt conditions. Such lands should be closed to any form of private acquisition. Those now in private hands should be brought into federal ownership by purchase or exchange. Once the federal establishment has acquired title to them, grazing should cease, and a research and action program for the control of sediment initiated promptly.

It is the settled policy of the United States government to set aside areas for the sustenance and protection of wildlife, and to encourage production of game for recreational hunting. The amount of land to set aside either wholly or partially for wildlife use is difficult to determine. Present wildlife areas include wildlife refuges, the national parks, and the national forests. The Taylor grazing lands furnish substantial amounts of forage for game animals, as do private ranch lands. No evidence indicates a pressing need for the reservation of additional areas to be used exclusively by wildlife. Nor is there a demonstrated need for an over-all increase in the supply of range forage available to wildlife.[19] If some restricted areas are of critical importance to certain species of wildlife, they may be classified and managed to give wildlife use priority over all possible conflicting uses, including grazing by domestic livestock. Certain areas containing unusual wildlife habitats might be similarly classified as primarily useful for wildlife purposes and closed to private entry.

The federal obligation directly or indirectly to develop facilities for public outdoor recreation is widely accepted. Effective work has been done by the Forest Service and the National Park Service in the areas under their jurisdiction; familiar examples are the camp grounds, cabins, and improved trails that these agencies have developed. Some public domain lands have outstanding recreational characteristics, and should be classified by the BLM as primarily valuable for recreational purposes. Certain areas should be set aside for public use (for example, riparian lands giving public access to fishing streams, or lands especially desirable for public picnic grounds),[20] while lands appearing to be most valuable presently or potentially for private recreational use should be so classified and then

[19] Up to a certain point probably regional income is increased more by wildlife grazing than by domestic stock grazing. Big game hunters will pay substantial sums for hunting privileges over and above their travel and maintenance expenditures in the region.

[20] All public domain lands are currently open for all recreational uses.

sold to individuals under the terms of the Small Tracts Act. Lands made available under the latter act would be closed to patent under other land laws. Such lands could be released for sale in relatively small quantities as demand developed. They might be sold at flat rates, by appraised value, by bid, by auction, or by some other pricing method. Judging by the government's unfortunate experience in pricing grazing leases on the Taylor lands, it would seem best to obtain the full market value of the land.[21]

Most of the irrigable lands in the public domain are already under reclamation withdrawal. Power sites are withdrawn, and so are known mineral lands. Under the measures proposed above, lands primarily useful for watershed purposes, wildlife sustenance, and recreation would likewise be set aside, as would major areas of silt production.

The remaining public domain would then consist of lands not especially useful for any generally accepted federal concern, and presumably, therefore, for the foreseeable future most useful as grazing lands for domestic livestock. Such lands could be sold into private ownership, since there seems to be no good reason for retaining them in federal tenure.

But such lands should not be offered for sale until the public domain land classification is complete. Moreover, there should be co-ordination with all branches of the federal establishment. A large acreage of public domain land in the Intermountain West lies in the right of way of authorized federal highways, and such land, obviously, should be reserved for highway use. The possibility that other government agencies may need certain tracts for special uses should be carefully investigated.

SALE AND EXCHANGE PROCEDURES

One of the most difficult problems under the program just proposed would be to devise a satisfactory scheme for the sale of lands classified as suitable for disposal to private owners. One necessary aspect of the sale program seems clear; in many cases several individual pieces of land would have to be offered for sale as a single package. If this procedure were not used, the traditional process of picking over the remaining federal lands would continue. Prospective purchasers would pick and choose among the offerings until finally the federal government was left with scattered pieces of worthless, unsalable property.

The sensible way to dispose of these lands is through an administered program of sale with a great deal of discretion given to the BLM personnel in charge. However, they should be instructed to try in general for

[21] Currently, in the Middle Rocky Mountain basins it appears that such lands are being sold at their true value.

the maximum return from all sales, to insure that the persons for whom the land held the highest economic utility could obtain title to it directly.

If all the land were offered for sale simultaneously, the market would be overwhelmed. Many ranchers would be unable to raise sufficient cash on such short notice to buy even the tracts they are currently using under Taylor leases. Under such circumstances the land would either not be sold, would be sold at a ridiculously low price (with much of it being concentrated into a relatively few huge corporate ownerships), or would sell at widely divergent prices to various purchasers.

Various properties should be offered in a single package to be sold to the highest bidder, but the BLM should have the right to refuse all bids. Under many circumstances if this were not done, ranchers, particularly the large operators, would bid in some properties at a low price because of the control they could exert over their use through ownership of adjacent lands and water sources.

To make the bidding procedure effective, it would be necessary for the BLM to charge maximum price for leasing such land for grazing purposes. In all of the Middle Rocky Mountain basins, various offers by the BLM to sell isolated tracts of range land to owners of the surrounding private land have been refused, because the ranchers preferred to rent the land at the prevailing low rates rather than invest their money in its ownership. As long as the alternative of low rentals is available, sales of many federal parcels will lag.

INTERIM MANAGEMENT

Final disposition of the Taylor lands under the program here proposed would take a considerable period; three decades seems a conservative estimate. During that time the lands would still need management. In general, the procedures recommended in the first part of this chapter would be satisfactory. Of prime importance would be a sharp increase in grazing fees to stimulate land sales. As soon as any tract of land had been classified as best suited for some federal use, it should be transferred promptly to the relevant agency.

THE ALTERNATIVE OF STATE OWNERSHIP

Historically one of the three major proposals for disposition of the public domain has been to turn the land over to the states. I am opposed to this solution, but largely on the basis of negative evidence. There is not in the literature any adequate, detailed study of the administration of western state lands; consequently, no basis exists for carefully substantiated conclusions about the administration of state lands. However, in the Middle Rocky Mountain basins state lands are managed and treated as though they were private lands, except that actual title and the mineral rights are retained by the state. State ownership seems in no way preferable to federal ownership. If the land is to remain in government ownership, it may as well be retained by the federal establishment.

DISPOSITION OF MINERAL RIGHTS

Federal policy with respect to mineral rights has been and still is somewhat ambiguous. Certain classes of minerals on or under federal lands are available for exploitation only under lease from the federal government; lands containing other classes of minerals (the metalliferous minerals) are open to entry and patenting. Mineral policy need not interfere with sale of public domain land to private buyers, because the mineral rights can easily be retained by the federal establishment if it so desires.

Conclusion

It is difficult to avoid the conclusion that national policy with respect to the public domain for the past seventy-five years has been a disappointment. As citizens we can take pride in our reservation policy for the national parks, the national forests, wildlife refuges, and reclamation and power projects. But our policies of disposal and management of the public domain present the opposite picture. Federal land policy has satisfied neither the proponents of state ownership nor the advocates of federal management or private ownership; neither easterners nor westerners; neither cattlemen nor sheep ranchers; neither the range livestock industry nor the conservationists. Federal management has produced little revenue, has not benefited the West in any fundamental way, has done relatively little to strengthen and stabilize the western range livestock industry as the Taylor Grazing Act directed. Under federal management the range lands and their plant cover have not been properly protected and conserved. Public domain land disposal has not met the test of justice, because alienation has been arbitrary, often fraudulent, and marked by opportunism and favoritism. It has been uneconomic because it has never been possible for lessees or buyers to bid in a straightforward manner for the land. Almost a hundred years ago John Wesley Powell, the first geographical writer on management of the western public lands, strongly advocated that the lands of the intermountain region be classified so that they could be disposed of and managed in a rational fashion. His recommendation was based on an appreciation of the fact that the lands of the intermountain region had widely varying inherent characteristics and these, in turn, gave strongly contrasting implications of their relative utility for the few and simple purposes of private individuals and the federal government at that time.[22]

Today the need for classification is greater than ever before, because the number and variety of public and private objectives has been steadily increasing and the need for most usefully fitting land potential to those objectives has increased proportionally. Land classification is a dull subject. It is so much easier and simpler to say sell the public domain, give it to the states, lease the Taylor lands by bid, or some other categorical solution. To a considerable extent the Taylor Act itself is this kind of solution. But one of the principal objectives of this study has been to show that lands in the Middle Rocky Mountain basins exhibit great contrasts both in natural and cultural characteristics. A land policy will be most successful that provides ways of handling these lands that take into account the lands' differing qualities, or that utilizes most effectively the contrasting characteristics of the various areas for national objectives. These differences from place to place are crucial. That is why in most cases the findings and recommendations in this study have been largely limited to conditions in the Middle Rocky Mountain basins. To some extent they are applicable to broad areas in the Intermountain West; but in many cases the conditions are highly localized. Only on the basis of similar detailed knowledge of the other lands of the intermountain region can all lands be used to serve most effectively our national and private interests.

The program presented in these latter sections would take account of the lands' potentials. The proposals may be summarized briefly as follows. (1) Land best suited for some legitimate government purpose be reserved promptly and then managed and used primarily for that purpose. This would carry to its logical conclusion one of the most successful of our public land policies. (2) Land that is primarily useful for private purposes should be transferred to private ownership, but it should be patented to that private citizen who places the highest value on it, as expressed by his willingness to pay the highest price for it. As I have been at some pains to show in the analogous case of grazing leases, the granting of land to a citizen at something less than the market price constitutes a pure gift to that citizen and confers no permanent benefit on subsequent owners, since the original recipient will immediately price the property

[22] J. W. Powell, *Report on the Lands of the Arid Regions of the United States* (Washington, D.C., 1879).

at its full value as nearly as he can estimate it. (3) The program here proposed suggests in effect that the Bureau of Land Management either by reservation or by sale should close out its function of managing the surface use of the remaining public domain lands. Perhaps it is unrealistic to propose that a bureau work diligently to terminate one of its principal functions. But the Bureau of Land Management has numerous other functions—management of the O. and C. lands of California and Oregon,[23] management of the public domain in Alaska, and management of minerals leasing on federal properties—which presumably would continue. The task of classification, reservation, and sale of the public domain lands would take many years; no wholesale transfers or dismissals of personnel would be necessary, no interruption of careers. Moreover, the BLM is only one division of the Department of Interior and a decade or so hence if the declining functions of the bureau necessitated some diminution of numbers, the transfers could easily be accommodated within the department.

If the program I propose is carried through, the Bureau of Land Management, the Department of Interior, the Congress, and the nation's citizens will view the result with satisfaction, recognizing that, whatever the shortcomings of earlier administration, the final disposition of the "vacant, unappropriated, and unreserved" federal lands was rational and just.

[23] O. and C. lands (Oregon and California revested lands) are lands that were originally granted for a railroad subsidy; but since the railroad was never built, the lands reverted to the federal government. The land was arranged in checkerboard fashion. Much of it contained valuable timber resources. The 2 million acres of O. and C. contain more than 60 billion board feet of timber, and their management is a major administrative job.

INDEX

PRINTED IN U.S.A.

INDEX